NRA FIREARMS
SOURCEBOOK

NRA FIREARMS SOURCEBOOK

Your Ultimate Guide
to Guns, Ballistics and Shooting

By Michael E. Bussard and
Stanton L. Wormley, Jr.

Edited by John Zent

A Publication of the
National Rifle Association
of America

ISBN 0-935998-26-8
Published 2006
Second Printing, March 2008

Printed in the United States of America

Published by the National Rifle Association of America
11250 Waples Mill Road, Fairfax, VA 22030-9400

Wayne R. LaPierre, NRA Executive Vice President

Produced by NRA Publications
Joe H. Graham, Executive Director
Lourdes F. Kite, Deputy Director
John Zent, Editorial Director
Harry L. Jaecks, Art Director

What The NRA Is
What The NRA Does

The National Rifle Association was organized as a non-profit membership corporation in the State of New York in November 1871, by a small group of National Guard officers. The object for which it was formed was the "...improvement of its members in marksmanship, and to promote the introduction of the system of aiming drill and rifle practice as part of the military drill of the National Guard..."

In 1877, its name was changed to the National Rifle Association of America. During its years of existence, NRA Headquarters has been located in New York, New Jersey, Washington, D.C. and, since 1994, Fairfax, Virginia.

The NRA represents and promotes the best interests of gun owners and shooter-sportsmen and supports their belief in the ideals of the United States of America and its way of life. It is dedicated to firearms safety education as a public service, marksmanship training as a contribution to individual preparedness for personal and national defense, and the sports of shooting and hunting as wholesome forms of recreation. It stands squarely behind the premise that the ownership of firearms must not be denied to law-abiding Americans.

The purposes and objectives of the National Rifle Association of America are:

To protect and defend the Constitution of the United States, especially with reference to the inalienable right of the individual American citizen guaranteed by such Constitution to acquire, possess, collect, exhibit, transport, carry, transfer ownership of, and enjoy the right to use arms, in order that the people may always be in a position to exercise their legitimate individual rights of self-preservation and defense of family, person, and property, as well as to serve effectively in the appropriate militia for the common defense of the Republic and the individual liberty of its citizens;

To promote public safety, law and order, and the national defense;

To train members of law enforcement agencies, the armed forces, the militia, and people of good repute in marksmanship and in the safe handling and efficient use of small arms;

To foster and promote the shooting sports, including the

advancement of amateur competitions in marksmanship at the local, state, regional, national and international levels;

To promote hunter safety, and to promote and defend hunting as a shooting sport and as a viable and necessary method of fostering the propagation, growth, conservation, and wise use of our renewable wildlife resources.

INTRODUCTION

"**N**o, it's not a flintlock. It's a miquelet lock, which was actually developed concurrently or slightly after the flintlock. You can tell the difference quickly because the mainspring is on the outside of the lockplate on a miquelet lock, not inside like on a flintlock," I said, settling a debate here in the offices of *American Rifleman* about an image of an antique Italian handgun sent to us by an NRA member.

"How did you know that?" asked one of my newer colleagues incredulously.

"It's easy, read your *Fact Book*," I replied. That is a pretty common refrain after answering an obscure question about guns or shooting. The key to gaining a better understanding of anything is having the right reference materials—or asking someone who has the right references. For shooters, collectors, handloaders, hunters—in fact, for anyone seeking more knowledge—this all-new *NRA Firearms Sourcebook* is indeed the right book to answer literally tens of thousands of general and specific questions about firearms and shooting.

The world of firearms and shooting is vast, and no one person can know everything—beware of anyone who says they do, as they are likely wallowing in self–deception or aren't savvy enough to know what they don't know. But having the right books on your shelf can help you learn more or at least get you started in the right direction. As one of my former *Rifleman* bosses told me years ago, "You need not know everything, but you should know where to look it up."

This book is a direct descendant of one of the most useful little desk references ever produced—the *NRA Firearms Fact Book*. I obtained my first copy in 1985, and it proved just how little I really knew. After reading it, I knew quite a bit more. More than 20 years later, I go to that battered little book at least once a day. Originally published in 1964 and revised in 1988, the *NRA Firearms Fact Book* from the NRA Technical Staff was a collective work of some of the greatest firearms authorities of the 20th century, including Major Gen. Julian S. Hatcher, Col. E.H. Harrison, M.D. "Bud" Waite, Ludwig Olson and Pete Dickey.

But the "little blue book," as we call it, was getting long in the tooth. Given the flood of recent developments in gunmaking and ammunition, and considering the many aspects of firearms, shooting, ballistics and optics not covered in the original, a revision was long overdue. A decision was made to drastically expand the scope and amount of material included in the book, so much so that a new title and a lot more pages were warranted. So some four decades after the *Fact Book* was first published, former NRA Technical Staff editors Michael E. Bussard and Stanton L. Wormley, Jr., with guidance from NRA Publications Editorial Director John Zent, tackled the project with a remarkably useful and informative volume as the result. I can finally retire my dog-eared, gun-oil-smeared copy of the *Fact Book*.

In reviewing the pages of *The NRA Firearms Sourcebook*, I was struck by the sheer amount of data presented here. Whether it's the amount of energy remaining for a .308 Win. FailSafe with a 180-gr. bullet at 400 yds., or identifying what other calibers can be fired out of a .357 Mag. revolver (the answer, by the way, is .38 Spl., .38 Long Colt and .38 Colt), there is a wealth of information in these pages, all in one place. Certainly this reference work will serve new shooters very well and help them gain know-how. For more advanced "gunnies," the ballistics tables and formulae presented herein will be invaluable. Whether you need the Greenhill rule to determine the optimum twist rate for a given bullet weight, or just want to calculate the recoil of your favorite plinking load, it's all here.

There's much misinformation about firearms today, particularly from mass media outlets, but there are also myths perpetuated amongst and by our fellow shooters. It could be an obvious gaffe like a complete cartridge flying through the air in the movie "Sniper," a reporter's bizarre claim that the FN 5.7 mm cartridge can shoot around corners like a guided missile or a guy at the gun club who insists that bullets rise after leaving the muzzle. Whatever the source, misinformation can lead to misunderstandings that can damage how firearms and their owners are judged by the non-shooting public. Moreover, such confusion can cost one on the firing line, in the field or, most critically, when a forceful response is necessary in a life-threatening situation. Erroneous thinking based on a lack of knowledge and repeated often enough can be just as damaging as the outright lies of anti-gunners, who obscure the facts behind a litany of half-truths, ignorance and deceptions about firearms and those who own and use them responsibly. Armed with a book like this, you can politely call them on the carpet, and do your part to ensure the firearms debate is based on facts, not myths and misconceptions.

When it comes to guns, there are, oddly, not a lot places you can go to the get the basics—and get them right. I recall a conversation with a shooting buddy some years ago during which he was almost ashamed to ask me the difference between a double-action-only semi-automatic pistol and a "regular" double-action semi-automatic. He was an enthusiastic reader of gun magazines, but in hyping the latest, greatest, Teutonic, polymer-framed semi-automatic handgun, we writers and editors had failed him. There was no place for him to find this basic information that he craved. Thankfully, that and much, much more is offered in these pages. The inclusion of chapters on safety, history and basic operation of firearms are great places to start whether you are new to the world of firearms or have been tinkering with guns for 80 years.

Another area where this book helps is in providing clear answers to subjects that often seem quite complex. Have you ever received a concise explanation of ballistic coefficient from anyone other than a ballistician? (Even then the term "concise" usually doesn't apply.) Sure, a lot of guys can tell you that the better the BC is, the less drop and energy loss you'll have at long range, but can they actually explain what it is and how it's calculated? In optics, the learning curve is even steeper in my view, and this book's chapter on optics is one of the best concise overviews I have read. There are a lot of terms thrown around out there, such as parallax and twilight factor, that if not understood, aren't helpful when used by writers or manufacturers.

Two other aspects of this book I found extremely useful are the chapters on manufacturing and, especially, the glossary. The more manufacturers attempt to differentiate their products from their competitors, the more complex they seem to get in their descriptions. While additional information on the "what and how" of their offerings is appreciated, it is easy for the average shooter to get bogged down in terms generally known only to engineers, machinists, metallurgists or (occasionally) advertising copywriters. When confronted with everything from "space-age polymer" to the chemical breakdown of a synthetic stock, it's no wonder many of us find ourselves nodding our heads and smiling vacantly. This book will help with those terms. (Well, maybe not with the creations of overenthusiastic copywriters.)

No one volume on any subject can be fully comprehensive, but this one can answer the vast majority of the numerous questions we field from NRA members. Every serious shooter, collector and firearms enthusiast needs to make room for the *NRA Firearms Sourcebook* on his or her shelf. Military units, police departments and security agencies will find it useful in supporting their missions. Equally well served will be members of the press and academicians who seek to write or speak intelligently about firearms. Make good use of this book and you, too, will soon know the difference between a miquelet lock and a flintlock. And that's just for starters.

Mark A. Keefe, IV
Editor-In-Chief, *American Rifleman*
Fairfax, Virginia, 2006

ACKNOWLEDGEMENTS

In spirit, this book represents the collective knowledge of shooters dating back to the invention of the first gun. More specifically, it is the latest and most comprehensive dissertation ever from NRA describing how guns and ammunition function. Since our founding in 1871, NRA has been the ultimate authority on such matters, and right from the start we have worked hard to share our expertise. While much has been accomplished face-to-face through massive firearms training, hunter safety and competitive shooting programs, it is telling that NRA has been an active publisher for 120 years. Over that time span the Association's journals, books and pamphlets have endeavored to educate our members and keep them abreast of new technology and developments relevant to gun owners.

Following in that tradition, *Sourcebook* authors Mike Bussard and Stanton Wormley have painstakingly distilled lessons learned on battlefields, shooting ranges and in the hunting woods. That practical knowledge is complemented herein by discussions on the design and manufacture of firearms and ammunition, as well as insight into aspects ranging from art and science to history and sociology. The authors are to be saluted for their extensive labor.

Many others also merit recognition for their involvement in the book's production. *American Rifleman* Editor in Chief Mark A. Keefe, IV, and Shooting Editor Glenn M. Gilbert, along with NRA Publications armorer Eric Poole, figured significantly in the editing and research. Other Publications Division staffers who contributed to the copy-editing and proofreading include Lourdes F. Kite, Linda J. Faulk, Wendy Maiello, Jeff H. Johnston, Michael O. Humphries, Frank Miniter, Brian C. Sheetz, Aaron Carter, Dave Campbell, Adam Heggenstaller, Chad Adams, Kyle Wintersteen, Mike Nischalke, J. Scott Olmsted, Maureen D. Hammerquist, Wendy LaFever, Traci Wright and Guy Sagi.

NRA Art Director Harry Lloyd Jaecks not only devoted many hours to the book's layout and design, but also shaped the final product in ways too numerous to detail. Senior Designer John T. Claman created the striking cover design, and Designers George Stump and Tom Rickwalder each contributed illustrations.

Assistance from other NRA divisions was provided by: NRA General Counsel Robert Dowlut and the attorneys in his office, in particular retired counselor James Warner; NRA-ILA Director of Research and Information William F. Parkerson, III; Division Director Bill Poole and colleagues in NRA Education and Training; Phil Schreier from the National Firearms Museum; and Jorge Amselle of NRA Community Service Programs.

Thanks also to John Robbins of NRA Community Service Programs and longtime *American Rifleman* Ballistics Editor William C. Davis, Jr., both of whom consulted on certain chapters. NRA Chief of Staff Mary Corrigan aided the cause by suggesting the title.

Production and marketing responsibilities were handled by Jeff Poole and Kathi Reca from NRA Membership, Mark Arndt of the NRA Purchasing Department, and NRA Publications Production and Advertising Director Mike Sanford.

Not to be overlooked are NRA Executive Vice President Wayne LaPierre and Executive Director of Publications Joe Graham whose leadership has fostered a professional environment where a work of this magnitude could be created.

—John Zent

AUTHORS' FOREWORDS

As shooters, hunters, competitors, collectors and reloaders, we can take pride in the fact that the development of firearms and ammunition remains the longest thread of technical achievement in recorded history. This historical thread stretches back over 765 years, and involved the participation of some of the great minds and leaders in world history.

What is the special appeal that sustains firearms and ammunition development? I believe there are two factors: 1) Firearms and ammunition development embraces an eclectic blend of art and science. Among the scientific elements are chemistry, metallurgy, physics, mathematics, measurement, ballistics, engineering, manufacturing and medicine. We find the art in aspects like architecture, tactics, sociology, law, international relations, politics and language. 2) Mankind has always been fascinated by flight, and very early on realized that controlled flying objects could be used to defeat powerful enemies at a safe distance. Viewed in this light, perhaps the great men of firearms and ammunition development recognized a basic truth that many people today have forgotten—self-defense is a non-negotiable birthright ingrained in all of us.

The historical thread of firearm and ammunition development is not broken. Rather, it continues with full vigor. Anti-gun advocates will privately despair because they are swimming upstream against the flow of history. Pro-gun supporters publicly note another fundamental truth: Private citizens who own firearms will never be slaves. Privately they note that Samuel Colt made all men equal.

The optimistic shooters among us will eagerly anticipate the avalanche of new developments in propellants, materials, optics, manufacturing and ballistics to come. Pessimists will opine there is nothing new under the sun and firearms development has peaked. But they are wrong. In 1900, firearms and ammunition technology was 99 percent guess and 1 percent knowledge. Today, over 100 years later, we have improved our situation to 98 percent guess and 2 percent knowledge. This leaves much to discover.

This new NRA publication is intended as an abridged, general-purpose reference book for shooters. As such, it is but one of the small mileposts in the sweep of firearms and ammunition history.

Michael E. Bussard
August 2005

It is difficult to comprehend the breadth of knowledge encompassed by the field of firearms. Firearm design, for example, involves a profound knowledge of not only engineering, metallurgy, materials science and manufacturing processes, but also human anatomy and ergonomics. While traditional firearm manufacture required only a thorough grounding in machine shop operations and woodworking, today's gunmakers must also master newer methods for fabricating metal components, such as metal injection molding (MIM) and investment casting, as well as technologies for making and working with fiberglass, carbon fiber, Kevlar and other man-made materials too numerous to list. Chemistry is crucial to the production of propellants used in ammunition, as is optics to the design and manufacture of telescopic sights; and the three types of ballistics—internal, external and terminal—involve areas of knowledge as disparate as the gas laws of physics, aerodynamics, and (in the case of hunting ammunition) animal physiology. History, too, is an integral part of the saga of the gun, as advances in firearm technology have been spurred by, and have contributed to, the unfolding of events in Europe, Asia, Africa and the Americas during the last half millennium or so. Even art features in the story, as can be plainly seen in the intricate patterns of metal engraving and woodcarving which have adorned firearms for centuries.

The *NRA Firearms Sourcebook* does not purport to be a complete and comprehensive reference covering all aspects of gun lore. Such a work would clearly be an almost impossible undertaking (and, if achieved, would need to be carried around on a hand truck). The authors of the *Sourcebook* had a more modest and realistic goal: to bring together as much essential and authoritative information on gun-related topics as can be presented in a work of reasonable and useful size.

While there are many people who have contributed to the *Sourcebook*, I'd like to give my special thanks to three who were particularly generous in the help they gave me. Kenneth D. Green, Director of Technical Affairs of the Sporting Arms and Ammunition Manufacturers' Institute (SAAMI), is one of the most technically savvy individuals around, and generously provided me with advice, information, and many of the excellent materials from SAAMI, including its Glossary of Industry Terms, from which many of the definitions in the *Sourcebook* were taken. Technical advice on ballistics was provided by William C. Davis, Jr., and Charles V. Fagg of Tioga Engineering. Neither man needs any introduction to serious students of ballistics. Davis in particular is credited as the developer of the VLD (Very Low Drag) bullet, which has revolutionized long-range shooting. Davis and Fagg are also well known to long-time readers of *American Rifleman*, to which they have contributed feature articles, answers to members' questions, and technical expertise for many years.

I'd also like to express my appreciation to Joe Graham, Executive Director of the Publications Division of the National Rifle Association, and Mike Bussard, former NRA Technical Editor, for giving me the opportunity to contribute to the *Sourcebook*. No one knew that what was originally to be a revision of the *NRA Fact Book* would evolve into a wholly new work of this scope. I'm proud to have been a part of this project, and I hope that the *NRA Firearms Sourcebook* gives firearm enthusiasts many hours of informative and enjoyable reading.

Stanton L. Wormley, Jr.
January 2006

CONTENTS

FIREARMS AND SOCIETY

Chapter 1
SAFETY

The Fundamentals

Safety is fundamental to all shooting activities. Whether you are practicing at the range, cleaning your gun in your workshop or defending your family from an attack, the rules of firearm safety always apply. Safe gun handling involves the development of knowledge, skills and attitudes—knowledge of gun safety rules, the skill to apply these rules and a safety-first attitude that arises from a sense of responsibility and an understanding of potential dangers. Though there are many specific principles of safe firearm handling and operation, all are derived from just three fundamental rules:

ALWAYS keep the gun pointed in a safe direction. This is the primary rule of gun safety. A safe direction means that the gun is pointed so that even if it were to fire, it would not cause injury or damage. The key to this rule is to control where the muzzle is pointed at all times. Common sense dictates the safest direction, depending upon the circumstances.

ALWAYS keep your finger off the trigger until ready to shoot. When holding a gun, rest your trigger finger ouside the trigger guard alongside the gun. Until you are actually ready to fire, do not touch the trigger.

ALWAYS keep the gun unloaded until ready to use. Whenever you pick up a gun, always keep the gun pointed in a safe direction, keep your finger off the trigger, engage the mechanical safety if possible, remove the ammunition source (magazine or ammunition from magazine tube), open the action, visually and physically inspect the chamber(s) and magazine area (which should be clear of ammunition) and leave the action open with the mechanical safety engaged. If you do not know how to open the action or inspect the chamber(s), leave the gun alone and get help from someone who does, or consult the owner's manual that came with the gun.

As a general rule, whenever you pick up a gun, point it in a safe direction with your finger off the trigger, engage the safety (if the gun is equipped with one), remove the magazine (if the gun is so equipped), and then open the action and look into the chamber(s) to determine whether or not the gun is loaded. Unless the firearm is being kept in a state of readiness for personal protection, it should be unloaded.

NRA Safety Programs

Over the course of its 137-year history, NRA has been synonymous with gun safety and hunter safety, so much so that "NRA safety rules" have become a part of our American lexicon. Largely because of the Association's ongoing emphasis on safety, shooting and hunting consistently boast some of the lowest accident rates among all participant sports, a fact confirmed annually in data released by the National Safety Council. Over the years NRA has produced hundreds of safety-oriented printed pieces, preached safety through its magazines, trained tens of thousands of firearms instructors, and been directly involved in hundreds of thousands of instructional classes and clinics in communities across America.

This legacy of safety continues today in many ways, including several highly successful programs geared to contemporary American culture.

Eddie Eagle GunSafe® Program

"If you find a gun: STOP! Don't Touch. Leave the Area. Tell an Adult." That's the life-saving message of the Eddie Eagle GunSafe Program. These simple, easy-to-remember instructions are the heart of NRA's safety program designed to protect young children from gun accidents.

Developed specifically for youngsters ranging from pre-schoolers to third-grade, the program uses the friendly Eddie Eagle mascot to teach children how to avoid gun accidents. This award-winning safety program was pioneered by past NRA President Marion P. Hammer, and developed in conjunction with teachers, reading and curriculum specialists, child psychologists and law enforcement professionals.

The Eddie Eagle GunSafe Program teaches gun accident prevention only. It has been taught by more than 25,000 schoolteachers, law enforcement officers and community safety activists. The program does not teach gun handling, gun nomenclature, or gun use. It makes no value judgments about guns, and does not promote gun use or participation in any shooting sports. The program never mentions the NRA and does not encourage anyone to become an NRA member.

Program materials include a colorful, animated video featuring Eddie Eagle, activity books, posters, and reward stickers. Anyone may teach the Eddie Eagle program by using the comprehensive instructor guides. The program can be taught in one-lesson or five-lesson sessions. Instructors may opt to present the entire program, or only parts of it, in order to fit their schedules and those of the children. Program materials, including videos, are available in both English and Spanish.

Through NRA's partnership with schools, law enforcement agencies, youth service organizations, and civic organizations, the Eddie Eagle program now reaches more than one million children each year. Since its inception, the program has reached more than 18 million children in all 50 states.

Deputy Sheriff Kelly Howell of the Rockingham County Sheriff's Office in Wentworth, N.C., is a big fan of the Eddie Eagle program. Concerned about accidental shootings, her office began looking for ways to educate the children of Rockingham County about gun safety. "We discovered the Eddie Eagle program," said Deputy Howell, "and we knew we had found something great!" The sheriff's office decided to implement the program, and has been delighted with the results. "This is a wonderful program," said Deputy Howell. "After we began teaching it to our children, we have not had a single gun accident!"

NRA's award-winning Eddie Eagle Gunsafe Program targets pre-schoolers through third-graders with an appealing, constructive message that can help prevent gun accidents. Since the program's inception in 1988, fatal gun accidents in the Eddie Eagle age group have dropped more than two-thirds, according to the National Center for Health Statistics.

Many recent studies have documented significant declines in gun accidents among children. In the Eddie Eagle age group, fatal gun accidents have dropped more than two-thirds since the program's inception in 1988, according to the National Center for Health Statistics. Gun accident prevention programs such as Eddie Eagle are widely considered to be a significant factor in that decline.

The Eddie Eagle Department at NRA Headquarters often receives testimonials about Eddie Eagle 'graduates' who found a gun and knew how to avoid an accident. These real-life examples demonstrate the program's effectiveness, and show how important the safety lesson is for America's youth. To cite just a couple of examples: In March 2005, eight-year-old Billy Thornton was with his father in a Knoxville, Tenn., credit union. While his father waited in line, Billy visited the restroom and found a handgun in plain view. Because he had been taught the

Eddie Eagle program, Billy did not the touch gun, and left immediately to tell his father what he'd found. Billy's father and the store manager retrieved and secured the gun at once. Ironically, the gun had been left there accidentally by a security guard.

In another instance, six-year-old Shae'Den Slette was playing in her Montana backyard when she found a loaded Colt .45 semi-automatic. She immediately ran to her mother, who secured the gun and notified police. The gun had been lost by a local resident.

In addition to accolades from individual citizens, a number of organizations and child safety experts have praised the program as well. Eddie Eagle has been endorsed or honored by: the National Safety Council, the National Sheriffs' Association, the American Legion, the Police Athletic League, the National Association of School Safety and Law Enforcement Officers and others. Governors of 24 states have signed resolutions recommending that the program be used in their school systems.

In addition, a study by Patricia Kunz, RN, printed in the Journal of Emergency Nursing Online, compared the top three gun safety programs. "Of the three programs evaluated," the study concluded, "the Eddie Eagle program best met the criteria. Strengths of the Eddie Eagle program include educational material appropriate for the intended developmental level and presentation appearance of the printed material."

For more information on the Eddie Eagle GunSafe Program, contact the Eddie Eagle Department, Community Service Programs Division, National Rifle Association, 11250 Waples Mill Road, Fairfax, VA 22030-9400. The toll-free number is 800-231-0752, and a Web site is available at www.nrahq.org/safety/eddie.

NRA Basic Firearm Training Programs

Carrying on one of its original missions, NRA provides basic training in the safe handling and proper use of firearms. Today, more than 50,000 NRA Certified Instructors throughout the United States continue this fine tradition of public service, training about 750,000 citizens a year. Course content covers the following topics:

- firearm handling and shooting safety
- firearm parts and their operation
- ammunition and its function
- shooting fundamentals and actual range time
- selecting, cleaning and storing a firearm
- shooting activities and opportunities beyond the basics.

Courses are offered in the following disciplines:

- Home Firearm Safety
- Pistol
- Rifle

- Shotgun
- Personal Protection
- Muzzleloading Pistol, Rifle and Shotgun
- Range Safety Officer
- Metallic Cartridge Reloading
- Shotgun Shell Reloading.

To obtain a list of NRA Certified Instructors in your area, call 703-267-1430 or visit www.nrahq.org/education/training/find.asp.

Another training option is an NRA First Steps course. First Steps (Firearm Instruction, Responsibility and Safety Training) is a program for new shooters. It provides a hands-on orientation to one specific rifle, pistol, or shotgun model in as little as three hours, including a one-hour shooting session on a range.

Refuse To Be A Victim®

Created in 1993, at first for women only, Refuse To Be A Victim is a three- to four-hour crime-prevention seminar that teaches methods to avoid dangerous situations and prevent criminal confrontations. Experts agree that the most important factor in surviving a criminal attack is to have an overall safety strategy before you need it. Seminar topics address personal safety issues as well as home, automobile, phone, technological, travel and personal security. Seminar participants are presented with a variety of common-sense crime prevention and personal safety strategies and devices they may integrate into their daily lives. Firearm instruction is not included.

Refuse To Be A Victim was developed by the women of the NRA in 1993 in response to requests from women nationwide for crime-prevention seminars. In 1997, the program became co-ed. Since that time, it has reached tens of thousands of women and men who have benefited from the program. With more than 3,000 instructors nationwide, seminars have been presented in 49 states and the District of Columbia.

Refuse To Be A Victim is also very popular with law enforcement agencies and crime-prevention groups. Numerous departments have had officers certified by NRA to conduct seminars. Many other organizations endorse it, such as the Virginia Crime Prevention Association (VCPA), which has incorporated it into its training schedule for crime-prevention officers. Patrick Harris, Executive Director of the VCPA, said, "This course is a valuable tool that helps crime-prevention officers show people how they can control their crime risks at home, work and while traveling, by removing the opportunities that lead to crime."

To locate Refuse To Be A Victim seminars, or for information on how you can become a certified instructor for the program, call 800-861-1166, send an e-mail to refuse@nrahq.org, or visit the program's Web site www.nrahq.org/rtbav.

Women On Target

Gun safety is the number-one priority of Women On Target instructional shooting clinics. Women On Target was launched in 1999 in response to persistent calls from women who wanted more opportunities to learn to shoot and hunt, preferably in the company of other women. The program involves women-only hunts and shooting clinics. NRA works with carefully screened outfitters and shooting clubs to host the women-only events. Instructional shooting clinics are designed primarily for beginners or for women who have experience with one type of firearm and want to try others. All clinics begin with a thorough safety orientation, followed by closely supervised shooting time. Women On Target focuses on basic recreational shooting, not self-defense.

Although the participants are women only, men play an integral part as guides and instructors. Participation in the program has grown dramatically—about 500 women attended Women On Target events in the year 2000. By the end of 2005, about 22,300 women had taken part.

For more information about Women On Target call 800-861-1166, or visit www.nrahq.org/women.

Accidental Firearm-Related Deaths

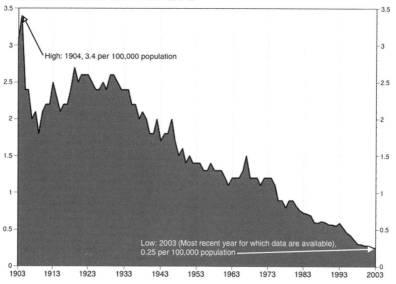

High: 1904, 3.4 per 100,000 population

Low: 2003 (Most recent year for which data are available), 0.25 per 100,000 population

Source: National Center for Health Statistics and National Safety Council

8

Rules For Using Or Storing A Gun

In addition to these three basic rules for safe gun handling, you must follow a number of additional rules when you use or store your firearm.

Know your target and what is beyond. Whether you are at the range, in the woods or in a self-defense situation, if you're going to shoot you must know what lies beyond your target. In almost all cases, you must be sure that there is something that will serve as a backstop to capture bullets that miss or go through the target. Think first, shoot second.

Know how to use the gun safely. Before handling a gun, learn how it operates. Read the owner's manual for your gun. Contact the gun's manufacturer for an owner's manual if you do not have one. Know your gun's basic parts, how to safely open and close the action, and how to remove ammunition from the gun. No matter how much you know about guns, always take the time to learn the proper way to operate any new or unfamiliar firearm. Never assume that because one gun resembles another, they both operate in exactly the same way. Also, remember a gun's mechanical safety device is never foolproof. Guidance in safe gun operation should be obtained from the owner's manual or a qualified gunsmith.

Be sure your gun is safe to operate. Just like other tools, guns need regular maintenance to remain operable. Regular cleaning and proper storage are a part of the gun's general upkeep. If there is any question regarding a gun's ability to function, it should be examined by a knowledgeable gunsmith. Proper maintenance procedures should be found in your owner's manual.

Use only the correct ammunition for your gun. Each gun is intended for use with a specific caliber or cartridge. Only cartridges designed for that particular gun can be fired safely in that gun. Most guns have the ammunition caliber stamped on the barrel and/or slide. The owner's manual will also list the cartridge or cartridges appropriate for your gun. Ammunition can be identified by information printed on the cartridge box and sometimes stamped on the cartridge head. Do not shoot the gun unless you know you have the proper ammunition.

Wear eye and ear protection as appropriate. The sound of a gunshot can damage unprotected ears. Gun discharges can also emit debris and hot gas that could cause eye injury. Thus, both ear and eye protection are highly recommended whenever you are firing live ammunition in your gun. Safety glasses and ear plugs or muffs should also be worn by any spectators or shooting partners present during live-fire sessions.

Never use alcohol or drugs before or while shooting. Alcohol and many drugs can impair normal mental and physical bodily functions, sharply diminishing your ability to shoot safely. These substances must never be used before or while handling or shooting guns. Note that these effects are produced not just by illegal or prescription drugs. Many over-the-counter medications also have considerable side effects, which may be multiplied when certain drugs are taken together or with alcohol. Read the label of any medication you take, no matter how innocuous, or consult your physician or pharmacist for possible side effects. If the label advises against driving or operating equipment while taking the medication, you should also avoid using a gun while taking it.

Store guns so they are inaccessible to unauthorized persons. It is your responsibility as a gun owner to take reasonable steps to prevent unauthorized persons (especially children) from handling or otherwise having access to your guns. You have a number of options for accomplishing this, which are discussed in greater detail in the Safe Firearm Storage section. The particular storage method you choose will be based upon your own particular home situation and security needs.

Be aware that certain types of guns and many shooting activities require additional safety precautions. There are many different types of firearms, some of which require additional safety rules or procedures for proper operation. These are commonly found in your gun's owner's manual. Also, most sport-shooting activities have developed a set of rules to ensure safety during competition. These rules are generally sport-specific; the procedures for loading your gun and commencing fire, for example, are different in NRA bullseye shooting than they are in NRA Action Pistol competition.

Defensive Shooting Safety

It may seem unrealistic to expect a person undergoing an attack to be conscious of the gun safety rules, much less adhere to them. Through constant repetition and mindfulness, however, safe gun-handling skills can become habits that function automatically even during the stress of a violent encounter.

Safe Firearm Storage

Safe gun storage is an integral part of gun safety. It is one of your prime responsibilities as a gun owner to take all reasonable precautions to prevent unauthorized persons from having access to your firearms.

Some jurisdictions have laws mandating secure firearm storage. Almost all jurisdictions have criminal negligence laws that can be applied to gun owners who do not take reasonable precautions in storing their firearms.

There are two main requirements for the storage of firearms. First and foremost, the storage method chosen must provide an adequate level of protection to prevent unauthorized persons from accessing the firearms. The determination of what is "adequate protection" is a matter of judgment on the part of the gun owner.

The second requirement is that the storage method or device used must allow the gun to be easily retrieved as needed to defend against an intruder or an attack. This is just as important to a shopkeeper behind a counter as it is to a homeowner awakening at night to the sound of an approaching intruder. Again, "easily retrieved" depends upon the particular circumstances of the environment.

There is no one best method of firearm storage nor one best type of locking or storage device. Each has advantages and limitations. You must choose the firearm storage method that is best for you given your circumstances and preferences.

It is also incumbent upon you as a responsible, law-abiding gun owner to know and observe all applicable state and local laws regarding safe gun storage.

Types of Locking Mechanisms

All storage methods designed to prevent unauthorized access utilize some sort of locking mechanism. Different types of locking mechanisms offer varying degrees of security and accessibility. Keyed locks, such as padlocks and the lockable drawers of desks and nightstands, can offer a reasonable level of security (depending upon the construction of the lock and the storage device). However, under stress or in darkness it may be difficult for some to locate the correct key or to manipulate it in the lock. A lesser concern, but one worth mentioning, is that inserting and turning a key in a gun box lock would likely create some sound—whether it is keys jingling together on a key ring or the movement of the lock's tumblers—that could alert a stealthy intruder.

Combination locks are often found on gun storage boxes and range from simple triple-rotary-tumbler models to units that rival the mechanisms found on bank vaults. For many people, combination locks are both secure and familiar to operate. Under stress, however, lock combinations can be confused or forgotten by the gun owner, and the tumblers can be challenging to manipulate quickly and accurately. Also, in darkness or even dim light, combination locks can be virtually impossible to operate, making them less than optimal for devices used for emergency firearm storage.

Simplex-type locks provide a good combination of security and quick access. Such locks feature a number of buttons that are pushed in a specific order to open the device and now some are designed to recognize fingerprints. With only minimal practice, these locks can be easily worked in total darkness. Locks with Simplex-type mechanisms can be just as strong and tamper-resistant as any other.

Another advantage of a Simplex-type lock is that incorrect entry blocks any further attempt to open the lock. A separate clearing code must be entered before the lock will accept the correct combination, making this lock even more resistant to unauthorized attempts to open it.

The basic Simplex-type lock is a mechanical lock, and thus does not depend upon house current or batteries. Some locking devices, however, combine Simplex principles with modern electronics. Typically, the storage device features a numeric keypad whose numbered buttons are pushed in a specific order to unlock. A variation on this involves five fingerpads, ergonomically placed on the top or front of the device, which can easily be felt in the dark and which are pressed in a sequence (such as thumb, middle finger, little finger, ring finger) to open the device. It is important to note that such locking mechanisms are usually disabled when electric power is lost (as from dead batteries or a failure in house current). There usually is a provision for opening the box with a key under such circumstances, but this could be problematic under stress or in the dark. Some units that use house current have provisions for a backup battery power supply to ensure continuous operation.

Types of Storage Devices

There are many different methods for storing firearms safely inside and outside the home, several of which may fit into your defensive plan.

Gun cases are commonly used for the transportation and storage of firearms. Gun cases are typically of synthetic material, though some more costly models are made of aluminum. Some have integral locks; others feature hasps for small keyed or combination padlocks.

Gun cases can be useful in several ways. When transporting your gun by air or other common carrier, and it must be in a gun case, some specific requirements as to the type and construction of the case may apply. Also, federal law mandates that a gun transported across state lines in your vehicle must be in a "locked container" (such as a gun case) when it cannot be transported in a compartment separate from the driver's compartment. Some states also have additional requirements for transporting guns within state boundaries. Even in jurisdictions or situations in which guns need not be transported in a gun case, it is still a good idea to do so, both to keep them out of sight and to protect them from being jostled together or damaged in your trunk, truck box and so forth. In the home, gun cases serve to protect firearms from dust and moisture. Often, guns kept in gun safes for long-term or permanent storage are first put into gun cases.

A pistol lock box allows you to store a gun in your vehicle or workplace so that it is protected from unauthorized access but can still be retrieved quickly. Typically, such boxes are made of steel and feature integral keyed, combination or Simplex-type locks; a few have electronic numeric keypads, fingerpads and fingerprint recognition. Some lock boxes are designed to store a gun securely out of sight while also providing quick access to that gun if it is needed for defensive purposes. Such boxes are typically located in desk drawers, under countertops or in the kneewells of desks. Some models are designed for automotive use. These lockboxes are attached using screws or bolts that can be accessed only when the box is open; easy theft of the box is discouraged. Quick-access boxes usually feature locks of the Simplex, electronic keypad or fingerpad type. Many novel mechanisms exist to provide quick access once the box is opened, from harnesses that swing out and present the gun grip-first to platforms that slide out for easy access.

Gun safes are designed to offer the greatest level of safety for your guns. Upper-end models provide walls and doors that are virtually impossible to defeat by brute force, high-security mechanical or electronic locks, and complex locking patterns that fasten the door to the frame in multiple locations with thick, hardened steel pins. Most of these models are too heavy and bulky for thieves to carry away easily, even when they are not bolted to the floor; some also offer a degree of fire protection.

Although appropriate for long-term firearm storage, gun safes may not be the best choice for the temporary storage of guns that you may need to retrieve quickly. The weight and size of gun safes often consign them to the basement of a building, far from your office or work location. Also, gun safes provide little concealment value. No matter where a gun safe is put, almost anyone seeing it will recognize it as a device for the storage of firearms or other valuable items, making it a target for thieves and burglars. Finally, the combination locks and heavy bolting mechanisms typical of such devices make it difficult to access your guns quickly and quietly. Even when equipped with a lighted keypad for quicker access, the sound of the handle being turned and the locking pins retracting will unquestionably alert an intruder in a quiet house.

There are a few alternative storage methods that should also be mentioned. Many people store guns in a **lockable drawer of a desk, nightstand, file cabinet or the like.** The decision to store a gun in this manner must be reached after careful consideration of the circumstances, needs and risks involved.

Another alternative form of storage is a **lockable gun rack** allowing firearms (particularly long guns) to be displayed or stored openly. This type of device typically features a locking bar (or sometimes a thick, plastic-covered steel cable) that passes through the trigger guard or around the frame, and is secured by a keyed or combination lock. Since a lockable gun rack does not protect a gun from moisture, dust or fingerprints, and does not conceal a gun from prying eyes, it is best mounted in a locked gun room or gun closet.

Also available are several types of **quick-access devices** that orient a handgun for a fast grab. Some of these devices are designed for nighttime use and orient a gun in a grip-upward position alongside the mattress. Others place a handgun in a horizontal position directly under a counter, drawer or desktop. These items may be useful in high-threat environments in which there may be no time to work even a Simplex-type lock and life or death may hinge on immediate access to a firearm. These devices do nothing to prevent gun theft or unauthorized access, and are thus not suitable for gun storage.

Storing a Gun Safely Outside the Home

Most of the time, when you are outside your home your concealed handgun will be on your person, carried in a holster, handbag, fanny pack or other concealment device. However, there will be occasions when you find it necessary to temporarily remove your gun and store it in a safe manner. Outside the home, handguns are usually temporarily stored either in a vehicle or in the workplace.

Vehicle Storage

At the very least, you should store your firearm in a locked gun case inside the vehicle's trunk, cargo box or other lockable area. Greater security and access can be afforded by special pistol lockboxes designed for automotive environments. Such devices are usually securely attached to part of the vehicle, such as the floorboard under the seat, the interior of the glove box, the underside of the dashboard or the interior of the storage compartment in the center console. Some of the units may slide or swing out to provide access; all normally require the entry of the proper combination or keypad sequence to access and withdraw the gun. Such units, properly installed, will provide no visual clue of the presence of a gun in the vehicle, but will allow ready access in only a few seconds.

Advance planning is essential when you will be traveling out of your home state and into a state where your carry permit is not valid. Always be aware that you are carrying a handgun; you must not become complacent and forget it is there or inadvertently go someplace where carry is forbidden.

Workplace Storage

Often a gun is stored in the workplace during the workday. As in the home, there are two types of workplace gun storage: long-term storage, in which the gun is kept locked up all day with little or no anticipation of defensive use; and quick-access storage, in which the gun is kept readily available to ward off robbers or other violent criminals.

Long-term workplace storage requires, at the very minimum, that you store your gun in a locked drawer or cabinet. Better security (but slower access) is attained when you place your gun in a locked gun case, and then lock it in a drawer or cabinet.

A locking pistol box securely attached to the inside of a locked desk drawer or cabinet provides the best practical level of security for long-term gun storage in the workplace. Such a device is highly resistant to theft and, if equipped with a keypad or fingerpad mechanism, can still be opened relatively quickly.

This type of device is also highly recommended for the quick-access workplace storage of a handgun kept hidden near a counter or register as protection against criminal attack. Some models feature a locking storage compartment that mounts completely under a counter and slides outward on rails for easy access. Other models can be mounted inside a drawer, on the side of a counter, under a shelf and so forth.

Miscellaneous Storage Methods Outside the Home

There may be occasions when you consider temporarily storing a gun in a location other than a vehicle or a workplace, such as in a locker at your gym or in a dressing room at a hair salon.

No single storage method addresses all situations. The responsible gun owner will use a mixture of storage methods to prevent any unauthorized access while facilitating easy retrieval when necessary. Research into the various storage options, and a carefully thought-out defensive plan, will help you decide which firearm storage options are appropriate for your situation.

Firearm Safety Devices

Most modern firearms have one or more mechanical subsystems designed to reduce the likelihood of an inadvertent discharge. These subsystems are collectively known as safeties. A safety is a device on a firearm intended to help provide protection against accidental or unintentional discharge under normal usage when properly engaged. Many firearms also incorporate other safety features, such as to prevent the action being opened when the gun is cocked, or to hinder use by unauthorized persons.

Generally, safety systems can be categorized as active or passive. Active safety systems are those that are intentionally activated and deactivated by the user, and serve to prevent firing unless and until the shooter is ready. The safety lever on a bolt-action rifle is an example of an active safety system. Passive safety systems work without the direct intervention of the user. For example, a firing pin block is a passive safety system.

Active Safety Systems

Active safeties, also often called manual safeties, are said to be on when the mechanism is engaged and the gun cannot fire, and off when disengaged to allow discharge. Such safeties are generally of three types: those that block the sear, those that block the trigger and those that block the hammer or firing pin.

Examples of sear-blocking safeties include the thumb safety on the M1911 Government Model and Browning Hi-Power pistols. The sliding tang safety on most break-action over/under shotguns is of the trigger-blocking type; and the swinging safety mounted on the bolt shroud of Winchester and Mauser bolt-action rifles retracts and locks the firing pin rearward, and thus is of the firing pin-blocking type.

Any of the three types of active safeties will reliably prevent firearm discharge—if the safety system is in proper working order. This may not always be the case with firearms that are older or much-used, or that have been abused or neglected. Even in a new firearm, the engagement between the trigger and the sear or hammer, or between the sear and the hammer or firing pin, may be only 0.020" to 0.025"—about the thickness of a single plastic credit card. Wear or improper trigger adjustment (either from the factory or, more commonly, from home gunsmithing) can sometimes reduce this slim margin to the point at which dropping the gun, or even closing the action briskly, can cause the trigger or sear to release even with the safety engaged. For this reason, some gunsmiths and firearm authorities consider a safety that solidly blocks the hammer or firing pin to be more secure than the other types of active safeties.

While there are only three basic types of active safety systems, there are many variations on the designs. For example, on some break-action shotguns, the tang-mounted sliding trigger-blocking safety automatically resets to the "safe" position each time the gun is opened and closed. Also, the safeties on bolt-action rifles may be two-position or three-position. The former can be moved to either the "fire" or "safe" positions, with the bolt locked in the latter condition. With three-position safeties, in addition to the "fire" and bolt-locked "safe" positions, a third, intermediary position still prevents firing but allows the bolt to be worked so as to remove a live round from the chamber. Safeties are generally located on the firearm in close proximity to the thumb or index finger of the shooting hand to allow disengagement without the grip being disturbed.

Note that not all firearms have active safety systems. Double-action revolvers, for example, typically lack such systems, as their long, heavy trigger pulls effectively minimize the likelihood of an accidental discharge. Firearms for certain types of shooting sports, such as benchrest competition, also often lack safeties. The exemplary safety record of competitive shooting demonstrates that, even in the absence of active mechanical safety devices, strict observance of the rules of firearm safety can create a safe shooting environment.

Passive Safety Systems
In contrast to active safety systems, which are voluntarily engaged/disengaged by the shooter, passive safety systems function more or less automatically. These safeties take many forms. A grip safety is an auxiliary device on the grip of some handguns (as well as some long guns) intended to prevent firing until depressed. This occurs when the gun is gripped naturally. The Browning .32 Auto and .380 Auto semi-

automatic pistols, and the Uzi pistol, carbine and submachine gun, for example, all incorporate grip safeties. Firing pin blocks, such as the mechanism on later-production Colt Government Model pistols, block forward firing pin travel unless the trigger is depressed and also qualify as passive safety systems. Inertia firing pins, in which the forward movement is restrained until it receives the energy from a hammer blow, serve as safety devices in that they help prevent firearm discharge if the firearm is dropped muzzle down onto a hard surface.

Most semi-automatic rifles and shotguns are designed such that the hammer cannot contact the tail of the firing pin unless the bolt is securely locked into the receiver or barrel extension. Also, many older bolt-action designs possess an interlock that blocks full forward movement of the firing pin until the action is closed. Several pistols, such as those produced by Glock, incorporate a pivoting lever in the trigger face which prevents trigger movement unless it is depressed by the trigger finger. Finally, some firearms, such as the Browning Hi-Power, have a magazine disconnect safety, which prevents the firing of a live round in the chamber if the magazine is removed.

Many modern firearms, particularly revolvers, incorporate transfer bars or hammer blocks that are activated by the trigger mechanism. In firearms utilizing transfer bars, such as Ruger revolvers, the hammer at rest contacts the frame, but sits back slightly from the frame-mounted firing pin. When the trigger is pulled, the transfer bar rises to fill that gap and transfers the blow of the hammer to the firing pin to discharge the gun. This prevents a heavy blow on the hammer from igniting the primer. The safety connector of Colt revolver mechanisms functions similarly. In contrast, the hammer block typical of Smith & Wesson revolvers functions in the opposite way: The hammer block sits between the hammer and frame when the hammer is at rest, preventing contact of the hammer nose with the cartridge primer even if the gun is dropped on the hammer spur. (A small tab on the rebound slide also serves to limit forward hammer travel at rest.) When the trigger is pulled, the hammer block drops to allow the descending hammer to hit and ignite the primer.

"Smart Gun" Safety Systems

Recent years have seen calls for the development of so-called "smart gun" technologies to prevent the use of firearms (primarily handguns) by unauthorized persons. The proposed designs use various strategies to allow the systems to "recognize" or detect an authorized user. For example, one such system would sense the pattern of pressure points on the grip frame produced by the firing hand, and would allow the gun to be fired only when the pattern corresponds to that of the owner. Such a system might prevent an authorized user from firing the gun if, due to stress or injury, his or her grip did not match the approved pattern. Another system employed a magnetic ring that, when worn on the user's shooting hand, would unlock an internal safety mechanism to allow gun discharge. Though simple, this system would penalize an authorized user who lost or forgot to wear the ring, or who, out of necessity, had to fire the firearm with the weak hand. A third system incorporates a combination lock in the firing mechanism that may be difficult to work under stress or in the dark, when a firearm may be quickly needed.

This critical problem—positively preventing firearm discharge by an unauthorized user while not limiting the authorized user's access to, and use of, his or her firearm under varying conditions—is one that has not been satisfactorily solved by any "smart gun" systems developed to date. A further problem is that such systems inevitably add to the mechanical complexity of the firearm, which decreases its reliability—a critical characteristic of firearms used by law enforcement or for home or personal defense. Surely, attempts to perfect this technology will continue.

Other Safety Systems

Beyond systems designed to prevent inadvertent discharge or unauthorized use, some firearms also incorporate features intended to minimize the danger from certain other potential hazards.

One such hazard is encountered when high-pressure propellant gas escapes from a split or separated case or through a punctured primer. This gas escape can damage the firearm and direct high-velocity particles of powder or brass into the shooter's eyes. Many bolt-action rifles chambered for high-intensity cartridges have features for handling escaping gas, including gas ports in the bolt body and receiver ring, gas-blocking baffles in the receiver raceways, counterbored bolt noses and bolt shrouds with gas-deflecting flanges. All such systems serve to either contain the gas in the action or divert it from the shooter's face.

Many early military bolt-actions feature a safety lug that engages a recess in the receiver, usually to the rear of the receiver ring. In some actions, the safety lug is simply the root of the bolt handle, which fits somewhat closely in a notch in the receiver. This safety lug provides extra safety in the event of failure of one of the primary bolt lugs. Few, if any, modern turnbolt actions are equipped with a safety lug.

It cannot be overstressed that mechanical safety devices do not, in themselves, guarantee safe firearm use. Any mechanical system can fail or be subverted by negligence, carelessness or willful disregard for the rules of firearm safety. Only strict adherence to those rules can prevent firearm mishaps having the potential to cause property damage or personal injury.

Ammunition Safety

Today's shooter enjoys ammunition of unprecedented variety and quality. Many contemporary factory hunting loads are more accurate than the target loads offered only a few decades ago and such is the reliability of commercial ammunition that problems are rarely encountered. Nonetheless, there are still a number of situations involving ammunition in which safety may be compromised if the proper precautions are not taken.

Interchangeable Calibers

Cartridge designations are normally highly specific and individual—that is, each designation will usually refer to a single cartridge having unique dimensions and/or ballistics. There are, however, occasions when this is not the case.

The most innocuous example arises when ammunition manufacturers use two or more different names to refer to the exact same cartridge. This actually arises fairly frequently with cartridges that are sold or manufactured in both the United States and Europe. For one thing, in America bore and bullet diameters are usually listed in decimals of an inch. Most European nations, however, use the metric system, in which the same dimensions are given in millimeters. Thus, in Europe the .25 ACP is known as the 6.35 mm Browning. Furthermore, current European practice is to designate cartridges using the bore diameter in millimeters, plus the case length in millimeters. This system transforms the .308 Winchester to the 7.62x51 mm.

Cartridges that have been adopted or manufactured by many different nations over a lengthy period may also pick up a variety of designations. Probably the classic example of this is the 9 mm Para, which is or has been also known as the 9 mm Luger, 9 mm Parabellum and 9x19 mm.

Occasionally, a manufacturer will introduce a cartridge under one name, and then subsequently change that name (often for marketing reasons). In 1957, Remington introduced the .280 Remington, essentially the .30-'06 necked down to take a .284"-diameter bullet. For various and sundry reasons, the new round did not sell as well as its originators had hoped, and in 1979 the company (perhaps hoping to capitalize on

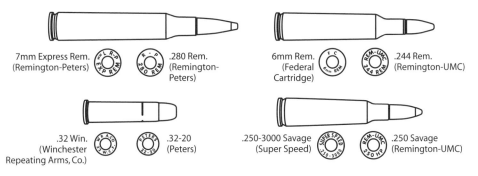

7mm Express Rem. (Remington-Peters) .280 Rem. (Remington-Peters) 6mm Rem. (Federal Cartridge) .244 Rem. (Remington-UMC)

.32 Win. (Winchester Repeating Arms, Co.) .32-20 (Peters) .250-3000 Savage (Super Speed) .250 Savage (Remington-UMC)

Several otherwise identical cartridges have been produced with different designations. The headstamps of these cartridges also may vary from one manufacturer to another.

19

the success the "7 mm" designation had conferred on several other contemporary cartridges) renamed it the 7 mm Express Remington. Although the "new" round was accompanied by some changes in factory loadings, its dimensions were identical to those of the original .280 Remington, and pressure levels increased only slightly (from 50,000 c.u.p. to 50,900 c.u.p.) for better performance. Eventually, because of confusion between the 7 mm Express Remington and the 7 mm Remington Magnum, the cartridge reverted to its original .280 Remington designation. Thus both of these cartridges (as well as the rifles chambered for them) are completely interchangeable.

Other examples of different names for the exact same cartridge include the .244 Rem. and 6 mm Rem., .25-20 Win. and .25 WCF, .250 Savage and .250/3000 Savage, .32-20 Win. and .32 WCF, and .44-40 Win. and .44 WCF. Many other cartridges have two or more names.

Less innocuous are those instances in which two cartridges have identical dimensions but markedly different pressure levels, which can permit a higher-pressure cartridge to be chambered in a firearm designed for lower pressure levels. Among handgun cartridges, for instance, the .38 Auto (or .38 ACP) and .38 Super Auto are the exact same length, and have the same diameter at the mouth, head and rim. However, while the .38 Auto was originally loaded to a pressure of about 23,000 c.u.p., the .38 Super Auto (which replaced it in 1929) was loaded to a pressure of around 33,000 c.u.p.—some 44 percent higher. This difference could create a problem when the powerful .38 Super Auto, designed for the strong M1911 pistol, is fired in the weaker Colt Model 1900, Model 1902 and Model 1903 pistols chambered for the lower-pressure .38 ACP. A more modern example of this involves the .45 ACP and the .45 Super. Both have the same dimensions, but the latter cartridge is loaded to considerably higher pressures (yielding more impressive ballistics) than the .45 ACP.

Finally, there are a few cartridges that come in two versions having different bullet diameters; this results in guns with varying bore dimensions being chambered for the same nominal cartridge. The prime example of this is probably the 8 mm Mauser (8x57 mm) which, for historical reasons, exists in two versions: the 8x57J, with a .318"-diameter bullet, and the 8x57JS, with a .323"-diameter projectile. Firing an 8x57JS cartridge in a barrel dimensioned for the smaller projectile of the 8x57J could result in dangerously excessive pressures.

It is also worth noting that some variation (on a smaller scale) may occur in custom barrels, as competitive shooters sometimes specify slightly tighter land and groove diameters. Excessive pressures may result when maximum loads developed in a standard-dimension barrel are fired in such a "tight bore" barrel. With any barrel of unknown origin, especially on a target arm, a cast of the chamber and part of the barrel should be performed to ascertain the exact bore measurements.

+P Ammunition

In addition to ammunition loaded to pressure levels standardized by the Sporting Arms and Ammunition Manufacturers' Institute (SAAMI), there are also "+P" versions of some handgun cartridges that operate at 10-20 percent higher pressures to produce greater velocity and muzzle energy. These loads are intended for use only in firearms designed to handle those higher pressure levels. The "+P" designation of these loads is usually found on the ammunition box and the cartridge headstamp. Firearms designed for such ammunition normally have a "+P" marking on the barrel, slide or frame.

Commonly encountered cartridges having a "+P" version include: .38 Spl., 9 mm Para and .45 ACP. (NOTE: To emphasize the pressure difference between the .38 ACP and the .38 Super Auto, all current .38 Super Auto ammunition has the "+P" designation.) To prevent firearm damage and possible injury, +P ammunition must be fired only in those firearms certified for it.

Finally, it must be mentioned that, for some cartridges, reloading manuals often contain both standard loads for older firearms, as well as higher-pressure loads for stronger, more modern firearms. For example, reloading data for the .45-70 Gov't. cartridge often comes in three varieties: loads for 1873 Springfield rifles, somewhat heavier loads for the Winchester Model 1886 lever-action, and even heavier loads for the Ruger No. 1 and No. 3 rifles, as well as other modern guns of similar strength. Some reloading manuals also list loads of different pressure levels for the .30-40 Krag. Higher-pressure loads for modern firearms must never be fired in older firearms, to avoid firearm damage and/or shooter injury.

Dangerous Cartridge/Chamber Configurations

For the most part, the dimensions for a given cartridge are unique, in theory ensuring that a firearm chamber will accept only one cartridge. In practice, however, dimensional similarities among cartridges as well as the manufacturing tolerances for both guns and ammunition can sometimes permit the wrong cartridge to enter a chamber. When that incorrect cartridge is fired in that chamber, excessive pressures capable of damaging the firearm or injuring the shooter can result.

Generally, there are two types of situations in which this can occur. Most commonly, when there are a number of cartridges based on a single parent case (such as the .25-'06, .280 Rem., .30-'06 and .35 Whelen, all of which are based on the .30-'06 case), it is occasionally possible to chamber a cartridge with a too-large bullet in a chamber of a gun with chamber or throat wear. Should the cartridge be fired in that chamber, excessive pressures would likely result from the attempt to jam an oversized bullet through an undersized bore. In most instances, the differences in neck size will preclude the larger round from entering the smaller chamber, but this may not always be the case with a chamber that has been cut grossly oversize, or when the neck of the cartridge brass has been thinned by turning.

Another dangerous combination may result when a short cartridge is inserted into the chamber of a much longer cartridge of the same head diameter. When this situation is compounded by the shorter cartridge carrying a larger bullet than the bore is designed for, excessive pressures may result. This can be a particular problem with belted magnum cartridges, in which the belt can prevent a shorter cartridge from going deep enough into the chamber to avoid the impact of the firing pin. For example, according to the published data on cartridge and chamber dimensions, a .350 Rem. Mag. cartridge could easily be chambered in an average-dimension chamber for the .300 Wby. Mag. Both are belted magnum cartridges; thus, the .350 Rem. Mag. would be held in proper firing position in the longer .300 Wby. Mag. chamber. If the firing pin were dropped on that cartridge, excessive pressures would be produced when the .358" bullet tried to enter a .308" bore, almost certainly damaging or destroying the rifle. Case splitting and/or an imperfectly-sealed chamber might also result, potentially releasing gas into the shooter's face.

Depending upon the condition of the rifle and the dimensions of the bore and chamber, a shooter may have the potential for such dangerous cartridge/chamber combinations lurking among the firearms he or she owns. A competent gunsmith can diagnose these conditions.

Wildcat Cartridges

In addition to factory-produced cartridges for which SAAMI has developed dimensional and pressure standards, there are also non-standard "wildcat" cartridges developed by ballistic experimenters. Often a wildcat round is produced simply by necking up or necking down the cartridge case of a factory standard cartridge; sometimes other case modifications, such as reducing case body taper or sharpening the shoulder angle, are also performed. By definition, wildcat ammunition must be produced by reloading.

In terms of safety, wildcat ammunition raises two issues. First, firearm chambers for wildcat cartridges may sometimes loosely accept other standard cartridges as well, creating a situation in which there is excessive headspace or case body clearance. If the standard cartridge is fired in a wildcat chamber, potentially dangerous case head separations or case body splits could result. (The exception to this is the "Improved" wildcat chamber, which is designed to allow the safe firing of factory ammunition.)

The second safety issue relating to wildcat cartridges relates to standardization. SAAMI publishes recommended cartridge and chamber dimensions, as well as maximum pressures, for factory ammunition produced in the United States; the Commission Internationale Permanente des Armes a Feu Portative (CIP) does the same for European-made ammunition. These standards provide a benchmark for ammunition manufacturers, gun makers, gunsmiths and others in the firearm industry, and ensure that all ammunition of a given caliber is safe to fire in virtually any firearm chambered for it.

No such standards exist for wildcat cartridges. Minute differences in the shoulder angle, neck length and body taper of a case, or the neck diameter or throat length of the chamber, as well as the lack of pressure standards and pressure-tested load data, all make the assembly of wildcat loads challenging, even for highly experienced reloaders.

Compounding the problem is the fact that many wildcat rounds were created for target competition, and were thus designed to be used in guns with competition-type chambers having tight necks, custom throats and/or minimum SAAMI dimensions.

Any shooter acquiring a gun (particularly a rifle) chambered in a wildcat caliber should first have a competent gunsmith make a cast of the chamber and throat. From this, proper cartridge dimensions can be obtained.

Note that NRA recommends reloading only using pressure-tested loading data published by reputable sources, such as the manufacturers of powder, bullets and other cartridge components.

Custom Chambers

Custom barrels, even in standard chamberings, may have non-standard features, such as tight necks, or throats that are longer or shorter than normal. Safety may be reduced when factory ammunition is fired in such chambers. For example, tight-neck chambers made for reloaded cases with turned necks may not provide sufficient clearance for the neck of a factory-standard cartridge to release the bullet upon firing, producing higher-than-normal pressures. Also, short throats may cause the bullet nose of a factory cartridge to jam tightly into the rifling upon chambering; this can also raise pressures. Custom chambers are sometimes also cut to minimum SAAMI dimensions, which can prevent chambering of cartridges produced to maximum SAAMI specifications.

Most of the time, such custom chambers are found on competition firearms, where they may contribute to accuracy. Minimum chambers and tight necks are sometimes found on varmint rifles as well. As a general rule, it's a good idea to have a competent gunsmith cast the chamber of any rebarreled rifle, regardless of the markings on the barrel. Accurate measurements of the cast will reveal if the chamber is made to standard or non-standard dimensions.

Squib Loads, Misfires and Hangfires

Modern manufacturing methods and strict quality control have made today's factory ammunition virtually 100 percent reliable in properly functioning firearms. However, occasionally the shooter may encounter one of four types of malfunctions with both factory and reloaded ammunition.

A **squib load** is defined as a cartridge or shell that produces projectile velocity and sound substantially lower than normal. Most commonly, the shooter will be aware of a squib load as a shot that does not produce the expected level of either noise or recoil. Such a condition can be caused by a number of factors: use of old or deteriorated ammunition; contamination of the primer or powder charge; or failure to load a primed case with a sufficient amount of powder. Under the best conditions, the squib load has sufficient power to propel the bullet out of the muzzle (albeit at less than normal velocity). Often, however, a squib load leaves a bullet lodged in the bore—and therein lies the danger. If the shooter fails to recognize that he or she has had a squib load and fires a successive shot with the bore obstructed, disastrous consequences may result for both the gun and the shooter.

Whenever the shooter senses something different about a particular shot—reduced recoil or muzzle blast, the failure of the shot to cycle the action of a semi-automatic firearm, the lack of a hole produced anywhere on the target, etc.—a squib load should be suspected. The shooter should not fire another shot, but instead should completely unload the firearm and then inspect the bore, visually or with a cleaning rod, to ensure there is no obstruction. A bullet that is just barely into the rifling (such as was fired from a case that was primed but not charged with powder) can sometimes be tapped out carefully using a cleaning rod inserted from the muzzle of the gun. Bullets that are more firmly lodged in the bore should be removed by a gunsmith. Note that in a revolver, a bullet fired from a primed case lacking powder may jam into the forcing cone, preventing cylinder rotation. Again, a gunsmith should be used to remedy such a situation.

A **misfire** is a failure of the priming mixture to be initiated after the primer (or rim of a rimfire case) has been struck an adequate blow by the firing pin, or the failure of the initiated primer to ignite the powder. This term is also commonly used to refer to a failure to fire caused by an insuf-ficient hit on the primer (perhaps more appropriately called a "light hit").

A misfire is experienced as the complete failure of a cartridge to fire when the trigger is pulled and the hammer or firing pin falls. A light firing pin hit is probably the most common cause of misfires, but occasionally they may also result from deteriorated or defective ammunition. When a light firing pin hit is the cause of the misfire, a shallow indentation of the primer cup will usually be seen when the misfiring cartridge is removed from the chamber.

Though not dangerous in themselves, misfires should be treated with caution, as it is impossible to initially distinguish a misfire from a hangfire. Thus, whenever there is a failure of a cartridge to ignite, the shooter should use the proper safety procedure for handling hangfires (see below).

A **hangfire** occurs when there is a noticeable delay between the impact of the hammer or firing pin on the primer and the actual discharge of the firearm. Typically, with a hangfire, the shooter will pull the trigger, causing the hammer or firing pin to fall, but no shot is produced immediately. Inside the case, however, the ignition process has been initiated and, after an unpredictable delay period, the gun discharges. Like a squib load, a hangfire can be produced by the use of deteriorated ammunition, or ammunition whose primer or powder charge has become contaminated.

The danger of a hangfire lies in the fact that it is often mistaken for a misfire. This, in turn, can result in two distinct types of hazards. First, a shooter who assumes that a non-firing round is a misfire may immediately open the gun's action to remove the malfunctioning cartridge. A cartridge that ignites when thus unconfined can cause damage to the gun and serious injury to the shooter. Moreover, a shooter who assumes that he or she has suffered a misfire may fail to exercise proper muzzle control, such that the gun may be pointing in an unsafe direction when it unexpectedly discharges.

Any time the hammer or firing pin falls and the gun fails to fire, a hangfire should be assumed. The firearm should not be opened or unloaded, but should be kept pointing in a safe direction for 30 seconds with a modern cartridge and two minutes with a muzzleloader. This is sufficient time for any hangfire to complete ignition. If one minute passes and the gun does not discharge, the situation is actually a misfire. The firearm should be unloaded and the offending cartridge inspected for light primer indentation, contamination, etc.

If a firearm that is normally reliable produces hangfires or misfires with a particular ammunition (particularly ammunition that is old or potentially deteriorated), discontinue use of that ammunition and dispose of it in accordance with local regulations.

For years, shooters have reported unpredictable pressure excursions capable of damaging or destroying a gun when light charges of very slow powders were used in large-capacity cases. This **detonation phenomenon** has thus far proved difficult to replicate under laboratory conditions. Nonetheless, many ballisticians regard the phenomenon to be real and have developed a variety of theories to explain it. One such theory postulates that a small powder charge in a mostly empty case can produce reinforcing shock waves inside the case. Another theory claims that the ignition of a small charge of very loosely packed powder granules can result in more or less simultaneous, rapid burning of the charge, producing excessive pressure.

Whatever its cause—or whether or not it occurs, in fact—detonation should not be ignored by the cautious shooter and reloader. Loads less than the minimum loads listed in published data should be avoided, as should any ballistic "experimenting" with slow powders for which reduced load data is not available.

Maximum Range of Ammunition

Whether hunting, target shooting or plinking, the shooter must be aware of the maximum range of the gun and cartridge combination used. The maximum range is the greatest distance a projectile can travel when fired at the optimum angle of elevation of the gun barrel. This optimal angle of elevation is usually around 30 degrees from horizontal. The maximum range is far greater than the effective range of the cartridge, which is the maximum distance at which a projectile can be expected to be useful. This is usually determined by factors such as accuracy and, for hunting or military uses, striking energy.

The importance of maximum range stems from the safety rule "Know your target and what is beyond." A bullet from an errant shot or a miss may fly several miles before it impacts the earth. A knowledge of maximum range (as well as what lies beyond the target area) can help a shooter assess whether it is or is not safe to fire.

The following table contains representative figures for the maximum range for many common rifle, handgun and shotgun cartridges. Note that these figures are approximate and are useful for rough comparison only. Variations in barrel length, the velocity level of the load, bullet ballistic coefficient and more will affect the actual distance attained by a particular load in a particular gun under specific conditions.

Maximum Range/Maximum Height

Maximum Range: Approximate maximum distance a bullet will travel to point of first impact with the ground at standard conditions with the muzzle elevated between 28 and 34 degrees.

Maximum Height: Approximate maximum height or altitude a bullet will travel at standard conditions with the muzzle elevated at 90 degrees.

Calibers, bullet weights and muzzle velocities listed are for factory-loaded ammunition having the longest average bullet flight distances. Other bullet weights or muzzle velocity figures in each caliber will have shorter average bullet flight distances. Entries in bold print are defining calibers in each category in that these bullets will travel the farthest.

Note that some military ammunition, special sporting ammunition and handloads may have greater average flight distances than those listed.

RIMFIRE CALIBERS FROM A RIFLE

Caliber	Muzzle Velocity (f.p.s.)	Bullet Weight (grs.)	Bullet Style	Maximum Range (yds.)	Height (ft.)
.17 Mach 2	2100	17	TP	2,200	4,400
.17 HMR	2550	17	TP	2,500	5,000
.22 Short Hi Vel.	1132	29	RN	1,231	2,770
.22 L.R. Std. Vel.	1145	40	RN	1,588	3,505
.22 L.R. Hi Vel.	1255	40	RN	1,622	3,650
.22 L.R.Ultra Hi Vel.	1640	33	HP	1,458	3,280
.22 WMR	2000	40	RN	1,715	3,860

MILITARY CALIBERS

Caliber	Muzzle Velocity (f.p.s.)	Bullet Weight (grs.)	Bullet Style	Maximum Range (yds.)	Height (ft.)
5.56 x 45 M193 Ball	3240	55	FMJBT	3,842	8,645
5.56 x 45 M855A1 Ball	3050	62	FMJBT	4,071	9,160
.30 Carbine M1 Ball	1970	111	FMJ	2,556	5,750
7.62x51 M80 Ball	2780	150	FMJBT	4,469	10,055
7.62x51 M118 Ball	2640	175	FMJBT	5,484	12,339
7.62x 51 M852 Match	2550	168	HPBT	4,752	10,692
.30 M1 Ball	2640	172	FMJBT	5,480	12,375
.30 M2 Ball	2780	152	FMJ	3,500	7,875
.30-40 Krag Ball	2000	220	FMJ	4,050	9,110
.50 BMG M2 Ball	2810	709	FMJBT	7,275	16,370
9x19 M882 Ball	1276	124	FMJ	2,350	5,290
.45 ACP M1911 Ball	825	230	FMJ	1,640	3,690

COMMERCIAL STANDARD RIFLE CALIBERS

Caliber	Muzzle Velocity (f.p.s.)	Bullet Weight (grs.)	Bullet Style	Maximum Range (yds.)	Height (ft.)
.17 Rem.	4040	25	HP	2,561	5,765
.204 Ruger	3900	40	SP	4,000	8,000
.218 Bee	2760	46	HP	2,095	4,715
.22 Hornet	2690	46	SP	2,084	4,690
.222 Rem.	3140	50	HP	2,727	6,135
.223 Rem.	3240	55	FMJBT	3,843	8,650
.225 Win.	3570	55	SP	3,211	7,225
.22-250 Rem.	3680	55	HP	3,501	7,878
.243 Win.	2960	100	SP	4,000	9,000
6 mm Rem.	3100	100	SP	4,649	10,460
.25-20 Win.	1460	86	SP	2,446	5,505
.25-35 Win.	2230	117	SP	3,183	7,162
.250 Savage	2820	100	SP	3,836	8,631
.25-'06 Rem.	2990	120	SP	4,656	10,470
6.8 Rem. SPC	2625	115	SP	3,400	6,750
.270 Win.	3050	130	SP	4,795	10,789
7 mm-08 Rem.	2875	140	SP	4,400	8,700
7 mm Mauser	2660	139	SP	4,196	9,441
.280 Rem.	2890	150	SP	4,446	10,003
.284 Win.	2860	150	SP	4,423	9,951
.30-30 Win.	2390	150	SP	3,010	6,773
.30-30 Win.	2200	170	SP	3,307	7,441
.308 Win.	2620	180	SP	4,655	10,473
.30-06 Sprg.	2700	180	SP	4,170	9,383
.30-06 Sprg.	2700	180	SPBT	5,670	12,758
.30-06 Sprg.	2600	200	SP	6,190	13,928
.30-40 Krag	2430	180	SP	4,551	10,240

27

COMMERCIAL STANDARD RIFLE CALIBERS continued

Caliber	Muzzle Velocity (f.p.s.)	Bullet Weight (grs.)	Bullet Style	Maximum Range (yds.)	Height (ft.)
.300 Savage	2350	180	SP	4,506	10,139
8 x 57 mm JS Mauser	2360	170	SP	2,871	6,460
.348 Win.	2520	200	SP	3,632	8,172
.35 Rem.	2020	200	SP	2,647	5,956
.35 Whelen	2400	250	SP	3,500	7,000
.358 Win.	2490	250	SP	3,964	8,919
.405 Win.	2200	300	SP	2,000	4,000
.444 Marlin	2350	240	SP	2,221	4,997
.45-70 Gov't.	1315	405	SP	3,500	7,875
.450 Marlin	2225	325	SP	3,500	7,000

COMMERCIAL MAGNUM RIFLE CALIBERS

Caliber	Muzzle Velocity (f.p.s.)	Bullet Weight (grs.)	Bullet Style	Maximum Range (yds.)	Height (ft.)
.243 WSSM	3250	95	SP	4,250	8,400
.25 WSSM	3060	115	SP	5,000	9,900
.257 Wby. Mag.	3400	115	SP	5,400	10,700
.264 Win. Mag.	3030	140	SP	4,875	10,969
.270 WSM	3275	130	SP	5,300	10,500
.270 Wby. Mag.	3280	130	SP	5,000	9,900
7 mm Rem. Mag.	2950	165	SP	6,951	15,640
7 mm Rem. Ultra	3325	150	SP	5,000	9,900
8 mm Rem. Mag.	2900	200	SP	4,850	10,913
.300 Win. Mag.	2960	180	SP	5,312	11,952
.300 Rem. Ultra	3450	150	SP	4,700	9,300
.300 Rem. SAUM	2900	190	SP	5,800	11,500
.300 WSM	3010	180	SP	5,700	11,300
.300 Wby. Mag.	3110	180	SP	5,800	11,500
.325 WSM	3060	180	SP	5,000	9,900
.338 Win. Mag.	2960	225	SP	5,179	11,653
.340 Wby. Mag.	2900	225	SP	4,400	8,700
.338 Lapua Mag.	2940	250	SP	7,000	13,900
.350 Rem. Mag.	2710	200	SP	3,877	8,723
.375 H&H Mag.	2530	300	SP	4,088	9,198
.375 Rem. Ultra	2760	300	SP	4,400	8,700
.416 Rigby	2440	400	SP	2,400	4,800
.416 Rem. Mag.	2400	400	SP	2,400	4,800
.416 Wby. Mag.	2850	350	SP	2,900	5,800
.458 Win. Mag.	2040	500	SP	4,235	9,529
.458 Lott	2300	500	SP	4,400	8,700
.460 Wby. Mag.	2700	450	SP	4,700	9,300

Abbreviations: TP—tipped; HP—hollow point; SP—soft-point; FMJBT—full-metal-jacketed boattail; SPBT—soft-point boattail; LRN—lead round-nose

COMMERCIAL PISTOL CALIBERS

Caliber	Muzzle Velocity (f.p.s.)	Bullet Weight (grs.)	Bullet Style	Maximum Range (yds.)	Maximum Height (ft.)
.25 ACP	760	50	FMJ	1,194	2,687
.30 Luger	1220	93	FMJ	2,280	5,130
.32 ACP	905	71	FMJ	1,505	3,386
.357 SIG	1350	125	FMJ	2,200	4,400
9x19 mm Luger	1140	124	FMJ	2,130	4,793
.38 Super Auto+P	1215	130	FMJ	2,295	5,164
.380 ACP	970	95	FMJ	1,090	2,453
10 mm Auto	1290	155	FMJ	2,227	5,010
.40 S&W	990	180	FMJ	2,200	4,400
.45 ACP +P	1140	185	JHP	1,840	4,140
.45 Win. Mag.	1200	260	FMJ	2,051	4,615

COMMERCIAL REVOLVER CALIBERS

Caliber	Muzzle Velocity (f.p.s.)	Bullet Weight (grs.)	Bullet Style	Maximum Range (yds.)	Maximum Height (ft.)
.32 Short Colt	745	80	LRN	1,030	2,318
.32 S&W Short	680	85	LRN	1,191	2,680
.32 S&W Long	705	98	LRN	1,277	2,873
.32 H&R Mag.	1100	85	JHP	1,800	3,600
.38 Short Colt	730	125	LRN	1,434	3,227
.38 S&W	685	145	LRN	1,411	3,175
.38 Special	755	158	LRN	1,739	3,913
.38 Special +P	945	125	JHP	2,257	5,078
.357 Mag.	1235	158	JSP	2,398	5,396
.41 Rem. Mag.	1300	210	JSP	2,095	4,714
.44 Special	755	246	LRN	1,879	4,228
.44 Rem. Mag.	1350	240	JSP	2,477	5,573
.45 Colt	860	250	LRN	1,853	4,169

SHOTSHELLS

Pellet Number/Type	Muzzle Velocity (f.p.s.)	Maximum Range (yds.)	Height (ft.)
10-ga. 1¾ oz. Foster rifled slug	1280	1,350	3,100
12-ga. 1¼ oz. Foster rifled slug	1600	1,300	3,000
12-ga. 1 oz. Foster rifled slug	1610	1,260	2,835
16-ga. ⁴/₅ oz. Foster rifled slug	1600	1,270	2,858
20-ga. ³/₄ oz. Foster rifled slug	1680	1,045	2,351
.410 bore ¼ oz. Foster rifled slug	1775	920	2,070
000 buckshot lead	1325	698	1,634
00 buckshot lead	1325	649	1,528
0 buckshot lead	1275	628	1,475
No. 1 buckshot lead	1250	593	1,396
No. 2 buckshot lead	1200	540	1,237
No. 3 buckshot lead	1200	507	1,201
No. 4 buckshot lead	1325	502	1,196
00 Buckshot Hevi	1325	692	1,615
No. 2 Hevi	1300	362	870
No. 4 Hevi	1325	322	776
No. 5 Hevi	1300	283	688
No. 6 Hevi	1325	281	679
No. 7½ Hevi	1325	248	604
BBB tungsten-iron	1450	398	956
BB tungsten-iron	1450	380	916
No. 2 tungsten-iron	1450	327	791
No. 4 tungsten-iron	1400	291	705
No. 5 tungsten-iron	1400	272	661
No. 1 tungsten-matrix	1375	345	831
No. 3 tungsten-matrix	1400	313	760
No. 5 tungsten-matrix	1400	276	672
No. 6 tungsten-matrix	1400	257	626
BB bismuth	1330	358	860
No. 2 bismuth	1330	308	745
No. 4 bismuth	1330	274	665
No. 5 bismuth	1330	257	624
No. 6 bismuth	1330	238	582
No. 7½ bismuth	1330	211	517
F steel	1350	356	858
T steel	1500	335	814
BBB steel	1500	321	782
BB steel	1500	307	749
No. 1 steel	1500	279	682
No. 2 steel	1500	264	648

SHOTSHELLS continued

Pellet Number/Type	Muzzle Velocity (f.p.s.)	Maximum Range (yds.)	Height (ft.)
No. 3 steel	1500	250	613
No. 4 steel	1500	235	578
No. 6 steel	1450	204	502
No. 7 steel	1300	185	455
BB lead	1330	399	958
No. 2 lead	1330	344	830
No. 4 lead	1400	308	749
No. 5 lead	1400	289	703
No. 6 lead	1400	269	656
No. 7½ lead	1400	238	583
No. 8 lead	1295	225	550
No. 8½ lead	1325	212	518
No. 9 lead	1230	200	486

Hunting Safety Afield

In addition to the fundamental firearm safety rules, there are additional safety rules that apply specifically to hunting.

- Be positive of your target's identity before shooting.

- Take time to fire a safe shot. If unsure, if you must move too quickly, pass up the shot. When in doubt—don't! When you wonder whether you should shoot—don't.

- If you fall, try to control where the muzzle points. After a fall, check your gun for dirt and damage and make sure the barrel is free of obstructions.

- Unload your gun before attempting to climb a steep bank or travel across slippery ground.

- When you are alone and must cross a fence, unload your firearm and place it under the fence with the muzzle pointed away from where you are crossing. When hunting with others and you must cross a fence, unload the gun and keep the action open. Have one of your companions hold the gun while you cross. When over the fence, take your gun and your companion's unloaded gun, so that he may cross safely.

- Never use a scope sight as a substitute for binoculars.

- When finished hunting, unload your firearm before returning to camp.

Rules are safe only when they are obeyed. If a companion doesn't follow the rules of safe firearms handling, discuss it with him immediately. Until the behavior is corrected it would be unwise to continue to hunt with him.

Miscellaneous Safety Topics

Bore Obstructions

Any object in the bore that impedes the progress of the bullet toward the muzzle has the potential of raising pressures to a hazardous level. There are many types of objects that can serve as bore obstructions: cleaning patches, snow, mud, dirt or other material that may be collected from the environment; even bullets from a squib load or portions of a bullet jacket.

The results of a bore obstruction vary, depending upon the thickness of the barrel walls, strength and type of action, the pressure of the cartridge, the weight of the obstruction and where the obstruction is located.

An obstruction in or just forward of the chamber has the effect of augmenting the weight of the bullet or shot charge and therefore increases chamber pressure. The potential for damage to the firearm depends upon the amount of this pressure increase, the construction of the action and breech, and the strength of the case. If the increase in pressure is only moderate, little or no damage may result.

An obstruction in the middle or forward part of the barrel may cause a ring bulge or, in some cases, bursting of the barrel at that point. This damage results from the impact of the projectile(s) with the obstruction. The weight of the obstruction, speed of the bullet or shot charge, and thickness of the barrel wall determines the extent of the damage. Cases have been seen in which a separated bullet jacket in the bore caused a small ring bulge and was ironed into the bore at that point, allowing the passage of subsequent bullets without other signs noticeable by the shooter.

Occasionally, a burst shotgun barrel is produced when a too-small shell is inadvertently dropped into a shotgun chamber and becomes lodged in the bore, and is impacted by the shot charge or slug of a subsequent shell. This can happen with a 20-ga. shell mistakenly inserted into a 12-ga. chamber: The undersize shell is lodged forward of the chamber and the shooter, seeing an empty chamber, loads a 12-ga. shell into that barrel and fires it. The 20-ga. shell not only acts as a bore obstruction, but itself often fires when hit by the 12-ga. load.

Barrel damage from defects in the structure or material of the steel (such as the bursting of a Damascus barrel fired with high-pressure smokeless powder loads) presents a different appearance than damage resulting from an obstruction. Also, while a heavy obstruction in the chamber end of the barrel may indeed damage an action, those in the middle or forward part of the barrel (such as occur when mud or snow get in the muzzle) may damage only the barrel and not the action.

Fortunately, it is fairly easy to avoid the hazards of bore obstructions. After cleaning the bore, visually inspect it for patches or other objects. In the field, keep the gun's muzzle away from snow, water and mud. At all times, if a squib load is suspected, unload the firearm, open the action and ensure the bore is clear, either by visual inspection or by running a cleaning rod the length of the bore.

Potentially Hazardous Guns

With millions of firearms having been produced, including firearms from almost every nation, in myriad types and models and by many different manufacturers, it is inevitable that there would be a handful of guns whose design flaws or manufacturing defects make them hazardous to use. The accompanying table lists a number of the more common of these "problem guns."

RECURRING PROBLEMS WITH SPECIFIC MODELS

GUN	PROBLEM	SOLUTION
Springfield M1903 rifles with serial numbers lower than 800,000 from Springfield Armory, or 285,507 from Rock Island Arsenal	Single-heat-treatment receivers are subject to sudden catastrophic failure.	Do not fire under any circumstances. Receivers cannot be heat-treated.
Japanese Type 94 semi-auto service pistols caliber 8 mm Nambu	Exposed sear bar can cause discharge if pressed without pulling the trigger.	Handle carefully.
U.S. military Krag M1892 rifles caliber .30-40 Krag	Some bolts develop cracks behind locking lug in rest.	Have gunsmith inspect gun. Scrap guns with cracked lug. Fire only factory ammunition of recent manufacture.
Ross straight-pull military rifles in calibers .280 Ross and .303 British	Bolt can be improperly reassembled after cleaning, causing bolt to be blown out of receiver when fired.	Reassemble correctly and double-check procedure.
Swedish M/40 semi-auto service pistols in caliber 9 mm Luger	Many examples made during World War II have weak steel frames that may crack.	Have gunsmith inspect gun. Do not fire high-velocity ammo. Retire guns with cracked frames.
Trapdoor Springfield military rifles in caliber .45-70 Gov't	Actions are weak.	Have gunsmith inspect gun. Fire only moderate pressure factory ammunition of recent manufacture.

Damascus Barrels

Up until the latter part of the 19th century, many shotguns featured so-called "Damascus" or "twist" barrels. These were produced by twisting and welding together long strips of steel and iron (which eliminated or minimized flaws in the metal), flattening out the twisted mass into a ribbon, and then wrapping it spirally around a mandrel. The edges of the spiral ribbon were then welded together to form a tube. Damascus barrels are identified from the beautiful and striking patterns often produced by the alternating layers of iron and steel. Acid etching was often used to accentuate these patterns.

It must be remembered that many, if not most, of the shotguns made with Damascus barrels were intended for use with blackpowder shotgun shells, which develop less pressure than even light smokeless powder loads (and also have a different pressure curve). Neither the actions nor the barrels of many Damascus-barreled guns were made sturdily enough in the breech area to handle smokeless powder ammunition.

The best Damascus barrels made by Belgian and English gunmakers were regarded as strong and elastic. However, differentiating these barrels from the plethora of inferior-grade Damascus tubes produced all over Europe is a job for an expert. These barrels, made of soft iron poorly welded together, are not only weak, but also tend to rust and pit readily.

Some authorities consider the best Damascus barrels, properly proofed, to be capable of handling light smokeless powder loads. However, considerable expertise, probably beyond that of the average gunsmith, is required to determine which Damascus barrels are safe with such ammunition. With these considerations in mind, the owner of even a "best quality" shotgun with Damascus barrels should avoid firing the gun with any smokeless-powder loads.

It should also be noted that many imitation Damascus barrels have been produced, such as by stencil-etching or through the application of contrasting patterns of varnish. Also, the finish of any barrel will wear and fade with time, often hiding the Damascus pattern. Determining barrel type can be made by polishing the finish off a small area of the barrel under the forearm and treating that area with a small amount of hydrochloric acid. Where the acid was applied, a solid gray patch will be seen if the barrel is solid steel; if Damascus, the original pattern of alternating iron/steel layers will be apparent.

Fire-Damaged Guns

Steel that has been heated beyond the critical point (around 1,400 to 1,500 degrees F for high-carbon steel) for a prolonged period, and then allowed to cool gradually, is essentially undergoing an annealing process that will reduce its hardness and strength. In a fire, a gun not protected by a gun safe may well be exposed to such temperature levels, potentially weakening its barrel or receiver and making it more susceptible to failure under the stresses of modern high-pressure ammunition. Any gun that has been in a fire should therefore be treated with suspicion, especially if there is evidence of exposure to high heat levels. An experienced gunsmith equipped with a Rockwell hardness tester should be able to assess the safety of any such gun.

Vision and Hearing Protection

In addition to observing the rules of gun safety, which primarily serve to protect the property and lives of others, shooters must also protect themselves through the use of appropriate eye and ear protection.

A shooter's eyes are vulnerable to many potential hazards while firing or handling a gun. During shooting, eye damage can occur from high-pressure gas escaping from a split case or pierced primer; flying particles of brass, copper, lead or powder; lead or copper back-splatter from the impact of a bullet on a steel target at close range; an errant shot pellet in the field, and even shards of metal and stock material in the event of a catastrophic gun failure. Hazards to vision may also occur during gun maintenance, cleaning and repair, from sprayed solvents as well as from spring-powered parts that may unexpectedly fly free of the gun during disassembly. For these reasons, eye protection should always be worn by anyone who is shooting, cleaning or disassembling a firearm, or who is in the proximity of a firearm discharge (such as a spectator at a shooting event).

While normal prescription eyeglasses provide some protection, safety glasses or goggles with tempered glass or synthetic lenses specifically designed for shooting or industrial use are preferable. Wraparound models generally provide better coverage than flat lenses. Some shooting glasses are designed to withstand the penetration of small shot pellets fired from a shotgun shell.

Shooting glasses or goggles for shooters also come in various tints; these typically improve clarity on cloudy days or cut glare on sunny days. Tint has no effect on the protection against penetration a lens provides.

Studies have shown that exposure of the unprotected ears to the sound of even a single gunshot can cause measurable permanent hearing loss. Thus, hearing protection should always be worn whenever one is shooting a firearm or in the proximity of gunshots.

Hearing protection generally takes the form of ear plugs and ear muffs. Both devices can be had in several versions. Ear plugs are just that: plugs of flexible material that fit in the auditory canal and reduce the strength of sound waves. Some are even molded to the shooter's ears. Ear muffs cover each ear with a cup of foam or other sound-reducing material, the two cups being connected by a flexible band that goes over or behind the head.

Both ear plugs and muffs come in electronic versions containing circuitry that passes sounds of normal intensity, such as conversation, to the ears, but which dampens high-intensity sounds, such as gunshots. Such devices would seem especially suitable for hunters, who often forgo conventional hearing protection altogether because it would hinder their ability to hear the approach of game animals.

Hearing protection devices are rated in terms of their ability to reduce sound intensity. The higher this Noise Reduction Rating (NRR), the more protection the ear plugs or ear muffs provide. An NRR rating of at least 22 is recommended for effective hearing protection. For even greater protection, some shooters wear both ear plugs and ear muffs.

Dry-Fire Safety

Dry firing, the releasing of the firing pin on an unloaded chamber of a firearm, is an inexpensive, safe and time-efficient way to enhance shooting skill. Dry-fire practice can be used to reinforce fundamentals, improve coordination and the speed of the draw from a holster, and to perfect the various shooting positions. Dry-firing involves practicing every phase of the firing process using an unloaded firearm. All that is missing is the blast and recoil of an actual discharge. When dry-firing a rimfire, it is strongly advisable that a snap-cap or dummy cartridge is used to relieve wear caused by the firing pin.

All dry-fire practice must be performed in accordance with the following safety rules:
- the firearm must be completely unloaded
- all dry-firing is done in a dedicated dry-fire area having a safe backstop at which the gun is pointed
- no live ammunition is allowed in the dedicated dry-fire area
- if reloading drills are performed, only dummy ammunition is used
- eye protection must always be worn.

Of course, even though the firearm is unloaded, it is still important to observe the first basic rule of gun safety—always keep the firearm pointed in a safe direction.

Range Safety and Etiquette

Most shooting is done at a range, which can be anything from an empty field with a suitable backstop to a modern indoor facility with automatic targets and state-of-the-art ventilation. All of the established rules of gun safety and safe gun handling apply when shooting at a range; however, additional rules and procedures also apply.

Identifying Range Areas—Whenever visiting a range for the first time, a shooter should identify important range areas, including:
- ready line or preparation area
- firing line(s)
- target holders

- backstop/impact area
- downrange (safe) direction(s)
- left/right range limits
- firing points and firing line numbers
- safety berms, walls, baffles
- entry and exit routes
- range flags or warning markers
- first-aid kit
- fire extinguishers
- telephone (with local emergency number if not 911).

Obey Range Safety Rules—Most ranges have their own safety rules, which are usually posted. It is the responsibility of the shooter to:
- know and obey all range safety rules
- know where others are at all times
- shoot only at authorized targets
- stop shooting immediately if you have experienced an ammunition malfunction.

Range Commands—At many ranges, there are range personnel—usually one or more range officers—who control range activities and can provide assistance to shooters when necessary. Range officers usually issue the following three basic range commands:
- "Load" (shooters may load their firearms, but keep safeties on)
- "Ready on the right, ready on the left? Commence firing" (shooters may take safeties off and fire in a safe direction)
- "Cease fire" (shooters must IMMEDIATELY stop firing, take their trigger finger off the trigger, keep the gun pointed in a safe direction and unload, then wait for further instructions from the range officer).

Note that "cease fire" is a safety command that can and should be given by anyone who observes an unsafe situation. Also, all shooters must immediately stop firing when anyone gives the "cease fire" command.

At many ranges, there may be additional commands to indicate to the shooters when the range is clear, or when shooters may go forward and change or mark their targets. Also, there are often special commands used in specific competitive shooting activities.

Handling Malfunctions at the Range—When a suspected hangfire or misfire occurs at the range, the shooter should:
- keep the gun pointed downrange or in a safe direction
- wait at least 30 seconds before opening the action on a modern cartridge firearm and two minutes with a muzzleloader in case the problem is a hangfire
- raise the non-shooting hand to notify any range personnel of a problem and to summon their assistance.

When a suspected squib load occurs at the range, the shooter should:
- stop firing immediately
- keep the gun pointed downrange or in a safe direction
- raise the non-shooting hand to notify any range personnel of a problem and to summon their assistance
- unload the gun and make sure the chamber is empty
- insert a cleaning rod down the bore from the chamber end, if possible, to make sure there is no bullet lodged in the bore.

Hygiene During and After Shooting—While firing or cleaning a firearm, a shooter may be exposed to potentially harmful lead particles or chemical residues. Thus, the following rules should be observed.
- While shooting or cleaning a firearm, don't eat, drink, smoke or otherwise place the hands close to the nose or mouth, to prevent the ingestion of lead or chemical residues.
- After shooting or cleaning a firearm, wash the hands and face thoroughly with soap and cold water before eating, drinking, smoking or engaging in any other activity (such as applying lipstick) that would put the hands in proximity to the nose or mouth.
- Change and wash clothing as soon as possible after shooting or cleaning a firearm to minimize exposure to lead.

Range Etiquette—There are a number of additional common sense rules which, though bearing but indirectly on safety, nonetheless promote mutual courtesy at the range.
- Do not handle any firearm while other shooters are downrange checking or changing targets. This includes cleaning, adjusting sights, moving the gun on the rest, etc.
- Do not handle any other shooter's gun, ammunition and/or equipment without his or her permission.
- Be aware of the firing cadence of the shooters next to you and try to avoid firing simultaneously with them.
- Avoid starting up unnecessary conversations with other shooters while they are firing, particularly if they are sighting-in, testing loads or engaged in some other activity requiring concentration.
- Police up all your brass, targets, empty ammunition boxes and other trash.
- Do not pick up another shooter's brass; he or she may intend to use it for reloading.
- Do not engage in boisterous, loud or distracting behavior that might annoy other shooters.

Safety Standards

With dozens if not hundreds of gunmakers and ammunition manufacturers in the United States, standards had to be developed to ensure that any given cartridge could be fired safely in any firearm chambered for it. This, in turn, required standardization of chamber dimensions, as well as cartridge dimensions, pressures and ballistics. In the United States, the organization responsible for setting, maintaining and reviewing such standards is the Sporting Arms and Ammunition Manufacturers' Institute, commonly known as SAAMI.

SAAMI uses the most modern technology and the highest available technical expertise in ballistics, metallurgy, chemistry, physics, engineering and many other relevant fields to develop safety standards for the manufacture and testing of firearms and ammunition. Although adherence to these standards is voluntary, acceptance of the standards by the firearms industry is essentially universal. SAAMI also distributes a variety of safety publications available to both the public and the industry, and has developed a glossary of standardized definitions for common firearms-related terms.

In Europe, the Commission Internationale Permanente des Armes a Feu Portative (CIP), an international association of proof houses headquartered in Liege, Belgium, performs much the same function. Adherence to CIP standards and proof procedures is mandated by law in most European countries, with many of these nations having additional regulations as well.

SAAMI and CIP standards for chamber and cartridge dimensions are similar; chamber pressure figures are not, however. In most cases, these variations reflect differences in the procedures used to measure chamber pressure. SAAMI and CIP are working together toward the development of international standards. Gunmakers in locations other than North America or Europe generally adhere to either SAAMI or CIP standards.

SAAMI
11 Mile Hill Road
Newtown, CT 06470
www.saami.org

CIP
Rue Fond des Tawes 45
4000 Liege, BELGIUM
www.cip-bp.org

Chapter 2
FIREARMS HISTORY

Mankind has always been fascinated by objects that fly through the air. Our ancestors quickly realized that harnessing the speed and power of such objects would provide them a powerful tool. Thus began a thread of technological development lasting thousands of years, starting with the rock, then the spear, sling, bow, crossbow...and eventually the gun. However, as nature gave up its secrets grudgingly, technology advanced only slowly for centuries.

Around 1248, the English monk Roger Bacon recorded the formula for gunpowder in his manuscript *De secretis operibus artis et naturae*. Bacon again mentioned gunpowder in his tract *Opus Majus* written in 1260. About the same time, Albertus Magnus recorded a formula for gunpowder in his *De mirabilius mundi ignium* and Berthold Schwartz experimented with gunpowder in Germany.

As these men ushered in the Age of Gunpowder, little did they suspect the major changes gunpowder would create in the social order, political systems, military tactics, architecture, science and industry.

By 1326, cannons were illustrated in Walter de Milimete's manuscript *De officiis regum* dedicated to Edward III's accession to the English throne. Edward III later became well known for his use of the cannon in battle. From this, note two interesting developments:
- Gunpowder's potential to propel objects through the air with great force was appreciated very quickly in Europe.
- Technical efforts to harness the potential of gunpowder in Europe proceeded at an unusually rapid pace.

As a direct result, development of firearms in Western civilization began and continues unabated to this day. Now, after nearly eight centuries, firearms development is one of the oldest threads of technological development in recorded history.

Gunnery is at once a science and an art. The science consists in varying parts of chemistry, metallurgy, engineering, physics, mathematics, geometry, ballistics and tactics. The art of gunnery comes from the ability to interpolate between the known and the unknown borders of science relying on experience and sober judgement tempered by prudence. These attributes can only be acquired by extensive study, experience and training.

For these reasons, throughout history gunners have been considered special people quite apart from the rest of an army. As early monarchs could not afford their full-time services, professional gunners became highly specialized mercenaries selling their skills wherever needed. Common uses for hired gunners were sieges and the defense of cities, ports and castles. Sieges often took months or even years. With the advent of cannon that could demolish defensive castle or city walls in a matter of hours, the tactics of sieges and their length changed dramatically.

Gunners closely held their expertise to maintain their profession and its value. It was common practice during a siege for gunpowder to be mixed and cannon cast on-site. During an engagement, gunners always held themselves apart from other members of an army as they considered themselves a professional elite. In addition to cash payments for services rendered, gunners were normally given the church bells of a city after a successful siege. From such bells, more cannon could be cast.

Gunpowder forever changed military tactics by making it possible for the common foot soldier armed with a gun to defeat an armored knight of the nobility. This development doomed the feudal social and political system and enabled the rise of nation-states and absolute monarchs.

With the rise of nation-states, monarchs could afford the full-time services of professional gunners who were incorporated into the standing, professional armies. From this came the traditions of ordnance corps in military service. Ordnance officers brought a new level of professionalism to the science and art of firearms.

Professional military and ordnance officers were very active in developing new ideas leading to technical advancements such as a breechloading flintlock rifle (Maj. Ferguson 1776), self-contained primers (Col. Boxer 1866 and Col. Berdan 1868), smokeless propellants (Capt. Schultz 1864), jacketed bullets (Lt. Col. Bode 1874 and Col. Rubin 1881), a self-loading rifle (Gen. Mondragon 1908) and the Thompson submachine gun (Gen. Thompson 1919).

Nations needed armies and armies needed guns—lots of them of a similar pattern. This was a serious problem until Eli Whitney developed mass production of interchangeable parts specifically for firearms. In so doing, Whitney laid the foundation for modern manufacturing.

Here, one must not forget the civilians who by their perseverance and determination advanced the science and the art of firearms with inventions such as percussion ignition (Forsythe 1807), percussion cap (Shaw 1814), Gatling gun (Gatling 1862), revolver (Colt 1836), smokeless powder (Vielle 1884), machine gun (Maxim 1884), bolt-action rifles (Mannlicher and Mauser circa 1890), semi-auto pistol (Luger 1900) and M1911 pistol (Browning 1911).

This thread of development continues today with military and civilian firearms designers such as Garand (M1 rifle 1936), Schmeisser (assault rifle 1944), Kalashnikov (AK-47 rifle 1947), Gal (Uzi submachine gun 1952), and Stoner (M16 rifle 1964).

Historic Notes

Early Formulas For Gunpowder

Take 1 lb. of native sulphur, 2 lb. of linden or willow charcoal, 6 lb. of native salpetre, which three things are very finely powdered on a marble slab. Then put as much powder as desired into a case to make flying fire or thunder. Note: ... The case for making thunder should be short and thick and half filled with the said powder and at each end strongly bound with iron wire.

Marcus Graecus
Book of Fires
Anno circa 1225

But however of stone of Tagus (salpetre), take seven parts, five parts of young hazelwood (charcoal) and five parts vapor of pearl (sulphur), and so you will make thunder and lightning ...

Roger Bacon
De secretis operibus artis et naturae et de nulliate magiae
(On the marvellous power of art and of nature and on the nullity of magic)
Anno circa 1248

The salpetre is the Soule, the Sulphur is the Life and the Coales the Body of it.

John Bate
The Mysteries of Nature and Art
Anno circa 1650

The Battle Of Crecy—
A Pivotal Event In Firearms History

On August 26, 1346, the English and French armies met in battle at Crecy in northern France. Led by King Philip of Valois, the French army numbered over 40,000 men while the English army led by Edward III consisted of less than 20,000 men. While the two armies seemed badly mismatched, Edward III introduced two new weapons to the battlefield for the first time—the longbow and the cannon. There were 11,000 longbowmen and two cannons in the English Army. The longbowmen practically annihilated the French knights, while it was recorded than the cannon caused the Italian mercenary crossbowmen "much discomfort." This is the first documented use of firearms in land warfare.

What It Takes To Be A Gunner

A gunner ought to be sober, wakefull, lusty, hardy, patient, prudent and a quick-spirited man, he ought also to have good eyesight, a good judgement and perfect knowledge to select a convenient place on the day of service, to plant his Ordnance where he may do most hurt unto enemies and be least annoyed by them ...

Nicolo Tartaglai
La Nova Sciento Invento
Anno 1537

The Art of Great Ordnance

See that every gunner is able to discharge his duty, and not for favor or affection to preferre such as say most and doe least, but that every man be preferred to place credit and esteem according to his honest behavior, and skill at his singular art...not to suffer every tagge and ragge to be a gunner as is too much used these days in Townes of Garrison, who are never practised in the Art, nor hath discretion nor desire to practise therein: A great number of such have but only the bare name of a gunner, although their standing hath been of a long time.

Having seen and observed the wonderful ignorance of many professors of the Gunner's Art I began to consider whether this neglect do rise from the gunners or the Commanders and I find the fault to be in both, in the Commanders because either they do not know how to exercise the gunners under their charge and command, and the idle laziness of the gunners that had rather spend their time potting and canning than in the knowledge of their Pieces or the practise of their profession.

Therefore, I call upon all that are Governors and Commanders of Castles or Forts to consider your gunner, of what disposition he be, as well towards God as Faithfull towards his Commander and Country, for it is most certain that a man that fears God cannot be disloyal to his Prince or Commander, to make such a man your Mr. Gunner, and let all the other gunners be ruled and directed by him.

The Art is like a circle without end, or like to a Labyrinth, where a man being well entered in, knoweth not how to get out againe, and therefore it must be exercise and industry that must make a perfect gunner.

William Eldred
Master Gunner of Dover Castle
Anno 1646

Historic Impact of Guns

The invention of gunpowder hath quite altered the condition of Martial Affairs over the world, both by sea and by land.

Robert Boyle
Anno 1664

Chaucer on Firearms

Swift as a pillet out of a gonne
When fire is in the pouder ronne

Geofrey Chaucer
House Of Fame **b. ii:**
Anno circa 1373

Time Line of Firearms Development

Year	Event
850 circa	Gunpowder first made in China
1004	First mention of gunpowder in Chinese literature
1067	Chinese emperor places production of salpetre and sulphur under state control
1225	Marcus Graecus reveals formula for gunpowder in his *Liber Ignum*
1250 circa	Roger Bacon records formula for gunpowder in *De secretis operibus artis ...*
	Albertus Magnus reveals formula for gunpowder in *De mirabilis mundi ignium*
	Berthold Schwartz experiments with powder in Germany
1259	City of Melilla in North Africa defended by a cannon
1280	First guns appear in China
1308	Guns used by Spanish in siege of Gibraltar
1325	Florentine Republic orders two officers to make cannon for city defense
1326	First known illustration of a cannon in Milemete's *De officiis regum*
1327	Scots record first seeing firearms at the Battle of Werewater in Britain
1338	Cannons recorded as equipment of English ship *Bernard de la Tour*
	Records show gunpowder being stored in Tower of London
1340	Guns first used at sea in Battle of Sluys by Edward III of England
	Powder mill built in Augsburg, Germany
1344	Edward III's household staffed with "artillers and gonners"
1346	English Army uses cannons against French at Battle of Crecy
1364	Metal hand-cannon made at Perugia, Italy
1370 circa	Frequent references in literature to guns on ships

1381	Town of Augsburg supplies 30 men with hand-cannon to Swabian forces
1400	Henry IV of England records payments for "quarrel gonnes, salpetre and wadding"
1410	Invention of matchlock
1411	Burgundy in France inventories 2,000 "volley guns" on carts
1421	Venetians employ primitive explosive shells called "granata" (grenade)
1428	Henry IV records show payments for *bastons a feu* (handguns)
1429	First mention of wet method of incorporating powder ingredients in France
1431	Hand-cannon figure conspicuously in siege of Lucca by Florentines in Italy
1432	Gunsmiths of Kunitomo chartered to make guns by shogun in Kyoto, Japan
1449	Bomarde (hand-cannon) illustrated in manuscript of Marianus Jacobus
1450 circa	Explosive shell perfected in Netherlands
	Corning (granulation) wet method of powder making perfected
	Gunmaking begins in St. Etienne, France
1460	Mons Meg giant cannon cast at Mons, Belgium
1463	Gunsmiths in Suhl, Germany, incorporate as craft guild
1470	Rifled barrels invented in Nuremberg, Germany
	Shoulder stocks and snapping matchlock developed
1473	First illustration of handgun in England in royal manuscript
1476	Swiss field 6,000 culveriners with hand-cannons at Battle of Morat
1490	Hand-cannon in widespread use as military weapon in Europe
1500	Improved metallurgy allows stronger gun barrels firing cast iron balls
	Leonardo da Vinci illustrates wheellock

1503	Firearms make first significant military impact at Battle of Cerignola in Spain
1515	Henry VIII inventories over 400 cannon in Tower of London
1516	Beretta manufactures arquebus barrels in Gardone, Italy, for doges of Venice
1518	Wheellock banned in Holy Roman Empire
1525	Peter Bawde casts first cannon in England for Henry VIII
1526	Pietro Beretta firm established in Brescia, Italy
1535	Jagd-und Sportwaffen (Merkel) firm established in Suhl, Germany
1537	First breechloading handgun made for Henry VIII in England
1540	Caminello Vitelli introduces his pistol in Pistoia, Italy
1543	Portuguese sell firearms in Japan
1544	First use of handguns by German cavalry at Battle of Renty
1545	Henry VIII employs craftsmen to make guns in Tower of London
1550	Invention of snaphaunce lock
	Corned powder replaces serpentine powder
	Rifled barrels now coming into use
1558	Ferlach Guild of gunmakers established in Ferlach, Austria
1570	Muskets fired from rest common in European armies
1577	Cataneo describes gun manufacture in Brescia, Italy
1578	Powder tester or *eprouvette* first described by Bourne in *Inventions and Devices*
1586	Paper cartridge containing bullet and powder invented
1587	Arndt Krupp founds Krupp armament dynasty in Germany
1588	British naval gunnery defeats Spanish Armada
1600	Invention of miquelet lock in Spain
1603	Valentine discovers gold fulminate

1604	Guy Fawkes Gunpowder Plot in England uncovered
1610	Invention of flintlock by Marin Le Bourgeoys in France
	Damascus barrel making becomes known in Europe
1627	Earliest record of gunpowder being used for blasting in mines
	Furtenburg invents improved powder tester in Germany
1637	London Gunmakers Guild obtains charter of incorporation
1650	Flintlock in common use
1672	Proof house established in London, England
	Proof of gun barrels becomes compulsory in Liege, Belgium
1674	John Maynow recognizes salpetre is potassium nitrate
1683	Birmingham gun trade established in England
1693	Proof house established in Birmingham, England
1720	British Army adopts Brown Bess Land Pattern Musket
1721	Vincenzo Bernardelli established in Brescia, Italy
1735	John Rigby & Co. (Gunmakers) Inc. established in Dublin, Ireland
1740	Incorporation milling of powder manufacture perfected
1742	Benjamin Robins conducts velocity tests, publishes *New Principles of Gunnery*
1748	Renato Gamba established in Gardone, V.T., Italy
1751	J.P. Sauer & Son established in Suhl, Germany
1770	Cogswell & Harrison Gunmakers Ltd. established in London, England
	Specialized dueling pistols emerge
1772	Gunpowder Act bans powder stamping mills in England as unsafe
1774	Bayen discovers fulminate of mercury in France
	British Parliament prohibits export of powder to America
1775	War of American Independence begins

1776	Maj. Patrick Ferguson patents breechloading carbine flintlock rifle
1777	Ferguson breechloader used in combat during Revolutionary War (Ferguson killed in 1780)
1781	War of American Independence ends
	Choke boring of shotgun barrels well known
1784	Capt. Henry Shrapnel invents the shrapnel shell
1793	Austrian sharpshooters adopt Girandoni repeating air rifle for combat
1795	Springfield Armory established in Springfield, MA
	U.S. Model 1795 Musket adopted as first standard American military arm
	Thomas Blanchard invents an interchangeable stock lathe at Springfield Armory, MA
1798	Eli Whitney institutes concept of interchangeable parts made to specification
	Whitney Arms Co. established in New Haven, CT
1800	Pierre Samuel du Pont de Nemours emigrates to America from France
	First barrel-straightening devices used
1803	Lewis & Clark's Corps of Discovery armed with rifles from Harpers Ferry Arsenal, either U.S. Contract 1792 or U.S. Model 1803. Lewis also notes use of an air rifle.
1804	E.I. du Pont de Nemours & Co. begins making powder in Delaware
1805	Auguste Francotte & Cie. S.A. firm established in Liege, Belgium
1807	U.S. Army/Navy adopt Harper's Ferry Model 1807 flintlock pistol
	Rev. Alexander Forsythe patents percussion system of firearms ignition (pill lock)
1808	Shrapnel shell first used in combat by British Army against French

1812   U.S. Ordnance Dept. established

Boss & Co. established in London, England
First cartridge breechloader patented by Jean Pauly
in Switzerland; Pauly perfects paper cap

Westley Richards & Co. Ltd. established
in Birmingham, England

1814   Joshua Shaw perfects percussion cap ignition in U.S.

James Purdy & Sons Ltd. established in London, England

Allegheny Arsenal established in Lawrenceville, PA

Watervliet Arsenal established in West Troy, NY

1816   Joseph Manton invents tube lock ignition in England

Jean Samuel Pauly patents principle of
cartridge-sealing breech

Remington begins making guns in Herkimer, NY

Frankford Arsenal established in Philadelphia, PA

Washington Arsenal established in Washington, DC

Watertown Arsenal established in Boston, MA

1817   U.S. Army adopts Hall Rifle—first breechloading
U.S. military rifle

1820   Verney-Carron established in St. Etienne, France

1825   Elongated bullets developed

1827   Kennebec Arsenal established in Augusta, ME

1828   Eley Bros. Ammunition Co. founded in England

1829   Nicolas von Dreyse invents needlefire ignition

W.W. Greener Co. founded in England

1831   August Demondion patents breechloading percussion gun
and cartridge in France

1832   Ethan Allen Co. established in Grafton, MA

St. Louis Arsenal established in MO

Henri Braconnot discovers nitric acid

1833   Henry Deringer introduces small concealable single-shot
pistol in U.S.

1835	Colt introduces Paterson No. 1 revolver
	New York Arsenal established on Governor's Island, NY
	Flobert Cap introduced in France
	Holland & Holland Ltd. established in London, England
1836	Samuel Colt patents revolver, establishes Colt's Firearms Mfg. Co. in Paterson, NJ
	E. Lefaucheux introduces pinfire gun and cartridge in France
	E. Lefaucheux devises first swinging breech gun
	U.S. Army converts Model 1836 flintlock pistols to percussion
1837	Allen & Thurber firm established in Grafton, MA
1838	British Army adopts percussion system; other European armies soon follow
1839	E. Remington & Sons firm founded
1841	U.S. Army adopts Model 1841 Harper's Ferry rifle, first U.S.-issue percussion rifle
1845	Dr. Edward Maynard patents tape primer ignition in U.S.
	Ethan Allen patents pepperbox pistol design
	Flintlocks becoming obsolete
1846	Zeiss Optik founded in Germany
	Leica founded in Germany
1847	Houllier patents metal cartridge case with various forms of primer in France
	Colt introduces the Walker Model revolver (Colt's first U.S. military contract)
	First Remington U.S. government contract for 1,000 carbines
1848	Christian Sharps patents breechloading, single-shot, dropping-block action
	Colt introduces First Model Dragoon revolver
1849	Capt. Claude Minie' perfects Minie' ball
	Lewis Jennings patents repeating rifle with toggle locking system in U.S.

1850   Most armies equipped with rifled muskets

1851   Colt introduces Model 1851 Navy revolver

Sharps Rifle Mfg. Co. established in Windsor, VT

British Army adopts modified Minie' ball bullet

Maynard Rifle Co. makes first commercially successful metallic cartridge

1852   Christian Sharps invents disc primer ignition in U.S.

William Armstrong perfects breechloading cannon in England

Daniel Wesson and Horace Smith form first partnership

Benicia Arsenal established near San Francisco, CA

1853   British Army adopts Pattern 1853 Enfield rifled musket

1854   Smith & Wesson patents Volcanic improvement of Jennings lock in U.S.

Allen, Thurber & Co. established in Worcester, MA

1855   U.S. Army adopts Model 1855 percussion rifle-musket, rifle, pistol and carbine with Maynard tape priming

Rollin White patents revolver with bored-through chambers

1856   J.G. Anschutz Co. established in Suhl, Germany

Smith & Wesson licenses White's revolver patents

1857   Smith & Wesson introduces Model 1 revolver

Smith & Wesson introduces rimfire cartridge (.22 Short) in U.S.

Oliver Winchester purchases assets of bankrupt Volcanic Arms in U.S.

Potet in France patents centerfire cartridge

1858   Robins & Lawrence exports factory tooling to England. First use of interchangeable firearms parts in U.K.

1859   Inside pinfire ignition invented

Remington introduces Rider double-action pocket revolver

1860   Spencer Repeating Rifle Co. established in Boston, MA; Spencer rifle introduced in U.S., first successful repeater

Lip-fire ignition invented

B. Tyler Henry redesigns lever-action Volcanic rifle

A.A. Hotchkiss patents design for bolt-action rifle

Colt introduces Army Model revolver

Remington introduces Remington-Beals Navy and
Army revolvers

Ft. Leavenworth Arsenal established at Ft. Leavenworth, KS

SIG established in Neuhausen, Switzerland

1861   U.S. Civil War begins

Colt introduces Navy Model revolver

Birmingham Small Arms (BSA) established
in Birmingham, England

1862   Dr. Richard Gatling patents Gatling gun in U.S.

Henry Peabody patents falling-block locking system in U.S.

Arsenals established in Indianapolis, Columbus and Rock
Island in U.S.

First use of Williams machine gun by Confederate Army at
Battle of Seven Pines

Kynoch, Lion Works Ammunition Co. founded in England

Berdan's Sharpshooters formed in Union Army

1863   Joseph Whitworth perfects hexagonal bore rifle in England

Leonard Geiger patents rolling-block locking system

Remington begins production of New Model Army revolver

Confederate government builds most modern powder plant
in the world in Columbus, GA

Hammerli established in Lenzberg, Switzerland

1864   Teat-fire ignition system invented

Boulenge chronograph developed in Belgium

J. Stevens Arms Co. established in Chicopee Falls, MA

Remington introduces Remington-Elliott New Model Army
and Navy revolvers

Schultz perfects bulk smokeless powder from wood cellulose
in Germany

1865   U.S. Civil War ends

Annular ignition invented in U.S.

U.S. Army selects Erskine S. Allin's camlocking system for new rifle

Winchester Firearms Co. established in New Haven, CT

Heym Waffenfabrik GmbH established in Suhl, Germany

Dynamit Nobel established in Nuremberg, Germany

Remington introduces Vest Pocket Derringer pistol

Luigi Franchi firm established in Brescia, Italy

1866   French Army adopts Chassepot version of von Dreyse needlegun

Winchester Model 1866 lever-action repeating rifle patented in U.S. by B. Tyler Henry

Remington purchases Geiger patent, introduces Rolling Block rifle

Swiss Army adopts Vetterli bolt-action rifle in .41 rimfire

Col. Edward Boxer patents Boxer primer in England

Parker Bros. established in Meriden, CT

Remington introduces M95 Over/Under Derringer

Roper obtains first patent on screw-in choke

Winchester introduces the Model 1866 lever-action rifle

1867   British Army adopts Snider-Enfield breechloading rifle

Hopkins & Allen Mfg. Co. established in Norwich, CT

Union Metallic Cartridge Co. founded in U.S., makes first Berdan-primed cartridge

1868   Remington introduces No. 1 Rolling Block rifle

Spencer Repeating Rifle Co. ceases operations

Col. Hiram Berdan patents the Berdan primer and case in the U.S.

Capt. Palliser invents first armor-piercing projectile in England

Capt. Nobel invents copper crusher system of measuring breech pressure in U.K.

1869   Remington introduces the Remington-Elliott Double Derringer pistol

United States Cartridge Co. established in Lowell, MA

William T. Eley patents first necked cartridge case in England

Mauser patents first successful bolt-action rifle and metallic cartridge in U.S.

1870   Franco-Prussian War begins

French Army adopts Montigny Mitrailleuse machine gun

Marlin Firearms Co. established in New Haven, CT

Gatling contracts with Colt to make Gatling guns

1871   National Rifle Association of America incorporated, New York City

Franco-Prussian War ends

British Army adopts Martini-Henry version of Peabody falling block system

Frederick Volkmann patents Collodin smokeless powder in Austria

Prussian Army adopts Mauser Model 1871 Infantry rifle

Nobel and Able begin first powder burning-rate tests with crushers in U.K.

Harrington & Richardson Co. established in Worcester, MA

Mauser Werke established in Oberndorf, Germany

1872   Du Pont, Hazard, Laflin & Rand form Powder Trust in U.S.

1873   First NRA full-scale Annual Matches held at Creedmoor range in NY

Winchester introduces Model 1873 lever-action rifle in .44-40 Win. caliber

U.S. Army adopts Springfield "Trapdoor" Model 1873 rifle in .45-70 Gov't.

Colt introduces Single Action Army revolver— "The Peacemaker"; adopted by U.S. Army

Smith & Wesson introduces the Schofield revolver; adopted by U.S. Army in 1875

Remington introduces its first shotgun, the Model 1873

1874   Lt. Col. Bode of the Prussian army develops the jacketed bullet

Capt. William Gardner designs Gardner repeating gun

Merwin Hulbert & Co. established in New York City

Needham introduces first successful ejectors for double-barrel shotguns

Greener introduces choke-bored shotgun barrels

According to legend, Billy Dixon makes 1,538-yd. shot with .50 Sharps at Battle of Adobe Walls, TX

1875   First Charles Daly shotgun marketed in U.S.

Explosives Act in the U.K. regulates propellant manufacture

Anson & Deeley patent first successful hammerless double-barrel shotgun

Remington introduces the Model 1875 single-action revolver

1876   Gen. George Custer's Last Stand at Little Bighorn River, MT; Custer leaves four Gatling guns behind

Grand Centennial Trophy Match held at Creedmoor; became Palma Trophy Match in 1878

1877   Colt introduces the Lightning double-action revolver

Battle of Plevna: Peabody single-shot rifles, Winchester repeaters make history

1878   U.S. Army purchases Hotchkiss bolt-action rifle, Winchester manufacture

1879   James Paris Lee patents box magazine for bolt-action rifle

Lewis Hepburn patents dropping-breech rifle design—Remington licenses as No. 3

George Greenhill's formula for rifling twist rates developed in U.K.

British Army uses Gatling guns in Zulu Wars

Krupp perfects sliding breech-block system

Battle of Rorke's Drift in South Africa: Martini-Henry rifle's finest hour

1880   L.C. Smith Co. established in Syracuse, NY

Sharps Rifle Co. goes bankrupt

1881   Col. Rubin perfects copper alloy-jacketed lead-core bullet in Thun, Switzerland

Gunfight at OK Corral fought in Tombstone, AZ Territory

1882   Swiss Army adopts Nagant revolver as M1882

1883   Iver Johnson Co. established in Fitchburg, MA

Winchester Arms Co. begins long relationship with John M. Browning

Ithaca Gun Co. established in Ithaca, NY

1884   Paul Vielle perfects smokeless powder manufacture in France

Hiram Maxim perfects recoil-powered, locked breech, full-automatic operation

Remington begins manufacture of the Remington-Lee bolt-action repeating rifle

Mauser firm becomes joint stock company Waffenfabrik Mauser in Germany

1885   **NRA begins publishing *The Rifle* magazine**

Lefever Arms Co. established in Syracuse, NY

Winchester introduces Browning single-shot low-wall rifle

1886   French Army introduces first smokeless powder rifle/cartridge 8x50 mm Lebel

Winchester introduces Model 1886 lever-action rifle

Austro-Hungarian Army adopts Mannlicher Model 1886 straight-pull rifle

Krieghoff Gun Co. established in Suhl, Germany

Walther established in Zella-Mehlis, Germany

1887   Alfred Nobel patents double-base smokeless propellants in Europe

Mannlicher-Scheonauer bolt-action rifle introduced

Hiram Maxim begins manufacture of his machine gun in U.K.

British Army adopts Webley Mark 1 revolver

Colt introduces the Lightning pump-action sporting rifle

Peters Cartridge Co. founded in U.S.

1888   **NRA begins publishing *Shooting And Fishing* magazine**

British Army adopts Lee Metford bolt-action rifle

1889   Belgian Army adopts Mauser Model 1889 bolt-action rifle

Fabrique Nationale (FN) established in Liege, Belgium, to make Mauser rifles

Marlin introduces the Model 36 lever-action rifle

Smokeless powders begin to replace blackpowder

Remington purchased by Union Metallic Cartridge Co.

Winchester purchases 50 percent interest in Remington

Rossi Co. founded in Brazil

John M. Browning discovers gas-operation with lever-action rifle fitted with a "flapper"

Kynoch produces first cordite propellant in England

1890   Winchester introduces the Model 1890 pump-action rifle

Remington introduces the Model 1890 revolver

Du Pont sets up propellant research facility at Carney's Point, NJ

Expanding rifle bullet developed at Dum Dum Arsenal, India, by Capt. Bertie-Clay

1891   Armies of Argentina, Bolivia, Colombia, Ecuador and Spain adopt Mauser M1891 rifle

Italian Army adopts Mannlicher-Carcano bolt-action rifle

Russian Army adopts Moisin-Nagant bolt-action rifle

First Maxim machine guns issued to British Army

E.J. Churchill Gunmakers established in High Wycombe, England

1892   **NRA National Matches move to Sea Girt, NJ, after Creedmoor closed in 1890**

U.S. Army adopts Krag-Jorgensen rifle

Schonberger introduces first successful semi-auto pistol in Austria

Winchester introduces the Model 1892 lever-action rifle

Bergmann Co. founded in Germany

1893   British Army uses Maxim machine guns in Battles of Shanghai and Matabeleland

Borchardt semi-auto pistol introduced

Remington introduces the Model No. 3 single-barrel shotgun

Tikka founded in Finland

Miroku Firearms Mfg. Co. established in Tokyo, Japan

Gatling patents electric-powered Gatling gun that fires 3,000 rounds per minute

Du Pont makes first smokeless powder in U.S.

1894   Winchester and Marlin introduce their respective Model 1894 lever-action rifles

Stevens introduces the Ideal Model 44 single-shot rifle, Favorite No. 17-29 rifles

1895   U.S. Navy adopts Lee Straight Pull rifle in caliber 6 mm USN (.236)

Mannlicher introduces gas-operated semi-auto rifle

Colt-Browning Model 95 machine gun introduced

Winchester introduces the Model 1895 lever-action rifle; first highpower smokeless-powder sporting rifle

Savage Arms Co. established in Utica, NY

1896   Swedish Army adopts Mauser Model 1896 bolt-action rifle

Mauser introduces C96 semi-auto "Broomhandle" pistol

U.S. Army adopts Colt-Browning "potato-digger" machine gun

1897   Japanese Army adopts Arisaka Type 30 rifle (Mauser design)

Winchester introduces the Model 1897 pump-action shotgun

Webley & Scott established in Birmingham, England

1898   Spanish-American War

German Army adopts Mauser Model 1898 bolt-action rifle

Stevens introduces Crackshot side-lever single-shot rifle

1899   Savage introduces the Model 99 lever-action sporting rifle

Capt. John Parker successfully uses Gatling guns as offensive weapons in Cuba

Hague Declaration outlaws bullets designed to flatten in human body

1900   Mannlicher introduces improved, gas-operated, semi-auto rifle

John M. Browning introduces his first semi-auto pistol, the Model 1900

Swiss Army adopts Model 1900 Luger pistol

1901   Webley-Fosbery Auto Revolver introduced by Webley & Scott

1902 British Army adopts Short, Magazine Lee-Enfield bolt-action rifle

National Board for the Promotion of Rifle Practice established in U.S.

1903 U.S. Army adopts Model 1903 Springfield rifle

Winchester introduces M1903 blow-back semi-auto rifle

FN Browning introduces Model 1903 semi-auto pistol

FN Browning introduces the Auto-5 semi-auto shotgun

Ferdinand Ritter von Mannlicher and Otto Schoenauer establish Steyr Mannlicher in Austria

1904 Machine guns play prominent part in Russo-Japanese War

U.S. Army adopts Vickers (Maxim) machine gun

Col. Kijiro Nambu introduces Nambu M1904 semi-auto pistol

1905 Japanese Army adopts Arisaka Type 38 bolt-action rifle

Remington introduces Model 11 semi-auto shotgun

Damascus shotgun barrels no longer made

1906 **NRA begins publishing *Arms And The Man* magazine**

Remington introduces Model 8 recoil-operated semi-auto rifle

Winchester introduces the Model 1906 rimfire rifle

A.H. Fox Co. established in Philadelphia, PA

American Eagle Luger entered in U.S. Army pistol evaluation

Shooting becomes an Olympic sport at games in Athens

1907 **NRA National Matches move to Camp Perry, OH**

Swedish Army adopts Browning Model 1903 semi-auto pistol

Remington introduces the Model 10A pump-action shotgun

First pointed, jacketed bullet in the U.S. made by Union Metallic Cartridge Co.

1908 German Army adopts Luger P 08 semi-auto pistol

1909 U.S. Army purchases Benet-Mercie light machine gun

Erfurt Convention devises European system of cartridge nomenclature; British and Americans agree but do not use it

1910   Samuel McClean patents Lewis gun design in the U.S.

FN Browning introduces Model 1910 semi-auto pistol

Rifle first fired from an aircraft from Wright flier in the U.S.

1911   U.S. Army adopts Colt/Browning Model 1911
semi-auto pistol

Remington introduces John M. Browning's Model 11
semi-auto shotgun

Winchester introduces the Model 1911 semi-auto shotgun

1912   First machine gun tested in U.S. airplane is Lewis
machine gun, College Park, MD

British Army adopts Vickers Mk.1 (Maxim) machine gun

Remington introduces the Model 14/14A pump-action rifle

Remington and Union Metallic Cartridge Co. merge into
Remington-UMC

Du Pont breaks up into Hercules Powder, Atlas Powder
and Du Pont Powder

1913   Armies of Britain, Belgium, France, Russia, Italy and Japan
adopt Lewis gun

1914   World War I begins

British airplanes armed with Lewis machine guns

Winchester introduces the Model 12 pump-action shotgun

Revelli in Italy introduces world's first submachine gun;
the Villar Perosa M15

Remington begins manufacture of Pattern 14 rifle for England

1915   Italian Army adopts Beretta Model 1915 semi-auto pistol

Colt introduces Woodsman semi-auto .22 pistol

Remington begins making the M1891 Moisin-Nagant rifles
for Russia in Bridgeport

Mondragon Model 1915 semi-automatic rifles issued
to German aircraft observers

1916   Benet-Mercie machine guns used to defend Columbus, NM
against Pancho Villa

Auto-Ordnance Corp. established in Cleveland, OH

1917   U.S. enters World War I

French Army adopts first semi-auto rifle—M1917, limited service

U.S. Army adopts Browning Model 1917 machine gun

Capt. Davis perfects first recoilless gun in U.S.

Colt and S&W introduce Model 1917 revolvers

S&W introduces Regulation Police double-action revolver

Remington begins making U.S. Model of 1917 rifles at Ilion, NY and Eddystone, PA; Winchester in New Haven, CT

Aguirre y Aranzabal (AyA) established in Eibar, Spain

1918   World War I ends

U.S. Army adopts Pedersen Device for Springfield rifle

U.S. Army adopts the Browning Automatic Rifle (BAR)

U.S. Army Air Corps adopts Marlin (Swebilius modified) Colt-Browning machine gun

Remington introduces the Model 51 semi-auto pistol

Beretta Model 1918 submachine gun (Villar Perosa action) adopted by Italian Army

German Army introduces first widely issued submachine gun, the MP18/I

Zbrojovka Brno (ZB) established in Brno, Czechoslovakia

A.F. Stoeger established in New York City

1919   U.S. Army adopts Browning M1919A2 machine gun

O.F. Mossberg & Sons established in New Haven, CT

Gen. John Thompson introduces Thompson M1919 submachine gun in U.S.

Irish Republican Army uses Thompson against British during Sinn Fein Rebellion

Vihtavuori established in Finland

Sporting Arms and Ammunition Manufacturers' Institute established in New York City

1920   Savage Arms Co. purchases J. Stevens Arms Co.

Gangsters in Chicago first use Thompson submachine gun

Auto-Ordnance Corp. stages test trial of Thompson SMG at Camp Perry

1921	U.S. Army adopts Browning M1921 heavy machine gun
	Sako, Ltd. established in Riihimaki, Finland
	Remington introduces the Model 30A bolt-action rifle
	Colt begins making Thompson SMGs
1922	Bullet performance tests begin at U.S. Army's Aberdeen Proving Ground in MD
	Federal Cartridge Co. founded in Anoka, MN
	Remington introduces the Model 24 semi-auto rifle
1923	**NRA begins publishing the *The American Rifleman* magazine**
	Griffin & Howe established in New York City
	Ceska Zbrojovka (CZ) established in Strakonice, Czechoslovakia
1925	Winchester introduces the Model 54 bolt-action rifle
	Valmet founded in Tourula, Finland
	Coxe and Burgess du Pont publish new ballistic profile tables
	Stoeger *Shooter's Bible* first published
1926	High Standard Mfg. Co. established in Hamden, CT
	U.S. Post Office orders Thompson SMGs
1927	Colt introduces the Detective Special compact, double-action revolver
	Remington introduces non-mercuric, non-corrosive Kleanbore primers
	Chesty Puller takes Thompson SMGs to Nicaragua with U.S. Marines
1928	Production of Thompson SMGs moves from Colt to Savage
1929	Walther introduces PP semi-auto pistol; first successful double-action, semi-auto pistol
	Ball powder invented by Dr. Fred Olsen at Western Cartridge Co.
	Winchester introduces the Model 52 bolt-action rimfire rifle and Model 21 over/under shotgun
	Capone Gang uses Thompson SMGs in Valentine's Day Massacre in Chicago

1930   U.S.S.R. adopts Tokarev TT30 semi-auto pistol

Weaver Scope Co. founded in Kentucky

1931   Walther introduces PP/K semi-auto pistol

FN Browning introduces Superposed over/under shotgun

Remington introduces the Model 32 over/under shotgun and Model 31A pump shotgun

Western Cartridge Co. purchases Winchester Repeating Arms

1933   U.S. Army Air Corps adopts Browning M2 heavy machine gun in .50 BMG

Winchester introduces the Model 63 semi-auto rifle

Du Pont purchases Remington-UMC

1934   U.S. Congress passes National Firearms Act 26 U.S.C. §5801 et seq.

Remington-UMC purchases Parker Gun Co. and Peters Cartridge Co.

1935   FN Browning introduces Hi-Power P35 pistol

British Army adopts Bren light machine gun

S&W introduces the .357 Magnum revolver and cartridge

Under J. Edgar Hoover, F.B.I. purchases Thompson SMGs

1936   U.S. Army adopts M1 Garand gas-operated, semi-auto rifle

Capt. Melvin Johnson introduces his recoil-operated, semi-auto rifle

Winchester introduces the Model 37 single-shot shotgun and the Model 70 bolt-action rifle

Remington introduces the Model 81 semi-auto rifle

1937   Ithaca introduces the Model 37 pump-action shotgun

1938   German Army adopts Walther P 38 pistol to replace P 08 Luger and adopts MP 38 submachine gun

Beretta introduces Model 1938A submachine gun

1939   World War II begins

Japanese Army adopts Type 99 bolt-action rifle/Type 99 light machine gun

Brownells firm founded in Montezuma, IA

1940   Remington Arms Co. switches to war production

German Army adopts MP 40 SMG

1941   U.S. Army adopts gas-operated, semi-auto M1 Carbine

British Army adopts Sten Mark 1 submachine gun

Johnson M1941 rifles sold to Dutch East Indies; limited U.S. use

Remington introduces the Model 720A bolt-action rifle

Remington begins making M1903 modified rifles
for U.S. government

Winchester Repeating Arms Co. switches to war production

Western Cartridge Co. switches to war production

Frankford Arsenal switches to war production

Armas Eibar S.R.L. (Laurona) established in Eibar, Spain

U.S. ordnance plants built at Lake City, Denver, St. Louis

Taurus founded in Brazil

Auto-Ordnance Corp. begins making Thompson SMGs
in Bridgeport, CT

1942   Last Luger P 08 pistols made by Mauser

U.S. Army adopts Springfield M1903A3 rifle/M1 Thompson
SMG/M3 SMG

Remington begins making M1903A3 rifle for U.S. government

Liberator pistol made by General Motors Guide Lamp Corp.

S&W introduces the Victory Model double-action revolver

Peters Cartridge Co. switches to war production

Ordnance plants now in Twin Cities, Des Moines, Utah,
Lowell, Allegheny, Milwaukee, Eau Claire, Evansville

1943   Remington begins making M1911A1 pistols for U.S. government

Ballistic Research Lab at Aberdeen Proving Ground, MD
begins operation

1944   John Inglis Co. begins manufacture of Browning Hi Power
pistols in Canada

Sako ownership to Finnish government and Red Cross

German Army adopts StG 44 "assault rifle"

Speer Bullets firm founded in Lewiston, ID

1945   World War II ends

French occupy Mauser factory in Oberndorf, production continues

Weatherby, Inc. established in South Gate, CA

Sierra Bullets founded in Santa Fe Springs, CA

1946   Sears, Roebuck & Co. introduces J.C. Higgins brand firearms

Husqvarna begins operations in Sweden

General Electric begins working on modern Gatling gun

Gun Digest first published

1947   U.S.S.R. develops AK-47 assault rifle

French close Mauser plant in Oberndorf, liquidate company, raze buildings

1948   Remington introduces Model 721 bolt-action sporting rifle

Marlin modifies the Model 36 lever-action rifle into the new Model 336

1949   Sturm, Ruger & Co. established in Southport, CT; Ruger introduces the Standard Model .22 semi-auto pistol

Israel Military Industries begins manufacture of military guns and ammo

Remington introduces the Model 48 semi-auto shotgun, 11-48 semi-auto rifle

Hornady Manufacturing Co. founded in Grand Island, NE

CCI founded in Lewiston, ID

RCBS founded in Oroville, CA

1950   Korean War begins

Remington introduces the Model 870 pump-action shotgun

Savage introduces the Model 24 over/under combination gun

1951   High Standard introduces Sport-King .22 pistol

Feinwerkbau established in Oberndorf, Germany

Mauser liquidation order lifted by French, limited manufacture resumes

1952   Israel introduces the Uzi submachine gun

Remington introduces the Model 760 pump-action rifle

S&W introduces the Model 39 semi-auto pistol

U.S.S.R. adopts Makarov semi-auto pistol

Hodgdon Powder Co. founded in Shawnee Mission, KS

1953   Korean War ends

Ruger introduces Single-Six single-action rimfire revolvers

1954   Fabrique Nationale introduces the FAL self-loading rifle

1955   Winchester introduces the Model 88 lever-action rifle

Remington introduces the Model 740 semi-auto sporting rifle

Colt introduces Python double-action revolver

Ruger introduces the Blackhawk single-action revolver

Perazzi established in Brescia, Italy

1956   Remington introduces the Model 58 semi-auto shotgun

S&W introduces the .44 Mag. double-action revolver

1957   U.S. Army adopts M14 rifle

S&W introduces the Model 41 .22 target pistol and Model 29 .44 Mag. revolver

Colt introduces Frontier Scout .22 rimfire revolver

1958   Savage introduces the Model 110 bolt-action sporting rifle

Weatherby introduces the Mark V bolt-action sporting rifle

Ruger introduces Bearcat single-action rimfire revolver

Remington introduces the Nylon 66 .22 semi-auto rifle; first production synthetic-stocked rifle

U.S. Army adopts M60 machine gun

1959   Yugoslavian Army adopts SKS carbine

U.S.S.R. adopts AKM assault rifle

Armalite established in Costa Mesa, CA

Uberti S.r.l. established in Serezzo, Italy

1960   General Electric revives Gatling design with 7.62x51 mm caliber Minigun

Winchester introduces Model 100 semi-auto sporting rifle

Remington introduces Model 742 semi-auto rifle

1961   U.S. Air Force adopts 20 mm General Electric M61 Gatling gun for aircraft

Ruger introduces a semi-auto carbine in .44 Mag.

S&W introduces the Model 52 target pistol

Herter's established in Waseca, MN

1962   U.S. becomes involved in Vietnam War

Remington introduces the Model 1100 semi-auto shotgun

Remington introduces Model 700 bolt-action rifle

Interarms begins operations in Alexandria, VA

Miroku in Japan begins making Charles Daly firearms

1963   Winchester introduces the Model 1200 pump-action shotgun

Colt introduces the SP-1 (AR-15) semi-auto rifle

Remington introduces the XP-100 pistol

Winchester introduces the Model 101 over/under shotgun

1964   U.S. Army adopts M16 rifle and companion 5.56x45 mm military cartridge

Winchester introduces the Model 1400 semi-auto shotgun

Winchester revises Model 70 and Model 94 rifle design

Winchester issues first modern commemorative M94 rifle at Wyoming Jubilee

Remington introduces the Model 600 and Model 40X bolt-action rifles

Ruger introduces the Model 10/22 semi-auto rifle

1965   Charter Arms introduces the Undercover double-action revolver

S&W introduces stainless steel M60 Chiefs Special revolver

1966   Heckler & Koch introduces MP5 submachine gun

1967   Remington introduces the Model 788 bolt-action sporting rifle

Browning introduces BAR semi-auto sporting rifle

Howa established in Tokyo, Japan

Thompson/Center Arms established in Rochester, NH

1968   U.S. Congress passes Gun Control Act 18 U.S.C. §921 et seq.

Ruger introduces Model 77 bolt-action and No. 1 single-shot sporting rifles

Daisy introduces V/L .22-cal. caseless rifle and ammunition

1969   Colt introduces Trooper double-action revolver

Armalite introduces AR-180 semi-auto rifle

1970   Ruger introduces Security-Six double-action revolver

Dan Wesson Arms Co. established in Palmer, MA

U.S. ammo makers begin conversion from crusher to piezo pressure measurement

1972   Sauer introduces Colt-Sauer bolt-action sporting rifle

1973   **NRA begins publication of the *American Hunter* magazine**

Remington introduces the Model 3200 over/under shotgun

Ruger introduces Super Blackhawk single-action revolver

First IWA Show held in Nuremberg, Germany

1974   Winchester introduces the Super X Model 1 semi-auto shotgun

Remington introduces the Model 3200 over/under shotgun

U.S.S.R. introduces new 5.45x39 mm military cartridge/ AK 74 rifle

1975   **NRA Institute for Legislative Action created**

Mauser becomes Mauser-Werke Oberndorf GmbH

1976   U.S. Congress passes Arms Export Control Act Sec. 38, Title 22 §U.S.C. 2778

Ruger introduces Mini-14 semi-auto rifle

Italian Army adopts Beretta 92 pistol

Miroku begins making some Browning firearms in Japan

Detonics Firearms Ind. established in Bellevue, WA

Talley purchases Rocky Mountain Arms, becomes North American Arms

1977   Ruger introduces Red Label over/under shotgun

1978   Steyr introduces the AUG 5.56 mm assault rifle, Austrian Army adopts as StG 77

1979   First SHOT Show held in St. Louis
French Army adopts FAMAS F1 5.56 mm assault rifle

1981   Winchester Firearms purchased from Olin, becomes U.S. Repeating Arms Co.

1982   U.S. Army adopts FN Minimi light machine gun as the M249

1983   Glock GmbH established in Austria

Bren 10 pistol introduced by Dornaus & Dixon

1984   Ruger introduces the Redhawk double-action revolver and M77/22 rifle

Canadian Army adopts M16 as the C7A1 5.56 mm assault rifle

Swift Bullets established in Quinter, KS

Cor-Bon Bullets & Ammo founded in Sturgis, SD

High Standard goes bankrupt

1985   Glock introduces Model 17 pistol to U.S. market

Springfield Inc. introduces M1911A1 series-pistols

Tony Knight introduces his MK-85, first modern in-line muzzleloading rifle

1986   U.S. Congress passes Firearms Owners Protection Act Public Law 99-308

Browning introduces Citori over/under shotgun

Ruger introduces the GP100 double-action revolver

1987   Remington introduces the Model 11-87 semi-auto shotgun

Springfield Inc. introduces M1A (M14 type) semi-auto rifle

Ruger introduces P85 Mark II semi-auto pistol and Super Redhawk revolver

Dakota Arms established in Sturgis, SD

1988   U.S. Army adopts M24 sniper rifle

1990   H.S. Precision established in Rapid City, SD

C.F. Holdings purchases Colt, becomes Colt's Manufacturing Co. Inc.

1991   Steyr introduces the SSG series of tactical bolt-action rifles

Ruger introduces SP-101 double-action revolver

1992   Voere introduces VEC 91 bolt-action sporting rifle for caseless 5.7x26 mm

GIAT of France purchases Fabrique Nationale in Belgium, Browning and U.S. Repeating Arms in U.S.

1993   U.S. Congress passes Brady Handgun Violence Prevention Act 18 U.S.C. §922 (s)

Kahr Arms established in Blauvelt, NY

Ruger introduces Vaquero single-action revolver

1994   U.S. Congress passes Omnibus Crime Control Act 18 U.S.C. §921 and 922; includes restrictions on imported firearms and magazine capacity

S&W introduces Sigma series of polymer-frame pistols

U.S. Marine Corps adopts FN MAG machine gun as M240B

Savage Arms purchases Lakefield Arms Ltd. of Canada

1995   German Army adopts Heckler & Koch G36 5.56 mm assault rifle

Eagle Arms purchases Armalite trademarks, begins new production

Lazzeroni Arms Co. established in Tucson, AZ

1996   Casull Arms Corp. established in Afton, WY

KBI of Harrisburg, PA, purchases Charles Daly trademark

1997   Browning discontinues Auto-5 shotgun production

GIAT sells Fabrique Nationale, Browning and USRAC (Winchester Firearms) to Wallonian government in Belgium

Henry Repeating Arms Co. established in Brooklyn, NY

Kimber Mfg. Co. re-formed in Yonkers, NY

1998   National Instant Check System (NICS) replaces Brady Act's five-day waiting period.

Taurus introduces Millenium-series polymer-frame pistols

1999   Winchester introduces the SuperX2 semi-automatic shotgun

Remington introduces the Model 700 Etronix VS SF electrically primed rifle

S&W introduces titanium-frame "Airlite" series double-action revolvers

Steyr introduces Model M polymer-frame semi-auto pistol and Scout rifle

Taurus introduces revolvers made of titanium

71

2000   Marlin buys Harrington & Richardson

Taurus introduces Millenium titanium-frame pistol

Beretta Holdings buys Sako, Stoeger and Tikka from Metso Oyj in Finland

Tristar Sporting Arms purchases American Arms

SAN Swiss Arms AG purchases SIG, Blaser, Mauser

2002   Employee group purchases S&W

2003   Smith & Wesson develops X-frame revolver for the .500 S & W cartridge

2005   NRA backs "Protection of Lawful Commerce in Arms Act" (S. 397) to end politically motivated lawsuits designed to bankrupt law-abiding American firearm manufacturers and retailers. S. 397 passes both chambers in Congress with broad bipartisan support.

2006   USRAC announces closure of New Haven, CT, plant; discontinues manufacture of Winchester Model 94 and Model 70 rifles and Model 1300 shotgun

2007   CVA develops the Elektra, an electrically primed muzzleloader

ArmaLite offers its first handgun, the semi-automatic AR-24

U.S. Army adopts a 7.62x51 mm Knight Armament Corp.'s semi-automatic rifle as the XM110 SASS (Semi-Automatic Sniper System), becomes U.S. M110

Smith & Wesson acquires Thompson/Center Arms

Remington, Bushmaster, Cobb Mfg., DPMS, and Marlin acquired by the same corporate owner, Cerberus Capital

Thompson/Center introduces Icon bolt-action rifle

Smith & Wesson introduces I-Bolt bolt-action rifle

Ammunition Time Line

Year	Cartridge Introduced or Event
1845	Flobert introduces the .22 BB Cap in France
1857	S&W introduces the .22 Short rimfire cartridge in U.S.
1860	S&W introduces the .32 Short rimfire cartridge
	.44 Henry Flat rimfire cartridge introduced
	Spencer introduces the .56-56 Spencer rimfire cartridge
1861	S&W introduces the .32 Long rimfire cartridge
	Springfield Armory introduces the .56-50 Spencer rimfire cartridge
1863	.41 Short rimfire cartridge introduced by UMC
1865	.38 Short and .38 Long rimfire cartridges introduced
1866	U.S. Army adopts .50-70 Gov't. cartridge
	Spencer introduces the .56-52 Spencer rimfire cartridge
1867	British Army adopts .577 Snider cartridge
	U.S. Navy adopts .50 Rem. pistol cartridge
	Union Metallic Cartridge Co. incorporated in Bridgeport, CT
1869	Sharps introduces the .40-50 Sharps cartridge
1870	Webley introduces the .320 and .380 revolver cartridges in England
	S&W introduces .44 S&W Russian and .44 S&W American revolver cartridges
	.44 Long rimfire introduced
1871	British Army adopts .577/450 Martini-Henry cartridge
	U.S. Army adopts .44 Colt revolver cartridge and .50 Remington pistol cartridge
	Sharps introduces the .40-70 Sharps (necked) cartridge
	.22 Long rimfire cartridge introduced
1872	Sharps introduces the .50-90 Sharps Straight cartridge
1873	U.S. Army adopts .45-70 Gov't. cartridge
	Colt introduces the .45 Colt revolver cartridge

Winchester introduces the .44-40 Winchester Center Fire (WCF) cartridge

Sharps introduces the .44-90 Sharps Necked cartridge

1874 Winchester introduces the .38-40 WCF cartridge

1875 Colt introduces the .32 Short and .32 Long Colt revolver cartridges

S&W introduces the .45 S&W Schofield revolver cartridge

1876 Winchester introduces the .40-60 and .45-75 Win. cartridges

1877 S&W introduces the .38 S&W revolver cartridge

Colt introduces the .41 Long Colt revolver cartridge

Peabody introduces the .40-70 Peabody cartridge

Sharps introduces the .45-110 Sharps Straight cartridge

Peters Cartridge Co. founded

1878 S&W introduces .32 S&W revolver cartridge

Sharps introduces the .45-120 Sharps cartridge

1882 Winchester introduces the .32-20 WCF cartridge and begins offering .44 Merwin & Hulbert ammunition

1884 Ballard/Winchester introduce the .32-40 and .38-55 Ballard cartridges

1885 Winchester introduces the .22 WCF cartridge

1886 Winchester introduces the .45-90 Win. cartridge

1887 Winchester introduces the .38-56 Win. cartridge

Peters introduces the .22 Long Rifle rimfire cartridge

1888 British Army adopts .303 British cartridge

Austro-Hungarian Army adopts 8x50R mm Austrian Mannlicher cartridge

.22 CB Cap introduced

1890 Winchester introduces the .22 Win. Rimfire cartridge

Peters introduces the .25 Stevens rimfire cartridge

1891 Russian Army adopts 7.62x53R mm Russian cartridge

Argentine Army adopts 7.65x53 mm Belgian Mauser cartridge

1892   Mauser introduces 7x57mm Mauser cartridge

U.S. Army adopts .30-40 Krag rifle and .38 Long Colt revolver cartridges

Franklin W. Olin founded Equitable Powder Manufacturing Co. in East Alton, IL, incorporated as Western Cartridge Co. in 1898

1893   Winchester introduces the .25-20 WCF rifle cartridge

Mauser introduces the 6.5x55 mm Mauser cartridge

1894   Swedish Army adopts 6.5x55 mm Mauser cartridge

.500 Nitro Express cartridge introduced in Britain

1895   U.S. Navy adopts 6 mm Lee USN cartridge

Winchester introduces .25-35 and .30-30 WCF and .32 Winchester Special cartridges

Savage introduces the .303 Savage rifle cartridge

1896   Mauser introduces 7.63x25 mm Mauser pistol cartridge

1897   British Army adopts .455 Webley Revolver Mark II cartridge

1898   Brenneke introduces first rifled shotgun slug in Germany

1899   FN Browning introduces 7.65 mm/.32 ACP pistol cartridge

.577 Nitro Express cartridge introduced

1900   FN Browning introduces the .38 Auto pistol cartridge

Holland & Holland introduces the .500/450 Nitro Express cartridge

Joseph Lang introduces the .470 Nitro Express cartridge

Jeffrey introduces the .600 Nitro Express cartridge

Mauser introduces the 9.3x57 mm Mauser cartridge

1902   9x19 mm Luger/Parabellum pistol cartridge introduced

S&W introduces the .38 S&W Special revolver cartridge

Winchester introduces the .33 Win. cartridge

9.3x74R mm cartridge introduced in Germany

1903   U.S. Army adopts .30-'03 cartridge

S&W introduces the .32 S&W Long revolver cartridge

FN Browning introduces the 6.35 mm/.25 ACP
pistol cartridge

FN Browning introduces 9 mm Browning Long
pistol cartridge

1904   Japanese Army adopts 8 mm Nambu pistol cartridge

Winchester introduces the .405 Win. cartridge

1905   FN Browning introduces .45 ACP pistol cartridge

Winchester introduces the .32 and .35 Win. Self-Loading
cartridges

Holland & Holland makes .400/375 Belted Nitro Express,
first belted case

1906   U.S. Army adopts .30-'06 Sprg. cartridge

Remington introduces .25, .30, .32 and .35 Rem. rifle cartridges

1907   S&W introduces the .44 S&W Special revolver cartridge

Kynoch begins making .470 Nitro Express ammunition in
England

Winchester introduces the .351 Win. Self-Loading cartridge

1908   German Army adopts 9x19 mm Luger pistol cartridge

8x56 mm Mannlicher-Schoenauer cartridge introduced

Remington introduces the .30 Rem. cartridge

1909   Jeffrey introduces the .404 Rimless Nitro Express cartridge

Westley Richards introduces the .425 Westley Richards
Magnum cartridge

1910   Winchester introduces the .401 Winchester Self-Loading
cartridge

1911   U.S. Army adopts .45 ACP pistol cartridge

Rigby introduces the .416 Rigby cartridge in England

Gibbs introduces the .505 Gibbs cartridge in England

1912   Austro-Hungarian Army adopts 9 mm Steyr pistol cartridge

FN Browning introduces the 9x17 mm/.380 ACP
pistol cartridge

Holland & Holland introduces the .375 H&H Mag. cartridge

Savage introduces the .22 Savage High-Power cartridge

1913 Western Cartridge Co. introduces the .256 and .30 Newton cartridges

1915 Savage introduces the .250 Savage rifle cartridge

1917 Wilhelm Brenneke introduces the 7x64 mm Brenneke cartridge

1918 Shotgun gauges larger than 10-gauge outlawed for hunting in U.S.

1920 Peters Cartridge Co. introduces the .45 Auto Rim revolver cartridge

Savage introduces the .300 Savage rifle cartridge

Mauser introduces the 8x60 mm Mauser cartridge

7 mm Nambu pistol cartridge introduced in Japan

1921 Winchester Super-X shotshells introduced

1923 U.S. Army adopts .50 Browning Machine Gun cartridge

1925 Winchester introduces the .270 Win. rifle cartridge

Holland & Holland introduces the .300 H&H Mag. cartridge

1929 Colt introduces the .38 Super Auto pistol cartridge

1930 U.S.S.R. adopts 7.62x25 mm Tokarev pistol cartridge

Winchester introduces the .22 Hornet sporting cartridge

1931 Olin family buys Winchester Repeating Arms Co.; forms Winchester-Western Co.

1932 U.S. Army develops .276 Pedersen military cartridge

1934 Remington introduces the .257 Roberts rifle cartridge

1935 S&W introduces the .357 S&W Mag. revolver cartridge

Winchester introduces the .220 Swift rifle cartridge

1936 Winchester introduces the .348 Win. rifle cartridge

Winchester introduces rifled slugs for shotguns

1937 Winchester introduces the .219 Zipper cartridge

1938 Winchester introduces the .218 Bee cartridge

1939 Japanese Army adopts 7.7x58 mm Arisaka cartridge

1941	U.S. Army adopts .30 M1 Carbine cartridge
1943	U.S.S.R. adopts 7.62x39 mm Soviet M43 cartridge
	Weatherby introduces the .270 Wby. Mag. rifle cartridge
1944	German Army adopts 7.9x33 mm Kurz cartridge for Stg. 44
	Weatherby introduces .257, 7 mm and .300 Wby. Mag. cartridges
1950	Remington introduces the .222 Rem. rifle cartridge
1951	Russian Army adopts 9x18 mm Makarov pistol cartridge
1953	Weatherby introduces the .378 Wby. Mag. rifle cartridge
1955	Remington introduces the .44 Rem. Mag. revolver cartridge
	Remington introduces the .244 Rem. rifle cartridge
	Winchester introduces the .243 and .358 Win. rifle cartridges
1956	Winchester introduces the .458 Win. Mag. cartridge
1957	U.S. Army adopts 7.62x51 mm NATO cartridge
	Remington introduces the .280 Rem. rifle cartridge
1958	Winchester introduces the .264 and .338 Win. Mag. cartridges
	Remington introduces the .222 Rem. Mag. cartridge
	Weatherby introduces .460 Wby. Mag. cartridge
1959	Norma introduces the .358 Norma Mag. cartridge
	Winchester introduces the .22 Win. Mag. Rimfire cartridge
1960	Norma introduces the .308 Norma Mag. cartridge
	Winchester introduces the .256 Win. Mag. cartridge
1962	Remington introduces the 7 mm Rem. Mag. cartridge
	Weatherby introduces the .340 Wby. Mag. cartridge
1963	Remington introduces the .221 Fireball cartridge
	Weatherby introduces the .224 Wby. Mag. cartridge
	Winchester introduces the .300 Win. Mag. and .284 Win. cartridges
1964	U.S. Army adopts 5.56x45 mm M193 cartridge
	Remington introduces the .41 Rem. Mag. revolver cartridge

Winchester introduces the .225 Win. rifle cartridge

Marlin introduces the .444 Marlin rifle cartridge

1965   Remington introduces the .22-250 Rem. and .350 Rem. Mag. rifle cartridges

1966   Remington introduces the 6.5 mm Rem. Mag. cartridge

1968   Weatherby introduces the .240 Wby. Mag. cartridge

1969   Remington introduces the .25-06 Rem. cartridge

Remington introduces the 5 mm Rem. Rimfire Mag. cartridge

1971   .44 Auto Mag cartridge introduced

Remington introduces the .17 Rem. rifle cartridge

U.S. Army develops 6 mm SAWS cartridge

First shotshells loaded with steel shot

1975   6 mm PPC cartridge introduced

Pyrodex blackpowder substitute patented by Daniel Pawlak and Michael Levenson; later introduced by Hodgdon Powder Co.

1976   Winchester introduces first steel-shot shotshells

1978   Remington introduces the 8 mm Rem. Mag. cartridge

Winchester introduces the .375 Win. and .45 Win. Mag. cartridges

NATO members adopt 5.56x45 mm Ss109/M855 cartridge

1980   Remington introduces the 7 mm-08 Rem. cartridge

Winchester introduces the .307 and .356 Win. rifle cartridges

1981   Remington introduces the .22 BR, 6mm BR and 7 mm BR cartridges

1982   Remington introduces the .357 Max. cartridge

1983   H&R introduces the .32 H&R Mag. cartridge

Norma introduces the 10 mm Auto cartridge

1987   Remington introduces .35 Whelen ammunition

IMI introduces the .41 Action Express cartridge

1988   Remington introduces the .416 Rem. Mag. cartridge

Weatherby introduces the .416 Wby. Mag. cartridge

Bell introduces the .700 Nitro Express cartridge

Winchester introduces the 9 mm Win. Mag. cartridge

Federal and O.F. Mossberg & Sons introduce 12 gauge, 3 ½" shotshell

Bismuth shotgun pellets patented by John Brown; partnered with Robert E. Petersen to form Bismuth Cartridge Co.

1989   Winchester introduces the .40 S&W Auto cartridge

Federal introduces the 9 mm Federal cartridge for revolvers

1991   IMI introduces the .50 Action Express cartridge

Federal introduces the .357 SIG cartridge

1996   Federal introduces High Energy cartridges in standard calibers

1997   Remington introduces the 7 mm STW and .260 Rem. cartridges

Lazzeroni introduces beltless magnum cartridge line

Winchester introduces factory .454 Casull ammunition

Tungsten-Matrix shot introduced by Kent Cartridge Co.

1998   Tungsten-Polymer shot introduced by Federal

Tungston-Iron shot introduced by Federal

1999   Remington introduces electrically primed Etronix ammunition

Remington introduces .300 Rem. Ultra Mag. cartridge

2000   Remington introduces the .338 and .375 Rem. Ultra Mag. cartridges

Hornady and Marlin introduce the .450 Marlin cartridge

Alliant Techsystems (ATK) acquires Federal Cartridge Co.

2001   Winchester introduces the .300 Win. Short Mag. (WSM)

Remington introduces 7 mm and .300 Rem. Short Action Ultra Mag.

Hornady introduces the .480 Ruger and .376 Steyr cartridges

2002   Winchester introduces .270 and 7 mm WSM calibers

Hornady introduces the .17 Hornady Mag. Rimfire

2003   S&W introduces the .500 S&W cartridge

Winchester introduces the .220 and
.243 Win. Super Short Mags. (WSSM)

Lapua introduces the Tanfoglio 9 mm FAR cartridge

Pyrodex Pellets blackpowder substitute introduced
by Hodgdon Powder Co.

2004   Triple Seven blackpowder substitute introduced by Hodgdon

Hornady introduces the .204 Ruger

Hornady introduces the .17 Mach2 rimfire cartridge

Remington introduces the 6.8 mm Rem. SPC

2005   Winchester Ammunition introduces the
.325 Win. Short Mag.

ATK Federal introduces Fusion ammunition

ATK Federal introduces the .45 Glock Automatic Pistol (GAP)
cartridge

S&W introduces the .460 S&W cartridge

2006   ATK Federal introduces .338 Federal cartridge

Hornady introduces LeverEvolution ammo line

2007   Remington introduces the .17 Fireball cartridge

Hornady introduces .308 Marlin Express, .375 Ruger, .450
Bushmaster and .30 TC rifle cartridges

Chapter 3
COLLECTING FIREARMS

Why Do Many Americans Collect Firearms?

Americans collect firearms for a wide variety of reasons.
A few of the most popular are:

- Historical interest and/or reference
- Family heirloom, war trophy or gift
- Participation in various types of hunting
- To compete in several different types of shooting sports
- Personal defense, practice, training and plinking
- Technical reference, study and research of operating mechanisms, construction materials, manufacturing technology, ergonomics, safety and applications
- Relaxing hobby
- Investment and appreciation in value
- Ammunition function testing
- Forensic reference
- Testing and proving materials, systems or concepts for scientific purposes

For most collectors, three or more reasons will apply.

Grading Criteria

Modern NRA Standards
These relate directly to the percentage of original factory finish remaining on the overall frame/receiver.

Mint—new in box, not sold previously at retail
New/Perfect—100 percent original finish with or without original packaging
Excellent—95-99 percent original finish
Very Good—80-94 percent original finish
Good—60-79 percent original finish
Fair—20-60 percent finish may or may not be original, but gun must function properly and fire
Poor—under 20 percent finish, functioning and firing not a factor

NRA Modern Firearm Condition Descriptions

New—not previously sold at retail, in same condition as current factory production

Perfect—in new condition in every respect

Excellent—new condition, used but little, no noticeable marring of wood or metal, bluing near perfect (except muzzle or sharp edges)

Very Good—in perfect working condition, no appreciable wear on working surfaces, no corrosion or pitting, only minor surface dents or scratches

Good—in safe working condition, minor wear on working surfaces, no broken parts, no corrosion or pitting that will interfere with proper functioning

Fair—in safe working condition, but well worn, perhaps requiring replacement of minor parts or adjustments which should be indicated in advertisement, no rust, but may have corrosion pits which do not render article unsafe or inoperable

NRA Antique Firearm Condition Descriptions

Factory New—all original parts; 100 percent original finish; in perfect condition in every respect, inside and out

Excellent—all original parts; over 80 percent original finish; sharp lettering, numerals and design on metal and wood; unmarred wood; fine bore

Fine—all original parts; over 30 percent original finish; sharp lettering, numerals and design on metal and wood; minor marks in wood; good bore

Very Good—all original parts; none to 30 percent original finish; original metal surfaces smooth with all edges sharp; clear lettering, numerals and design on metal; wood slightly scratched or bruised; bore disregarded for collector firearms

Good—some minor replacement parts; metal smoothly rusted or lightly pitted in places, cleaned or reblued; principal lettering, numerals and design on metal legible; wood refinished, scratched, bruised or minor cracks repaired; in good working order

Fair—some major parts replaced; minor replacement parts may be required; metal rusted, may be lightly pitted all over, vigorously cleaned or reblued; rounded edges of metal and wood; principal lettering, numerals and design on metal partly obliterated; wood scratched, bruised, cracked or repaired where broken; in fair working order or can be easily repaired and placed in working order

Poor—major and minor parts replaced; major replacement parts required and extensive restoration needed; metal deeply pitted; principal lettering, numerals and design obliterated; wood badly scratched, bruised, cracked or broken; mechanically inoperative, generally undesirable as a collector's firearm

BILL OF SALE FOR FIREARM (Sample, may be copied)

Buyer's Full Name
_____

Buyer's Address:
_____

_____

(city) _____ (state) _____ (zip code) _____

(_____)   _____—_____
area code   telephone number

Received from the above named individual residing at
the address indicated, the sum of:

U.S. $_____ in full/partial payment
for the following firearm described as:

Make: _____ Model:_____

Serial Number: _____ Caliber/Gauge: _____

Barrel length: _____ inches   Overall Length: _____ inches

Weight: _____ Country/Date of Manufacture: _____

Action Type: _____

Accessories Included (if any):
_____

_____

Condition Per NRA Standards:
_____

Markings, Inscriptions, Engraving:
_____

_____

Stock(s): _____

Repairs, Replacements, Alterations:
_____

_____

Historical Value/Claims:
_____

_____

Name and Address of Previous Owner (optional):

_____

_____

_____

I certify that I have the right to sell or trade possession of the firearm described, and that the information on this Bill of Sale is true and complete to the best of my knowledge.

Day: _____ Month: _____ Year: _____

Full Name of Seller _____

Address of Seller _____

_____ _____ _____
(city)   (state)   (zip code)

(_____) _____—_____
area code   telephone number

Authorized Signature of Seller:

_____

I certify that I have received the firearm described in the above Bill of sale in the condition noted.

Day: _____ Month: _____ Year: _____

Full Name of Buyer: _____

Authorized Signature of Buyer:

_____

Attachments:

Photocopy of buyer's driver's license: _____
Photocopy of buyer's completed Form 4473: _____
Certified copy of seller's/buyer's Federal Firearms License: _____
Copy of letter from independent appraiser: _____
Photograph(s) of firearm: _____
Documents of historic authentication: _____
Extended payment agreement: _____
Factory operator's manual: _____
Photocopy of buyer's check or money order: _____

Chapter 4
FIREARMS LAWS

I n the United States, firearms are regulated by more than 24,000 federal, state and local laws governing manufacture, transfer, ownership, transport, carry, storage, use, taxation, import and export.

State and local laws differ from one state and locality to another, so be certain to check with your personal attorney, local law enforcement agency or state attorney general's office to determine applicable firearms laws in your area.

In addition, check with your local fire marshal's office to determine applicable regulations for storing propellants, primers and loaded ammunition.

The NRA Institute For Legislative Action (ILA) offers the following booklets on:

- A Citizen's Guide To Federal Firearms Laws
- Federal Firearms Laws
- State Firearms Laws (by state)
- Compendium of State Firearms Laws
- Interstate Transportation of Personally-Owned Firearms
- Right-to-Carry Reciprocity Guide

These may be obtained by contacting ILA at the resources address at the end of the chapter.

Most federal laws pertaining to firearms are administered by the Bureau of Alcohol, Tobacco, Firearms and Explosives (ATF) which is part of the Department of Justice. Contact the ATF at the resources address with any questions regarding federal firearms laws and regulations.

Business enterprises trading in or manufacturing firearms require a Federal Firearms License (FFL) from the Bureau of Alcohol, Tobacco, Firearms and Explosives.

Applications for a FFL (ATF Form 7) are available from: BATFE, 2600 Century Parkway, N.E., Suite 400, Atlanta, GA 30345; (404) 417-2750.

There are nine types of FFLs depending on the type of business. Below is a listing current to 2005.

Types of Federal Firearms Licenses

Type 01 Dealer In Firearms 18 U.S.C. §923(a)(3)(B)
Dealer in firearms other than destructive devices. Includes rifles, shotguns, pistols, revolvers, gunsmith activities and National Firearms Act (NFA) weapons.
Fee: $200 for first three years; $90 on renewal.

Type 02 Pawnbroker 18 U.S.C. §923(a)(3)(B)
Pawnbroker in firearms other than destructive devices. Includes rifles, shotguns, pistols, revolvers, gunsmith activities and National Firearms Act (NFA) weapons.
Fee: $200 for first three years; $90 on renewal.

Type 03 Collector Of Curios And Relics 18 U.S.C. §923(b)
Pertains exclusively to firearms classified as curios and relics. Its purpose is to facilitate a personal collection. It is **not** a license to buy and sell curios and relics.
Fee: $30 for three years.

Type 06 Manufacturer Of Ammunition For Firearms 18 U.S.C. §923(a)(1)(C)
Manufacturer of ammunition for firearms other than for destructive devices or armor-piercing ammunition.
Fee: $30 for three years.

Type 07 Manufacturer Of Firearms 18 U.S.C. §923(a)(1)(B)
Manufacturer of firearms other than destructive devices.
Fee: $150 for three years.

Type 08 Importer Of Firearms Or Ammunition For Firearms 18 U.S.C. §923(a)(2)(B)
Importer of firearms other than destructive devices or ammunition for firearms other than destructive devices, or ammunition other than armor-piercing ammunition.
Fee: $150 for three years.
Note: Importers of handguns and rifles MUST register with the ATF under the provisions of the Arms Control Export Act. For further information on registration, contact the Firearms And Explosives Imports Branch of the ATF at (202) 927-8320.

Type 09 Dealer In Destructive Devices Or Ammunition For Destructive Devices 18 U.S.C. §923(a)(3)(A)
Fee: $3,000 for three years.

Type 10 Manufacturer Of Destructive Devices, Ammunition For Destructive Devices Or Armor Piercing Ammunition 18 U.S.C. §923(a)(1)(A)
Fee: $3,000 for three years.

Type 11 Importer Of Destructive Devices, Ammunition For Destructive Devices Or Armor Piercing Ammunition 18 U.S.C. §923 (a)(2)(A)
Fee: $3,000 for three years.

Major Applicable Laws*

1. The National Firearms Act (1934)
   Title 26, United States Code, Chapter 53, Internal Revenue Code (26 U.S.C. §5801 et seq.)
   Purpose: to apply registration, rules and Special Occupational taxes on importers, manufacturers and dealers and possessors of machine guns, destructive devices and certain other firearms.

2. The Gun Control Act Of 1968, Public Law 90-618
   Title 18, United States Code, Chapter 44 (18 U.S.C. §921 et seq.)
   Purpose: to control interstate traffic in firearms; to provide support to federal, state and local law enforcement officials.

   3. Arms Export Control Act Of 1976, Sec. 38, As Amended, Title 22, U.S.C. §2778
   (International Traffic in Arms Regulations or "ITAR")
   Purpose:
   a. establishes Presidential control of exports and imports of defense articles and services, guidance of policy, etc.
   b. designation of United States Munitions List
   c. issuance of export licenses
   d. condition for export
   e. negotiations information

   Note: Import provisions administered by ATF (Part 47 of 27 CFR). Export provisions administered by Department of State.

4. Firearms Owners Protection Act (1986) Public Law 99-308
   Purpose:
   a. helps remedy abuses and clarify laws
   b. defines "dealer" and eligibility requirements

ATF Definitions *

Firearm

GCA 1968 Firearm
a. any weapon (including a starter gun) which will or is designed to or may readily be converted to expel a projectile by the action of an explosive

---

* **Note:** This is a brief discussion of various laws and is not all-inclusive. Please contact the BATFE with any questions regarding federal firearms regulations.

    b. the frame or receiver of any such weapon
    c. any firearm muffler or firearm silencer
    d. any destructive device

NFA 1934 Firearm

    a. a shotgun having a barrel or barrels of less than 18" in length
    b. a weapon made from a shotgun if such weapon as modified has an overall length of less than 26" or a barrel or barrels of less than 18" in length
    c. a rifle having a barrel or barrels of less than 16" in length
    d. a weapon made from a rifle if such weapon as modified has an overall length of less than 26" or a barrel or barrels of less than 16" in length
    e. any other weapon (see definition)
    f. a machine gun
    g. any silencer
    h. a destructive device

The definition does not include antique firearms or any other device (other than machine guns or destructive devices) which the Secretary finds by reason of the date of its manufacture, value, design and other characteristics is primarily a collector's item and not likely to be used as a weapon.

Antique Firearm

GCA 1968 Antique Firearm 18 U.S.C. §921(a)(16)

The term "antique firearm" means:

a. any firearm (including any firearm with a matchlock, flintlock, percussion cap or similar type of ignition system) manufactured in or before 1898, or

b. Any replica of any firearm described in subparagraph a if such replica:

    (i) Is not designed or redesigned for using rimfire or conventional centerfire fixed ammunition, or
    (ii) Uses rimfire or conventional centerfire fixed ammunition which is no longer manufactured in the United States and which is not readily available in the ordinary channels of commercial trade, or

c. Any muzzle loading rifle, muzzle loading shotgun, or muzzle loading pistol, which is designed to use black powder, or a black powder substitute, and which cannot use fixed ammunition. For purposes of this subparagraph, the term "antique firearm" shall not include any weapon which incorporates a firearm frame or receiver, any firearm which is converted into a muzzle loading weapon, or any muzzle loading weapon which can be readily converted to fire fixed ammunition by replacing the barrel, bolt, breechblock, or any combination thereof.

NFA 1934 Antique Firearm 26 U.S.C. §5845(g)

The term "antique firearm" means any firearm not designed or redesigned for using rimfire or conventional centerfire ignition with fixed ammunition and manufactured in or before 1898 (including any matchlock, flintlock, percussion cap, or similar type of ignition system or replica thereof, whether actually manufactured before or after the year 1898) and also any firearm using fixed ammunition manufactured in or before 1898, for which ammunition is no longer manufactured in the United States and is not readily available in the ordinary channels of commercial trade.

Rifle 18 U.S.C. §921(a)(7)

The term "rifle" means any firearm designed or redesigned, made or remade, and intended to be fired from the shoulder and designed or redesigned and made or remade to use the energy of an explosive to fire only a single projectile through a rifled bore for each single pull of the trigger.

Shotgun 18 §921(a)(5)

The term "shotgun" means any firearm designed or redesigned, made or remade , and intended to be fired from the shoulder and designed or redesigned and made or remade to use the energy of an explosive to fire through a smooth bore either a number of ball shot or a single projectile for each single pull of the trigger.

Handgun 18 U.S.C. §921(a)(29)

The term "handgun" means:

a. A firearm which has a short stock and is designed to be held and fired by the use of a single hand; and
b. Any combination of parts from which a firearm described in subparagraph a can be assembled.

NFA 1934 Machinegun 26 U.S.C. §5845(b)

Any weapon which shoots, is designed to shoot, or can readily be restored to shoot, automatically more than one shot, without manual reloading, by a single function of the trigger.
This definition also includes:

a. The frame or receiver of any such weapon
b. Any part designed and intended solely and exclusively, or combination of parts designed and intended, for use in converting a weapon into a machinegun
c. Any combination of parts from which a machinegun can be assembled if such parts are in the possession or under the control of a person.

NFA 1934 Destructive Device 26 U.S.C. §5845(f)
a. Any explosive, incendiary, or poison gas:

   (i)   Bomb

   (ii) Grenade

   (iii) Rocket having a propellant charge of more than 4 ounces

   (iv) Missile having an explosive or incendiary charge of more than one-quarter ounce

   (v)   Mine

   (vi) Device similar to any of the devices described in the preceding clauses

b. Any type of weapon (other than a shotgun or shotgun shell which the Secretary finds is generally recognized as particularly suitable for sporting purposes) by whatever name known which will, or may be readily converted to, expel a projectile by the action of an explosive or other propellant, and which has any barrel with a bore of more than one-half inch in diameter, and

c. Any combination of parts either designed or intended for use in converting any device into a destructive device described in a or b above and from which a destructive device may be assembled.

Note: The term "destructive device" shall not include:

a. Any device which is neither designed nor redesigned for use as a weapon

b. Any device, although originally designed for use as a weapon, which is redesigned for use as a signaling, pyrotechnic, line throwing, safety, or similar device

c. Surplus ordnance sold, loaned or given by the Secretary of the Army

d. Any other device the Secretary of the Treasury finds is not likely to be used as a weapon, is an antique, or is a rifle which the owner intends to use solely for sporting, recreational or cultural purposes.

NFA 1934 Any Other Weapon 26 U.S.C. §5845(e)
Any weapon or device capable of being concealed on the person from which a shot can be discharged through the energy of an explosive; a pistol or revolver having a barrel with a smooth bore designed or redesigned to fire a fixed shotgun shell; weapons with combination shotgun and rifle barrels 12″ or more, less than 18″ in length from which only a single discharge can be made from either barrel without manual reloading;

a. Definition shall include any such weapon which may be readily restored to fire;

b. Definition shall not include a pistol or revolver having a rifled bore, or rifled bores, or weapons designed, made or intended to be fired from the shoulder and not capable of firing fixed ammunition.

Ammunition 18 U.S.C. §921 (a)(17)(A)
Loaded cartridge or round of ammunition including the cartridge case, primer, propellant powder and bullet designed for use in a firearm.

Armor Piercing Ammunition 18 U.S.C. §921(a)(17)(B) and (C)
a. A projectile or projectile core which may be used in a handgun and which is constructed entirely (excluding the presence of traces of other substances) from one or a combination of tungsten alloys, steel, iron, brass, bronze, beryllium copper, or depleted uranium, or
b. A full-jacketed projectile larger than .22-caliber designed and intended for use in a handgun whose jacket has a weight of more than 25 percent of the total weight of the projectile.
c. Armor Piercing Ammunition does not include:
(i) Shotgun shot required by federal or state environmental or game regulations for hunting purposes
(ii) A frangible projectile designed for target shooting
(iii) A projectile which the Secretary finds is primarily intended to be used for sporting purposes
(iv) Any other projectile the Secretary finds is intended to be used for industrial purposes, including a charge used in an oil or gas well perforating device.

Curios And Relics 27 C.F.R. §478.11
Firearms that are of special interest to collectors by reason of some quality other than is associated with firearms intended for sporting use or as offensive or defensive weapons. To be recognized as a curio or relic, a firearm must fall within one of the following categories:
a. Firearms which were manufactured at least 50 years prior to the current date, but not including replicas thereof.
b. Firearms which are certified by the curator of a municipal, state, or federal museum which exhibits firearms to be curios or relics of museum interest.
c. Any other firearms which derive a substantial part of their monetary value from the fact that they are novel, bizarre, rare, or because of their association with some historical figure, period or event.

Resources

National Rifle Association
Institute for Legislative Action
11250 Waples Mill Rd.
Fairfax, VA 22030-9400
800-392-8683
www.nraila.org

Bureau of Alcohol, Tobacco, Firearms and Explosives
    Department of Justice
    Office of Public and Governmental Affairs
    650 Massachusetts Ave., Room 8290
    Washington, DC 20226
    email: atfmail@atf.gov

Directorate of Defense Trade Controls
    PM/DDTC, SA-1, 12th Floor
    U.S. Department of State
    Washington, DC 20522
    202-663-29804

Export Counseling Division (for export of shotguns only)
    U.S. Department of Commerce
    Washington, DC 20230
    202-482-4811

Nationwide Instant Check System (NICS)
    www.fbi.gov/hq/cjisd/nics/indes.htm

Traveler's Guide to the Firearm Laws of the Fifty States
    859-647-5100
    www.gunlawguide.com

FIREARMS TECHNICAL

Chapter 5
PARTS NOMENCLATURE

As firearm design standardized around prevailing types of locks, a unique nomenclature evolved for describing specific parts common to most or all guns. That terminology grew along with the emergence of different kinds of guns and operating systems, and today, those who manufacture, sell, repair and shoot firearms rely on a highly developed vocabulary. Even though certain models contain parts unique only to that particular gun, and while some makers may call a similar part by different names, everyday firearms nomenclature is in fact very functional. Language differences aside, gun folks the world over know that a "slide" is the moving top piece of a semi-auto pistol, that "locking lugs" can be found on the "bolts" of various rifles and shotguns, and that the majority of "repeaters" have an "ejection port."

Specialized gun-speak certainly can appear arcane and mysterious to the novice shooter, but for many firearm enthusiasts, learning to talk the talk is part of the fascination and fun.

Parts Common to Most Guns

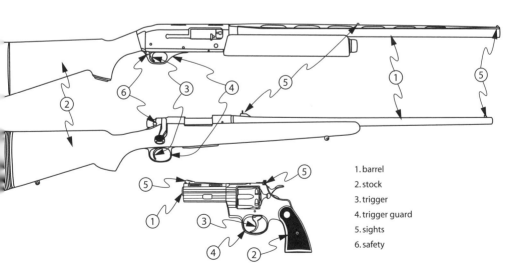

1. barrel
2. stock
3. trigger
4. trigger guard
5. sights
6. safety

Bolt-Action Rifle

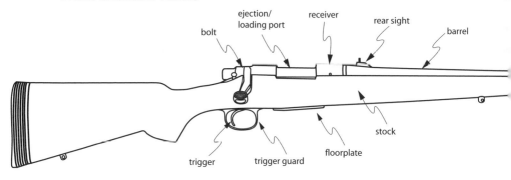

bolt

ejection/
loading port

receiver

rear sight

barrel

trigger

trigger guard

floorplate

stock

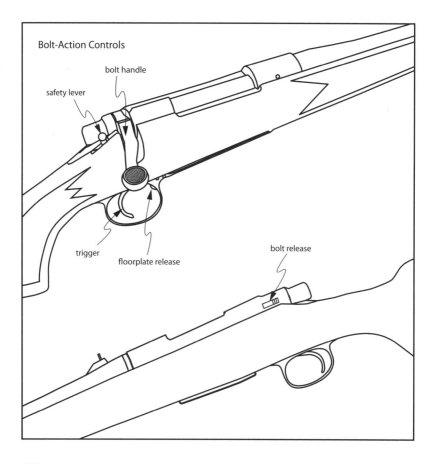

Bolt-Action Controls

bolt handle

safety lever

trigger

floorplate release

bolt release

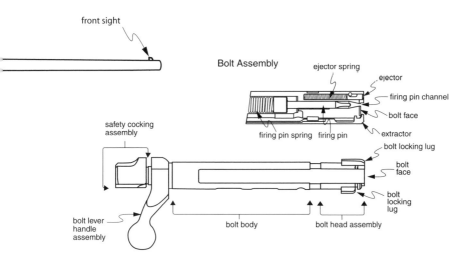

front sight

Bolt Assembly

ejector spring

ejector

firing pin channel

bolt face

extractor

firing pin spring   firing pin

safety cocking
assembly

bolt locking lug

bolt
face

bolt
locking
lug

bolt lever
handle
assembly

bolt body

bolt head assembly

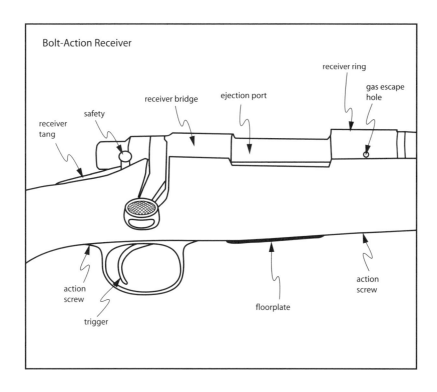

Bolt-Action Receiver

receiver ring

gas escape
hole

receiver bridge

ejection port

receiver
tang

safety

action
screw

trigger

action
screw

floorplate

Revolver

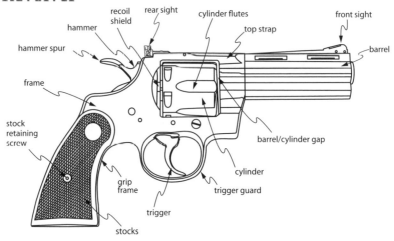

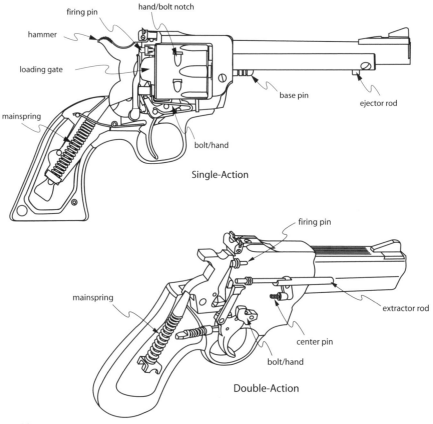

Single-Action

Double-Action

Semi-Automatic Pistol

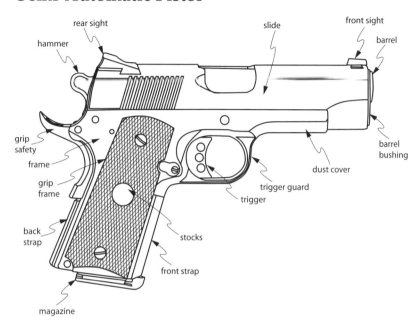

rear sight

slide

front sight

hammer

barrel

grip
safety

frame

grip
frame

back
strap

magazine

stocks

front strap

trigger guard

trigger

dust cover

barrel
bushing

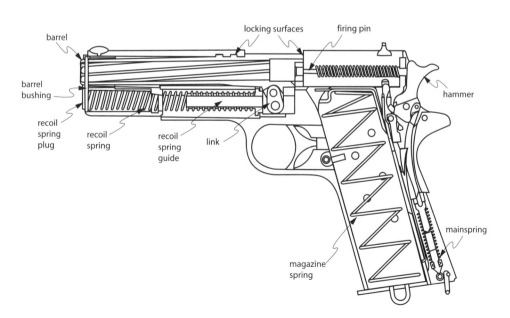

barrel

locking surfaces

firing pin

barrel
bushing

hammer

recoil
spring
plug

recoil
spring

recoil
spring
guide

link

magazine
spring

mainspring

Over/Under Shotgun

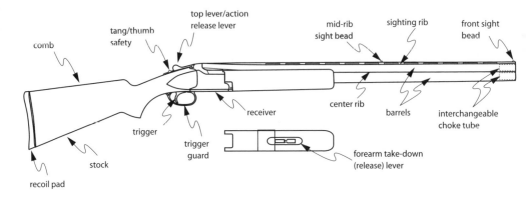

comb

tang/thumb
safety

top lever/action
release lever

mid-rib
sight bead

sighting rib

front sight
bead

center rib

barrels

interchangeable
choke tube

receiver

trigger

trigger
guard

forearm take-down
(release) lever

stock

recoil pad

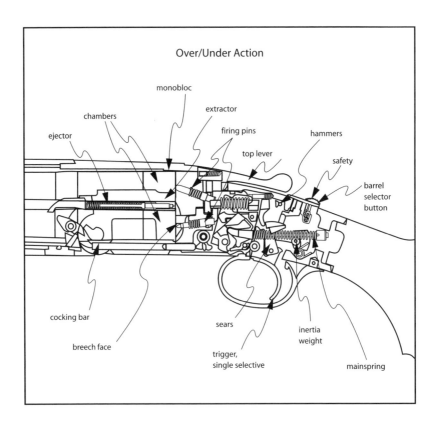

Over/Under Action

monobloc

extractor

chambers

firing pins

ejector

hammers

top lever

safety

barrel
selector
button

cocking bar

sears

inertia
weight

breech face

trigger,
single selective

mainspring

Semi-Automatic Shotgun

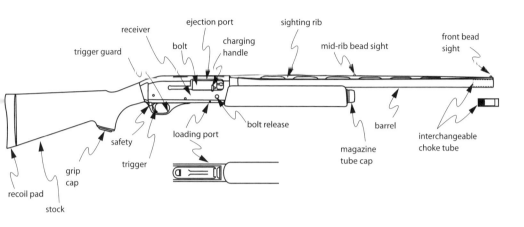

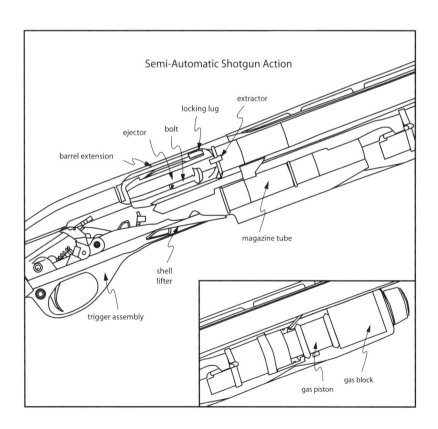

Semi-Automatic Shotgun Action

Chapter 6
OPERATING PRINCIPLES

Cycle of Operation

Regardless of design, every firearm must follow a strict sequence of mechanical events known as the cycle of operation. The cycle of operation consists of the following eight steps:

Firing

Pulling the trigger releases one of the following:

- the hammer, allowing it to strike the firing pin, or
- the spring-powered striker, or
- the bolt, allowing the fixed firing pin on the bolt face to strike the primer as the bolt reaches the end of forward travel.

When the firing pin, striker or bolt reach the end of forward travel, the firing pin strikes the primer in the cartridge base. As the firing pin's tip indents the primer cup, the priming compound is crushed between the indent and the primer anvil. The priming compound explodes, sending hot gases through the flash-hole into the propellant powder. The pressure and temperature of the propellant powder rises quickly causing it to begin burning rapidly. As the propellant burns, it produces hot, expanding gases that accelerate the bullet or shot charge down the barrel.

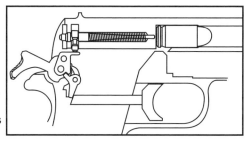
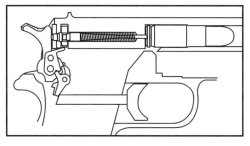

Pulling the trigger of a cocked pistol (top) releases its hammer to strike the firing pin, which indents the cartridge's primer cup, igniting the priming compound and powder. The burning powder produces burning gases that force the bullet down the barrel.

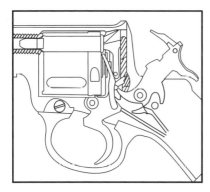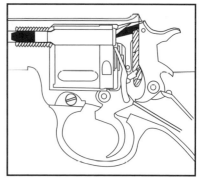

In revolvers like the one depicted here, the firing pin is fixed to the hammer (left) and strikes the primer directly when the trigger is pulled. That ignites the priming compound and subsequently the propellant powder to drive the bullet down the barrel.

Unlocking

After the bullet or shot charge has cleared the muzzle, breech pressure quickly drops to ambient levels. The bolt or breech block can then be unlocked by the operating mechanism.

Extraction

As the breech pressure drops, the cartridge case springs back to its original dimensions. When the bolt unlocks, one or more mechanical extractors on the bolt grasp the rim of the cartridge case, loosen it with primary extraction, then pull it out of the chamber as the bolt moves rearward. Note the cartridge may be fired or unfired.

There are two types of extractor:
- internal—located inside the bolt face
- external—located outside the bolt face.

Ejection

The empty, fired case or unfired cartridge is thrown clear of the action through the ejection port cut into the receiver by one of two types of ejector:

- internal—spring-loaded plunger inside the bolt face
- external—fixed pin or projection in the receiver.

Cocking

The rearward motion of the bolt resets the fire-control mechanism by cocking the hammer or striker.

Feeding

As the bolt moves forward, the magazine presents a fresh cartridge into the bolt path. The bolt contacts the base of the presented cartridge, pushing it forward until it has cleared the magazine lips and is released. If the extractor engages the case rim, the feed is "controlled." If it does not, then it is a "push feed" system.

Chambering

The bolt continues its travel, pushing the cartridge fully forward until it seats completely in the chamber of the barrel.

Locking

At the end of its forward movement, the bolt locks securely to the barrel or receiver and the gun is ready to fire the next shot. The operational cycle then repeats.

Some arms may not go through every step in the cycle above. For example, blowback-operated guns are not locked, so both the locking and unlocking steps are eliminated. Also, in many break-action rifles and shotguns and some single-shot rifles, when the action is opened, the fired shell is extracted from the chamber, but not ejected. In another instance, some bolt-action rifles cock on closing as the bolt is pushed home while others cock on opening.

Modes Of Operation

Manual (Single-Shot)

After a single shot has been fired, the mechanism of the firearm must be manually cycled by the shooter to unlock, extract, eject, feed, chamber and fire a subsequent cartridge.

Semi-Automatic

After manually loading the first round, this method of operation uses recoil or gas from the fired cartridge to power the action cycle. A single shot will be fired each time the trigger is pulled until the magazine is empty.

Full Automatic

A fully automatic firearm will fire repeatedly with a single pull of the trigger until the trigger is released or the magazine is empty unless the gun is equipped with a burst-limiting device.

- unrestricted automatic—The firearm keeps firing until the trigger is released or the magazine is empty.
- burst limited—Every time the trigger is pulled, a burst of two, three or five shots is fired. The trigger must be manipulated again to fire another burst.

Powering an Operating System

Manual

Human muscle performs the cycle of operation.

Self-Loading

The forces generated by firing the cartridge are harnessed to perform the cycle of operation.

Externally Powered

An outside mechanical power source is used to perform the cycle of operation.

Rimfire Firing Sequence

Cartridge in
chamber

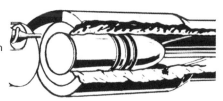

Firing pin
strikes and
ignites
primer
which in
turn ignites
powder

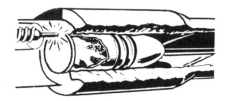

Gases from
powder
expand in
case

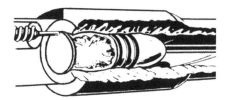

Gases push
bullet out to
force...

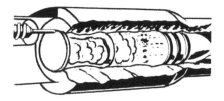

...speeding
bullet out
through
barrel

Bolt-Action Mechanisms

The bolt-action is the quintessential rifle action for military, hunting and target-shooting applications. Many shooters believe turnbolt-action rifle design reached its zenith in Paul Mauser's classic Model 98.

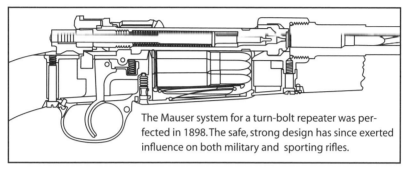

The Mauser system for a turn-bolt repeater was perfected in 1898. The safe, strong design has since exerted influence on both military and sporting rifles.

Action Lengths

Bolt-actions come in four basic lengths:
- miniature
- short
- long
- magnum

The most popular are the short and long actions; the miniature is scarce, while the magnum is growing in popularity.

Cocking

Bolt-action rifles are cocked in one of four different ways:
- On bolt opening—This is very popular as it makes the bolt glide effort very low. However, bolt opening forces can be high as primary extraction and cocking occur at the same time.
- On bolt closing—This method substantially lowers the effort needed to open the bolt as it separates the cocking operation from the opening effort. Not as popular as cock-on-opening.
- Partially cocks on opening/completes cocking on closing—This system divides the cocking effort more or less evenly. A rare design.
- Firearm must be manually cocked—The shooter must cock the striker or hammer every time the gun is fired as a separate operation.

Magazines

Most bolt-action rifles have an internal magazine holding three to five rounds of ammunition. The magazine capacity depends on the size of the cartridge for which the rifle is chambered. The magazine may be blind with no floorplate, have a hinged floorplate or be a detachable box.

Feeding can be either:
- Controlled—In this system the extractor grips the case rim

111

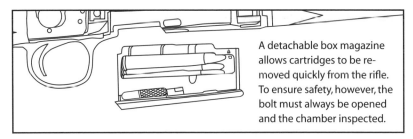

A detachable box magazine allows cartridges to be removed quickly from the rifle. To ensure safety, however, the bolt must always be opened and the chamber inspected.

immediately after the magazine releases the cartridge in order to control it. This has the advantage of allowing the cartridge to be withdrawn without chambering it. Many hunters prefer this system although it is more expensive to manufacture.

- Push Feed—In this system, the extractor does not control the cartridge until it has been seated in the chamber and the extractor snaps over the case rim. This has the advantage of being somewhat easier to manufacture, but the cartridge must be fully seated before the extractor can withdraw it. It is a common system found in many popular rifles.

Bolt Throw

Standard throw, bolt rotates 90 degrees to unlock

Advantages: strong primary extraction; large, opposed locking lugs; low loading on cocking surfaces.

Disadvantages: bolt handle interferes with scope; slower operation.

Short throw, bolt rotates 60 degrees or less to unlock

Advantages: fast operation; no scope interference; multiple locking lugs.

Disadvantages: high loading on cocking surfaces; weaker primary extraction; more expensive to manufacture.

Straight-pull bolt

Bolt handle does not rotate. Cam-actuated, rotating bolt head with multiple locking lugs or pivoting wedge unlocks as bolt is pulled rearward and locks as bolt is pushed fully forward.

Advantages: faster operation than turnbolts; easier to train shooters.

Disadvantages: more complex and expensive; weak primary extraction; heavier.

While straight-pull bolt-actions have been tried with some success on military rifles, such actions have not proven popular on sporting rifles. Reasons for this include higher cost of manufacture and weak primary extraction. The potential for faster operation has not proven significant for sporting purposes.

Single-Shot Mechanisms

A single-shot is a manually loaded and operated action without a magazine. It is capable of being loaded with and firing only a single shot at a time.

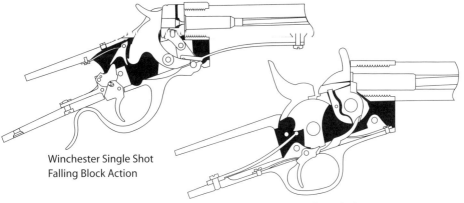

Winchester Single Shot
Falling Block Action

Remington No. 1 Rolling Block Action

Falling block

An operating lever under the action moves the bolt vertically in slots cut into the receiver walls. Moving the bolt upward to the bore axis locks the action; moving the bolt downward unlocks the action and recocks the striker. Most modern single-shot rifles employ this type of system as it is strong and can easily handle cartridges generating high breech pressures.

Pivoting block

The breech block is hinged to the receiver at the rear, leaving the front free to pivot up and down. An operating lever under the action pivots the forward part of the breech block upward to lock and downward to unlock. Unlocking recocks the striker. This system is now considered obsolete as it can not handle cartridges generating high breech pressures.

Break-open

This type of action is hinged in the middle to allow the barrel muzzle(s) to pivot downward on the frame to expose the chamber(s) for loading or unloading. The barrel(s) lock to the frame by a variety of means including sliding wedges, cuts in the receiver fences, retractable plungers and sliding top wedge locks. The break-open mechanism may have strikers or hammers recocked on opening or have an external hammer that must be manually recocked. This is a very popular system for single- and double-barrel shotguns. It is not normally considered suitable for high-breech-pressure cartridges without added locking devices.

Rolling block

This system is similar to the pivoting breech block in that it is
hinged at the rear leaving the front free to move. Whereas the
pivoting block pivots upward to lock, the rolling block pivots
forward to lock and unlock. A small operating handle on the
breech block provides finger purchase. The hammer must be
recocked manually for each shot. This system is now considered
obsolete. It is a weak design not capable of handling modern, high-
pressure cartridges.

Trapdoor

This system features a breech block hinged at its upper front to the
barrel. To lock this system, the breech block is pivoted downward
until it aligns with the bore axis and is held in place by a small
lock. To unlock the system, push the small lever to release the
lock and swing the breech block upward. The hammer must be
manually recocked for each shot. This system is now considered
obsolete. It is a weak design not capable of handling modern, high-
pressure cartridges.

Slide (Pump) Actions

The slide- or pump-action rifle or shotgun is a uniquely American
operating system. While it has only a handful of devotees in the rifle
category, a high percentage of shotgunners prefer this system. For this
reason, there are presently only a few manufacturers of slide-action
rifles, with Remington and Taurus being the major brands. Others have
come and gone. On the other hand, nearly every major manufacturer,
both domestic and foreign, offers a pump-action shotgun. Most pump-
action guns have a tubular magazine under the barrel.

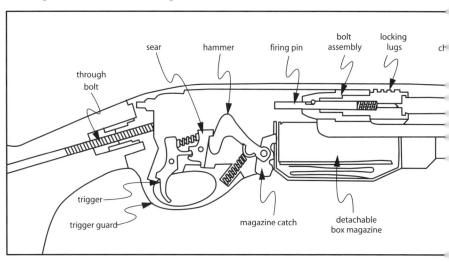

Operation is by means of a sliding fore-end that travels back and forth under the barrel and parallel to the bore axis. Action bars cycle the bolt. Often nicknamed a trombone- or pump-action. The receiver may be stressed or unstressed with the latter being the most popular.

> **Advantages:** reliable operation; inexpensive to manufacture; popular type offered in many brands; can handle high-pressure cartridges.
>
> **Disadvantages:** dual operating rods needed to avoid binding; may prove too noisy in some scenarios; operation difficult for some shooters.

Lever-Actions

The lever-action rifle is a classic American design that matured between 1866 and 1900 in the hands of cowboys, pioneers and lawmen in the Old West. According to legend, Winchester lever-action rifles "Won the West." The lever-action remains a popular favorite among American hunters today.

Operation is by means of a full loop hand lever rotating on a pivot under the receiver. The lever is keyed to the bolt; pulling the lever downward unlocks the bolt, extracts and ejects the cartridge case and recocks the hammer. Pulling the lever upward feeds and chambers a fresh cartridge and locks the bolt to the receiver. The hand lever remains against the pistol grip when the action is closed and locked.

Most lever-action rifles have an exposed hammer with a tubular magazine under the barrel. The receiver on most lever-action rifles is a stressed part in that the bolt locks to it. Many lever-action designs are weak in that they cannot handle cartridges with breech pressures above 40,000 p.s.i.

While lever-action rifles offer accuracy suitable for most hunting

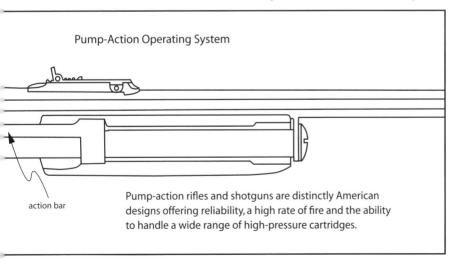

Pump-Action Operating System

action bar

Pump-action rifles and shotguns are distinctly American designs offering reliability, a high rate of fire and the ability to handle a wide range of high-pressure cartridges.

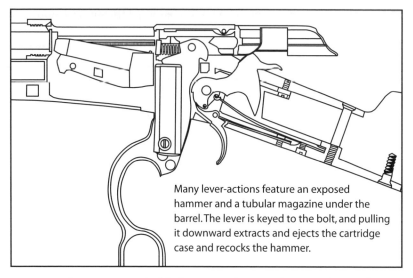

Many lever-actions feature an exposed hammer and a tubular magazine under the barrel. The lever is keyed to the bolt, and pulling it downward extracts and ejects the cartridge case and recocks the hammer.

purposes, they are not suitable for general target shooting due to the two-piece stocks and the lack of stiffness in the thin-walled receivers.

Most lever guns are rifles, although lever-action shotguns were offered around 1900 and have recently been reintroduced.

Advantages: fast operation; classic, trim styling; light weight.

Disadvantages: many models unsuited for high pressure cartridges; mediocre accuracy potential; hard to disassemble for cleaning/maintenance.

Revolvers

There are three types of revolver operation:
- Single-action—For single-action operation, the hammer of the revolver must be manually cocked for each shot.
- Double-action—For double-action operation, the shooter has two choices. The hammer can be manually cocked for each shot in similar manner to a single-action. This provides a light trigger pull for best accuracy, but is slow to operate.
  Or the trigger can be pulled with hammer down. Doing so will cock then release the hammer for a fast first shot in an emergency. However, the heavy trigger pull is not conducive to accuracy.
- Semi-auto—The trigger must be manually cocked or operated double-action with the trigger for the first shot. Afterward the cylinder advances to the next chamber powered by recoil through a series of guide channels and traveling pins. This design is rare and expensive.

Note: *See pg. 102 for illustrations of revolver operating mechanisims.*

Self-Loading Mechanisms

Recoil Operation

When the cartridge is fired, the barrel and bolt are allowed to recoil rearward for a short distance while locked together. The bolt and barrel are then unlocked, further rearward movement of the barrel stopped, and the bolt allowed to continue rearward against the pressure of the recoil spring. At the end of the bolt's travel, the recoil spring returns the bolt and barrel into battery. The length of bolt travel determines whether the system is short- or long-recoil.

- Short-recoil—Bolt travel less than overall cartridge length. This system is very popular as it is compact and light.
- Long-recoil—Bolt travel distance is the same or more than overall cartridge length. This system is rare as it is expensive and heavy.

Gas Operation

This operating mechanism uses hot, expanding propellant gases bled from the barrel or trapped at the muzzle to cycle the action. There are two basic systems of gas-operation:

- Direct impingement on the bolt via gas tube—Propellant gases bled from the barrel through a small hole, travel through a gas tube to be directed against a surface on the bolt. The energy in the gas causes the bolt to unlock and move rearward against recoil spring pressure.

- Indirect impingement via piston and rod.

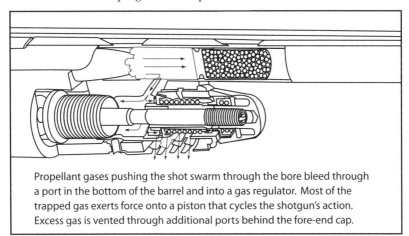

Propellant gases pushing the shot swarm through the bore bleed through a port in the bottom of the barrel and into a gas regulator. Most of the trapped gas exerts force onto a piston that cycles the shotgun's action. Excess gas is vented through additional ports behind the fore-end cap.

Short-stroke piston

Propellant gases are bled from the barrel through small axial hole(s) into a gas block. The gas block redirects the gas flow against a captive but movable piston in the gas block, a fixed piston on the operating rod or an intermediate piston rod. The

short power stroke acts on the operating rod(s), causing them
to move rearward, unlocking the bolt and pushing it rearward
against the pressure of the recoil spring.

Long-stroke piston
Propellant gases are bled from the barrel through small, axial
hole(s) into an expansion tube where they act directly on a gas
piston attached to the operating rod. Many systems of this type
have an adjustable valve assembly that enables the shooter to vary
the amount of gas bled into the expansion tube to suit climatic
conditions and ballistic variations. Also common are gas vent holes
in the expansion chamber to bleed off any excess gas pressure.

Muzzle gas trap
This type of system traps propellant gas at the muzzle in a
chamber that redirects the gas pressure against a piston attached to
the operating rod. This system has not proven popular.

Blowback/Inertia Operation
- Direct or Straight—The unlocked bolt is pushed rearward
  against its own inertia and recoil spring pressure by the back
  thrust from the breech pressure on the fired cartridge case.
  The inertia and recoil spring delay opening long enough to
  allow the breech pressure to drop to safe levels. This system is
  suitable for use with cartridges developing less than 40,000 psi
  of breech pressure.
- Delayed—Engagement surfaces or gas pressure delay the
  opening of the bolt until the breech pressure drops to safe
  levels. This system is suitable for use with cartridges having
  average breech pressures in excess of 40,000 psi. This system
  requires a fluted chamber.

Externally Powered
Externally powered gun systems are operated by an independent
power source off the gun and are not dependent on the gun's action
for operation. The power source provides energy to operate the gun by
several methods:
- manual—powered by human muscle
- electric—a variable-speed electric motor operates the system
- hydraulic—a variable-speed hydraulic motor operates the system
- gas—a propellant gas powers the system.

Externally powered gun systems include the Gatling, Gardner,
Nordenfelt, chain gun and the Meroka. Externally powered guns will
extract and eject dud cartridges as well as fired cases.

Chapter 7
STOCKS

The Sporting Arms and Ammunition Manufacturers' Institute defines a stock as the wood or synthetic component(s) to which the metal parts of a firearm are attached and that enable the shooter to hold the firearm. Within this definition stocks exhibit a wide variation in design and construction. Stocks may serve additional purposes as well.

Long Gun Stocks

Long gun stocks are either one-piece or multi-piece designs. One-piece stocks are common on most bolt-action sporting rifles and many ultra-modern bullpup military rifles, while multi-piece stocks are found on lever-action, pump-action and semi-automatic rifles and almost all shotguns.

All long gun stocks can be divided into a forward part, called the fore-end or (particularly on multi-piece stocks) the forearm that is grasped by the non-firing hand, and a rear part called the buttstock that is held into the shoulder by the shooter's firing or trigger hand. Long gun stocks come in a wide variety of styles, including hunting, target, tactical, competition and folding designs. One-piece stocks normally attach to the firearm using two or more stock screws in the underside of the stock. For this purpose, one-piece rifle stocks are inletted to create a channel for the receiver and the barrel. The inletted

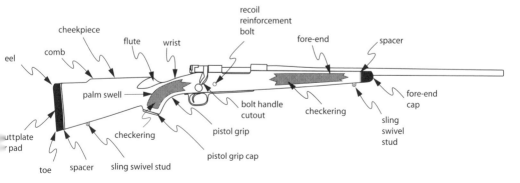

Rifle Stock Nomenclature

121

channel contains one or more bedding areas for the action and barrel. The forearm of a break-open shotgun normally attaches by way of a spring-loaded latch that engages a hook or stud on the underside of the barrel. The forearm of a pump- and semi-auto shotgun is normally secured by the threaded magazine tube cap. Rifles equipped with multi-piece stocks have the fore-ends secured by screws threaded into barrels or hangers.

The upper surface of long gun buttstocks on which the shooter's face rests is called the comb. Some buttstocks have a cheekpiece on the right or left side used for a face rest. Just rearward of the trigger guard is the wrist which is grasped by the shooting or trigger hand. At the end of the buttstock is a buttplate or buttpad that contacts the shoulder. Buttplates

Basic Stock Types

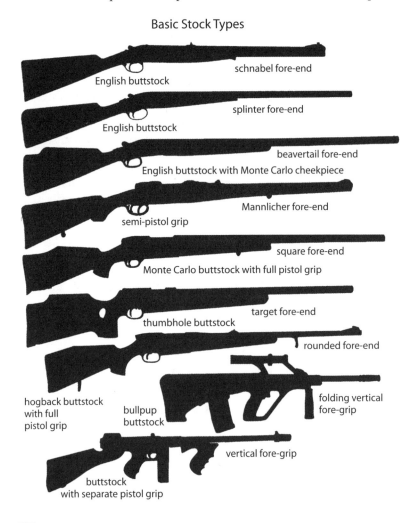

schnabel fore-end

English buttstock

splinter fore-end

English buttstock

beavertail fore-end

English buttstock with Monte Carlo cheekpiece

Mannlicher fore-end

semi-pistol grip

square fore-end

Monte Carlo buttstock with full pistol grip

target fore-end

thumbhole buttstock

rounded fore-end

hogback buttstock with full pistol grip

bullpup buttstock

folding vertical fore-grip

vertical fore-grip

buttstock with separate pistol grip

are commonly made of steel, brass, aluminum, wood or synthetic material, while buttpads are commonly made of soft or hard rubber. The top of the butt is called the heel, and the bottom is called the toe.

Most long gun stocks for hunting or general utility have checkering on the gripping areas of the fore-end/forearm and wrist. Target gun stocks may have checkering, stippling or no surface modification, and may have other features not found on general-purpose stocks.

Shotgun Stock Nomenclature

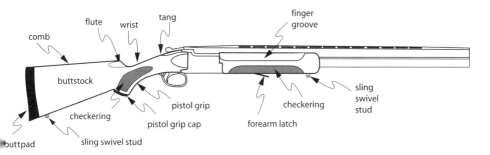

Handgun Stocks

Handgun stocks usually take the form of two slabs attached to the sides of the grip frame with one or two screws. One-piece stocks of molded synthetic material are also common; these usually consist of a U-shaped unit that slides onto the grip frame.

Since they are not subject to large mechanical stresses under normal use, handgun stocks can be made of a considerable variety of materials such as wood, plastic or synthetic material, and they take a number of shapes.

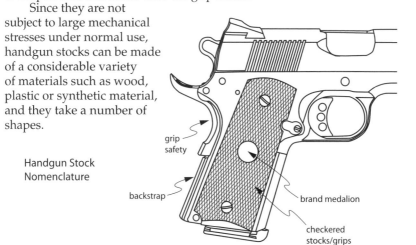

Handgun Stock Nomenclature

Other Stock Functions

In addition to enabling the shooter to hold the firearm, many rifle and shotgun stocks perform other important functions as well. For example, stocks may house critical parts of the operational mechanism such as recoil springs, buffers or magazines. The stocks of some revolvers serve to retain springs, trigger bars and other parts of the fire-control mechanism. Many rifles have hollowed-out areas in the buttstock under the buttplate suitable for storing cleaning equipment, takedown tools, extra cartridges and survival items.

Stocks also serve to prevent dust, sand, dirt, mud, water and debris from easily entering the action. For many shooters, the type, shape, finish, figure and ornamentation of the stock is a major factor contributing to a gun's aesthetic appeal. Finally, stock materials, stock dimensions (fit) and stock bedding play a critical role in how well a particular gun may perform in the hands of a particular shooter.

Stock Material Characteristics

Stock materials must be:
- strong enough to withstand rough handling
- strong enough to withstand recoil over thousands of shots
- typically made of common, inexpensive materials
- easily shaped, molded or formed
- lightweight
- dimensionally stable and rigid
- made of materials that resist oils, solvents, alcohol, fuels and/or moisture.

Wood Types

For centuries wood has been the material of choice for both long gun and handgun stocks. Although many woods have been (and continue to be) used for firearm stocks, long experience has led most stockmakers to favor only a handful of hardwood types such as walnut.

A specific type of wood's serviceability as a gun stock is based on its physical properties such as hardness, shock resistance, weight and volumetric shrinkage.

The dimensional stability of a given wood species used for a gunstock will affect the shooting accuracy of a rifle. Volumetric shrinkage values are a criterion of the subsequent shrinking-swelling that takes place in wood as a result of normal atmospheric moisture changes. With each one percent change in moisture content below the fiber saturation point (defined as 30 percent M.C.), approximately one-thirtieth of the total possible shrinkage will occur.

Physical properties are directly related to the appearance and strength of a wood species. For stockmakers, hardness, shock rating, weight and stability are key indicators for a particular wood's potential.

PROPERTIES OF POPULAR WOODS FOR STOCKMAKING

WOOD	HARDNESS	SHOCK RATING	WEIGHT	STABILITY
Amer. black walnut	1010	10.7	38	10.2%
Bastogne walnut	1460	12.3	42	—
beech	1300	15.1	45	13%
black cherry	950	11.4	33	9.2%
claro walnut	950	9.0	35	—
English walnut	1200	9.8	40	—
shagbark hickory	1820	25.8	63	13.4%
myrtle	1270	8.2	39	9.9%
rosewood	1450	13.1	53	small
sugar maple	1450	16.5	44	11.9%
screwbean mesquite	2335	15.0	54	4.5%
yellow birch	1260	20.8	43	13.4%

All values are approximate.

Hardness scale — Janka Hardness Test

Shock Rating — static bending values in in.-lbs. per cu. in.

Weight = in lbs. per cu. ft.

Stability = volumetric shrinkage during drying

Adapted with permission from *Gunstock Woods and Other Fine Timbers*, by Virgil Davis, Southland Press, 1988.

Wood Grain

By far the favorite wood for gunstocks is walnut. Light, strong, resilient and stable, with a fine, dense grain, walnut is hard enough to take sharp, fine checkering and precise inletting without being brittle. Properly sealed, it offers excellent dimensional stability. For high-grade factory or custom arms, walnut offers excellent figure, the unique pattern or design on the wood's surface. Grain and figure are not the same (although the pattern and flow of the grain largely determines the figure produced). Technically, grain refers to the organization or orientation of the wood fibers. There are six types of grain patterns, and an even greater variety of figure patterns.

There are seven types of wood grain:

- straight
- irregular
- diagonal
- spiral
- interlocked
- wavy
- curl.

There are six types of wood figure:

- fiddleback
- bird's-eye
- burl
- marble-cake
- crotch
- quilted.

Worldwide, there are some 50 species of walnut (genus *Juglans*). In addition, many other species are mistakenly called walnut. In terms of walnut best suited for gunstocks, most is taken from three species: *Juglans regia* (Circassian, English or French walnut; also many other types), *Juglans nigra* (American, eastern and Oregon black walnut) and *Juglans hindsii* (California black, claro and Hinds walnut). Also suitable for high-grade stocks, but very rare, is Bastogne walnut, a hybrid of *Juglans regia* and *Juglans hindsii*.

Most favored of these is *Juglans regia* (Circassian, English or French), which in Latin means "royal walnut." This species originated in Asia, but has been transplanted widely throughout Europe and the Americas, resulting in many subclassifications that exhibit slight differences in color and figure resulting from variations in growing conditions. All woods of this species, however, have a fine, dense grain, excellent hardness and workability, high strength and shock resistance, good stability, and appealing grain and figure. *Juglans nigra* (American, eastern and Oregon) the name for varieties of true black walnut, and *Juglans hindsii* (California, claro and Hinds), collectively known as claro walnut, are very similar in properties to the *Juglans regia* varieties, though they are both slightly weaker and not as shock resistant as the Circassian or Bastogne varieties. Black and claro walnut are also known for their distinctive grain and figure.

Other popular hardwoods for gunstocks include beech (*Fagus grandofolia*), black cherry (*Prunus serotina*), hickory (*Carya ovata*), maple (*Acer* species), mesquite (*Prosopis pubescens* or *glandulosa*), myrtle (*Umbellularia californica*), rosewood (*Dalbergia* species) and yellow birch (*Betula alleghaniensis*). Beech and yellow birch have fairly plain grain and figure, but are strong and inexpensive. Thus, they are popular choices for inexpensive or utility-grade firearms, usually with a walnut stain.

Other woods, including bubinga (*Guibortia tessmanni*), ebony (*Diospyros* species), and zebrawood (*Microberlinia brazzavillensis*), are not appropriate or practical for entire rifle or shotgun stocks, but are frequently used for handgun stocks, pistol-grip caps and fore-end tips.

From Tree to Finished Stock

According to some authorities, only trees 24" or more in diameter should be used for gunstocks. The best wood for stocks is found in the first five or six feet of the trunk at the junction of the stump and the roots and in the crotch area where the trunk splits into branches. With many walnut trees, the stump is not cut off at ground level, but dug out to take advantage of the figure in the vicinity of the roots.

Once cut to length, the stump is cut into a number of rough-sawn pieces of wood called "blanks" having the approximate external outline of the stock prior to final shaping. There are several ways to cut blanks from the trunk. The best method is quarter sawing, but this method produces considerable waste. A modified form of quarter sawing, called splitting, yields a greater number of blanks, as do the slab and modified slab sawing methods. Each blank ends up as a block of wood approximately 36" long, 15" wide and 3" thick with its ends sealed with paraffin wax.

Up to 40 percent of the weight of a newly cut stock blank is moisture; this must be reduced to around 10-12 percent before the blank can be made into a stock. Air drying is the best method of reducing moisture in stock woods, however it typically takes years. Kiln drying is a popular and faster alternative. Kiln drying is a two-stage process. For the first stage, the 3"-thick blanks are stacked with sticks separating the layers to allow air circulation. After drying, they are cut into rough blank shape, with a section about 8" wide at the rear tapering to about 3" wide at the front. Following this, they are again stacked with the ends sealed for final drying. After this, the stock is shaped and inletted.

Various systems are used to grade stock blanks based on considerations such as color, figure, grain flow, texture, lack of sapwood, the ability of the stock to take fine checkering, and more. Grades generally range from Utility or Common at the low end to Exhibition or Special Select at the top. Some suppliers have premium grades higher than Exhibition. There is no single classification system universally accepted or used by stock wood suppliers.

Considerable experience is required to properly cut a block of wood into a blank, then to make the blank into a stock. Grain orientation is critical for strength in highly stressed areas such as the pistol grip. Ideally, the grain should flow with the lines of the stress. Breakage can occur when the grain flows in the wrong direction. For example, the convoluted patterns of light and dark produce the best figure, but also signal where the wood is weak. Thus, figure should be restricted to the area of the buttstock behind the wrist.

Stock inletting and shaping can be performed manually, with machine tools or a combination of both. In this phase, walnut quickly demonstrates why it is the first choice of stockmakers. It is easily cut with sharp tools, does not embed in rasps or files, and is not brittle—characteristics that allow the precise wood-to-metal fit that is the *sine qua non* of fine stockmaking.

After shaping and inletting, the stock is checkered either by hand or by machine. In this process, the surface of the wood in selected areas of the pistol grip and fore-end is cut away to form a series of intersecting lines.

These lines and the pattern they form provide superior adhesion to the shooter's hands. If called for, sling swivel studs are installed at that time.

Application of the stock finish is the final phase. It serves to seal the stock against moisture, strengthen the wood fibers at the surface, and preserve the color and figure of the wood. The stock must first be smoothed with successively finer grades of sandpaper until it is free of scratches and tiny "whiskers" of wood. With many (but not all) woods, a separate sealer is applied to inhibit moisture changes. Coarse-grain woods, such as some of the walnuts, must also have their pores filled to the level of the surrounding wood. This is frequently accomplished using thick coats of the same material to be used for final finishing; the thick filling coats are allowed to dry and then brought back to the level of the wood with fine sandpaper, leaving only the pores filled.

There are three types of preservatives used for finishing gun stocks: oil, varnish (lacquer) and synthetics such as polyurethane. Hand-rubbed tung or linseed oil finishes are beautiful, but each coat must be laboriously hand-applied, dried and smoothed, then the process repeated until the desired depth of finish is produced. Modern synthetic finishes such as acrylics and polyurethanes apply easily and can fill, seal and finish a stock in only one or two coats. They are also very durable. Lacquer and varnish finishes offer an attractive finish but one that is not quite as durable as synthetic finishes. Although not as durable as synthetic, lacquer, varnish and oil finishes are the easiest to repair in the event of a scratch or ding.

The final finish, ranging from glossy to matte, can be obtained by using very fine abrasive paper or rubbing compound followed by a final coat of wax.

Other Stock Materials
Laminated Wood

Solid-wood gun stocks often suffer from dimensional instability when exposed to moisture, high humidity or changes in temperature. When this happens, the stock swells and warps, thereby significantly degrading accuracy and dramatically shifting the point of aim.

These problems can be ameliorated by using laminated-wood stocks made from one or two types of wood cut into strips and glued together longitudinally. High-strength epoxy glue at high pressure impregnates the wood and ensures a good bond. For additional strength and stability, the grain of each wood layer is oriented at right angles to its neighbors. The thickness and type of laminates vary, though most commercial laminated stocks use layers of birch about 1/16" thick.

Because laminated stocks are considerably more stable than solid-wood stocks, they are a favorite choice for target or varmint rifles. For many shooters, the distinctive appearance of laminated stocks adds to their appeal. However, laminated-wood stocks are heavier and can be more expensive than solid-wood stocks of the same dimensions, and they can still warp if excess moisture is absorbed.

Fiberglass and Other Synthetics

Even when properly sealed, solid- or laminated-wood stocks are vulnerable to warpage, swelling, or other dimensional changes due to the absorption or release of moisture. Additionally, wood can deteriorate from exposure to solvents or gun oils; in fact, softening of the wood in the bedding area by repeated exposure to gun oil is a common problem. Wood also can crack as the result of accumulated stress from recoil, or from weakness at a critical point, such as the wrist. Consequently, stockmakers have long sought stronger alternatives to wood.

In the 1970s, several companies began producing gunstocks made of laid-up fiberglass cloth. Fiberglass cloth is strong, dimensionally stable, resistant to solvents, and is unaffected by humidity, moisture or temperature variations. Additionally, it has shock-absorbing properties that reduce the amount of perceived recoil. The original technique developed for making fiberglass stocks remains in use today. It involves hand-laying fiberglass cloth in layers in a mold, with epoxy resin to bind the layers into a solid shape. Next, the void inside the stock is filled with polyurethane foam and catalyst, which expands outward, pressing the layers of resin-impregnated fiberglass cloth tightly against the inside of the mold. Some manufacturers use an expandable rubber air bladder inside the mold pressurized to 60-80 p.s.i. to force the fiberglass layers outward against the mold. When the bladder is deflated and removed, the space filled with fiberglass beads or strands mixed with epoxy. Color can be added to the fiberglass layers during the molding process to produce an integral finish that will not chip, peel or crack and needs no maintenance. Alternatively, a gel coat around .040" thick can be applied to the finished stock. Such paint finishes can become showcases of art with complex designs, scenes and various colors.

Recently, other cloth materials have been used in conjunction with fiberglass, such as Kevlar and carbon fiber. In most cases, such materials have been used to supplement fiberglass cloth rather than replace it, for example, in high stress areas such as the wrist or fore-end. One such example, Dupont's Kevlar para-aramid fiber, renowned for its use in bullet-proof vests, is five times stronger than steel on an equal-weight basis. However, it is substantially more expensive than fiberglass cloth, insufficiently rigid as the sole cloth material in a long gun stock and harder to lay up in a mold. Carbon or graphite fiber cloths offer light weight with a high stiffness-to-weight ratio, making them useful on stocks that must be ultra-light but rigid, such as benchrest and other competition stocks. However, carbon or graphite fibers are extremely expensive and their directional strength often requires complex lay-up patterns.

Synthetic stocks of injection-molded plastics such as nylon have been used successfully for gunstocks since the early 1960s. This type of inexpensive, light and stable gunstock is suitable for rimfire rifles and airguns, but lacks to strength necessary for center-fire rifles or shotguns.

In recent years, reaction molding technology has matured using new resins, new molding processes and fiberglass filling materials. These advances allow a significant increase in the strength of molded gunstocks such that they are sufficienly strong for use in center-fire rifles and shotguns. Though they are less rigid than the laid-up fiberglass stocks, molded gunstocks are inexpensive, weather-resistant, require little or no maintenance and can withstand considerable punishment. Reaction-molded stocks offer other benefits as well: They can be molded into shapes difficult or impossible to create in wood, and the color or camouflage pattern can be molded into the stock material itself.

Synthetic materials for handgun stocks include a variety of molded plastics of various colors as well laminates such as Micarta, a high-pressure laminate of layers of linen cloth and resinous binders. Also popular are various soft-rubber units of one- or two-piece construction. Rubber grips absorb recoil as well as provide a more secure gripping surface, for more enjoyable range sessions, however rubber grips may not be suited for concealed carry as their non-slip surface tends to cling to clothing and reveal the presence of a gun.

Metal

Metal stocks have been common on some firearms since the 1930s, primarily in the form of telescoping, folding or collapsible stocks. Popular examples of such stocks include those found on the German MP38/40, American M3 "Grease Gun"and British "Sten"submachine guns of World War II, as well as postwar submachine guns such as the Israeli "Uzi", Swedish "K" and Danish Madsen M1950. Other well-known examples are the M1 "Paratrooper" Carbine and many special models of military assault rifles. Folding or collapsing metal stocks are also found on some contemporary law enforcement and home-defense shotguns and pistol-caliber semi-auto carbines. Metal stocks are common also in some types of competitive shooting such as three-position rimfire (Anschutz, Walther and Feinwerkbau) and unlimited benchrest rifle as well as the occasional trap shotgun and handgun uses.

Hybrids

Hybrid stocks combine metal with wood or synthetic materials to produce a gunstock that is rigid, impervious to moisture, solvents and oils, and never loses its bedding. Probably the first widespread use of aluminum as a structural stock material was among benchrest shooters. Another pioneer in this area was Accuracy International in England with their metal frame and wood side panel design. In the 1980s, H-S Precision of South Dakota, introduced the present standard hybrid stock for sporting rifles. The H-S Precision design features a precision-machined aluminum backbone with a laid-up synthetic molded around it. The cloth layers include fiberglass, Kevlar and carbon fiber laid-up where their characteristics are needed. The H-S Precision backbone design offers solid bedding that never needs replacing while still allowing the action to be taken out of the stock and reinstalled with little or no loss of zero.

Ornamentation

Many custom handgun stocks utilize materials such as ivory, mother of pearl, stag horn or synthetic replicas of these. Such stocks offer no functional advantage over wood or synthetic units, and are used primarily for ornamental purposes.

Target Stocks

As target arms are required to consistently perform at a higher level of accuracy and reliability than other firearms, this requires additional refinement to the stock. Target rifle stock designs vary widely according to the demands of the individual shooter and his discipline. Today, solid-wood stocks have yielded to laminated-wood, hybrid or synthetic stocks because of their greater stability and more consistent accuracy in varying conditions over longer periods of time. Bedding is commonly in the form of fiberglass/epoxy compounds, steel or aluminum backbones or aluminum bedding blocks (*see Stock Bedding*).

Design variations on target stocks can include fore-end accessory rails and counter weights as well as adjustable buttplates and combs. Benchrest rifle stocks have wide, flat fore-ends to ride sandbag rests solidly and high combs to position the shooter's eye properly for viewing through a scope. Stocks for metallic silhouette competition have high combs, a short length of pull and a short, lowered fore-end that are more conducive to accurate shooting from a standing position. Long-range prone rifle stocks usually have high, straight combs, a long length of pull and a nearly vertical pistol grip. Perhaps the most adjustable gunstocks are those on free rifles that offer adjustments for length of pull, pitch, vertical and lateral buttplate position, vertical buttplate angle and hand position on the fore-end. Also common on such rifles are palm rests and hook buttplates that help stabilize the gun in the standing position.

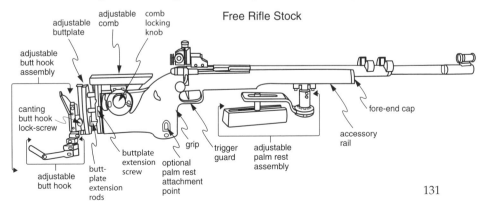

Free Rifle Stock

Stocks for trap, skeet and sporting clays shotguns commonly offer some or all of the following features:

- beavertail forearms
- pistol grips with or without palm swells
- adjustable combs
- adjustable pitch and variable length of pull.

On the other hand, competitors involved in shotgun slug and "turkey-shoot" matches are mostly concerned with getting their sighting eye high enough to see through a low-powered optical or red-dot scope commonly used in such matches. For this reason, wood or synthetic stocks with high Monte Carlo combs are often favored for such guns.

Pistols used in center-fire and .45-caliber phases of three-gun bullseye competition are often fired with their factory stocks. By contrast, many .22 rimfire handguns used in bullseye competition are equipped with stocks having thumb rests, finger grooves and oversized dimensions for shooter comfort. For ISSF (International Shooting Sport Federation) competition, orthopedic stocks fitted specifically to the shooter's hand are used in order to provide maximum support. Practical handgun competitors (especially those using fat-bodied pistols for high-capacity magazines or those with small hands) sometimes utilize extra-thin stocks. Maintaining a secure, consistent grip under recoil is of utmost importance, so sharply checkered wood or synthetic grips of the wrap-around type are popular.

Stock Modifications

Surface Treatments

Most firearm stocks have some form of surface treatment intended to improve the shooter's grip in specific areas, such as the wrist, pistol grip or fore-end. Such treatments take a few common forms.

Checkering consists of intersecting lines on the wood or synthetic surface, most often a diamond pattern with borders. Checkering may be accomplished by one of four methods:

- cutting, done either by hand or by machine
- laser etching, done by machine
- impressing, using a heated metal die the reverse of the desired pattern to displace the wood surface
- molding in the case of synthetic stocks.

Checkering patterns may have different line spacing, which is expressed in L.P.I. (lines per inch). The higher the number, the more lines per inch and the finer the pattern. Most factory hunting rifles and shotguns are coarsely checkered with 16, 18 or 20 lines per inch. High-grade rifles and shotguns normally have finer checkering of 22, 24 or 26 lines per inch. For decorative purposes, some checkering is produced in a French or skip-line pattern, in which lines are omitted or skipped at regular intervals.

Stippling is not as aesthetically pleasing as checkering, but produces an excellent gripping surface. For this reason, stippling is seen primarily on target arms. Stippling may also be seen on the frontstrap and backstrap of the grip frames of some target and defensive handguns.

Carving is uncommon on contemporary factory firearms, and is usually found only on high-grade custom arms. In a process analogous to metal engraving, the carver produces scroll, floral or other patterns, game scenes, or other types of artistic designs. Unlike checkering or stippling, whose primary purpose is functional, the carved patterns are primarily ornamental, and thus are not restricted to the gripping surfaces of the wrist and fore-end.

Synthetic stocks are very hard to checker by means of cutters, as the resin and fiberglass quickly wear cutter blades out. For this reason, many manufacturers of synthetic stocks cut checkering patterns into the molds to produce a checkered stock. Other synthetic stockmakers use rough surface paints or add non-slip materials such as fine sand or rubber-like inlays to the stock finish.

Stock Accessories

Although the needs of most shooters are well met with factory stocks, a wide variety of aftermarket stock accessories are available including:

- sling swivels and studs
- detachable bipods
- recoil pads
- recoil reducers
- cartridge or magazine holders.

Recoil reduction devices reduce the perceived recoil of a firearm and take the form of soft rubber buttpads, mercury-filled devices that fit inside the gun butt and telescoping buttstocks that use spring or hydraulic resistance to soften the kick. Often seen on original and reproduction blackpowder rifles as patch boxes, cartridge or magazine carriers are sometimes equipped on modern rifles such as those used for biathalon competition and hunting. Other accessories, such as fore-end accessory rails, palm rests, hand stops, and adjustable combs and buttplates, are normally found only target guns.

Stock Bedding

Properly inletting and then fitting the barreled action of a rifle to the stock is called bedding. The purpose of bedding is to securely hold the barreled action in the stock so that the vibrations and stresses produced as the bullet accelerates down the bore are transferred and controlled in a uniform pattern of movement. By so doing, inconsistencies in flex and vibration are held to a minimum, thus reducing bullet dispersion and increasing accuracy and consistency.

Ideally, when the stock screws are tightened, the stock should produce as little stress as possible on the barreled action—that is, it shouldn't cause the receiver to bend or the barrel to flex from pressure. Some stress or pressure is unavoidable; existing stress must remain consistent from shot to shot. This requires bedding that conforms exactly to the receiver surface.

Many wood and some synthetic stocks are inletted either by machine or by hand. Many synthetic stocks are molded with inletting to accept a specific barreled action. Hybrid and metal stocks must be machined and fitted to the action. The quality of the bedding fit is determined by the precision of the inletting or molding process. With wood and synthetic stocks, fit is improved by applying bedding compound to the bedding area. Bedding compound consists of fiberglass or powdered metal such as steel or aluminum in a thick liquid solution of epoxy or similar material. The bedding compound is spread onto the bedding surface, and the barreled action (treated with release agent to prevent adhesion of the compound) is seated firmly into it. The bedding compound is then allowed to dry, forming a hard, moisture- and solvent-resistant layer that conforms precisely to the barreled action. This holds the action securely in the stock so that stresses on the receiver and barrel remain consistent.

There are many different bedding techniques. For example, bedding compound can be applied to the full length of the receiver or only at the receiver ring and receiver tang.

Pillar bedding is a popular option. In this technique, cylindrical steel or aluminum tubes for the stock screws are bedded into the stock. The tubes are cut to a length so that they become pillars that control the fit of the action and magazine in the stock. When properly fitted, both the bottom metal and receiver are tensioned against the pillars and not the stock, giving secure metal-to-metal bedding contact.

Aluminum bedding blocks are another popular option, especially with heavy-barrel tactical rifles and varmint rifles. In this method, an aluminum bedding block is inletted and bedded or molded into the stock and the action, then bedded to the block. This provides a stable bedding solution that maintains accuracy and point of impact over a wide range of temperature and humidity conditions.

Barrel Bedding

Barrel bedding is a vital component of accuracy. Many rifle shooters prefer the free-floating method of barrel bedding in which the barrel does not contact the stock at all. This method is preferred for its stability, consistency and accuracy. Other shooters prefer to bed the first 1½" or so of the barrel in front of the receiver, then free-float the barrel for the rest of its length. Many hunters maintain that thin sporter-weight barrels prone to considerable vibration shoot best when stabilized by contact with the stock at the tip of the fore-end. A few gunsmiths and rifle builders advocate full-length bedding—bedding the barrel with compound the full length of the barrel channel.

Stock Fit

As the physical interface between the shooter and a firearm, stock fit can and does significantly affect shooter performance.

Because they are pointed and not aimed, stock fit is especially critical for shotguns. Comb height and width, cast-on or cast-off, stock pitch, pull length and wrist contours must be tailored to the individual shooter so that when held in a normal shooting position, the shotgun points where the shooter is looking. Top shotgun competitors and serious bird hunters often have their shotgun stocks fitted to their physical characteristics. Some competition shotgun stocks, such as those used for trap or sporting clays shooting, often have adjustable combs and buttpad spacers for easier fitting.

Stock fit is also critical with most hunting rifles. The most important aspect of rifle stock fit is comb height. The comb must be high enough to position the shooter's eye directly behind a riflescope if a scope is to be used. For this reason, comb angle is also significant. A comb that angles sharply downward toward the butt will transfer more recoil to the shooter's face than a comb that rises toward the rear. A straight comb is a popular compromise, as it allows the head to be slid slightly forward or rearward on the stock (as might occur in different shooting positions) without changing the height of the eye in relation to the scope sight.

Handgun stock fit is important in order to stabilize contact with the shooter's hand. In this respect, the girth of the grip frame, the width and length of the grip area and the trigger reach (the shortest distance from the backstrap to the trigger face) all influence how a handgun is held and controlled. For example, shooters with small hands often find it difficult to achieve a proper firing grip on large-frame handguns. Shooters with large hands find it difficult to grip small-frame handguns.

The girth of many handguns can be modified easily by installing thinner grip panels if such are available. Smooth grip panels can be replaced with checkered rubber panels to increase retention. Grips with integral non-slip surfaces covering frontstraps or backstraps can be used to increase trigger reach and retention. Lastly, several firms offer slip-on rubber units designed to meet some of the above needs.

For target shooting, handgun stocks can facilitate optimal alignment of hand, wrist and forearm, allowing the shooter to achieve a comfortable shooting position that naturally aligns his eye with the target. Stocks for target handguns used in bullseye or ISSF competition are shaped to give maximum ergonomic benefit through the use of thumb rests, palm swells, adjustable palm shelf, trigger reach, grip angle and cant. A handgun stock offering all or a majority of these features is termed an orthopedic grip and may (depending upon the latitude allowed by the rules) nearly envelop the hand and wrist. Handgun competitors often purchase oversize stocks and then shape them to their shooting hand for the best fit.

Stock Dimensions

Long Guns

For most rifle and shotgun shooters, fit of the stock to the face and shoulder, eye alignment with the sights, and position of the shooting hand in relation to the trigger determine how comfortable a particular gun feels. These factors effectively determine how well a shooter can handle a rifle or shotgun. These comfort features can be expressed in a number of important stock measurements.

Cast—This is the lateral displacement of the centerline of the buttplate (pad) from the centerline of the bore. For a right-handed shooter, this displacement is usually to the right and is called cast-off. For left-handed shooters, with stock displacement to the left, it is called cast-on. A stock with an abnormally large amount of cast-off or cast-on is designed for shooters who mount the gun on the right or left, but who have an opposite side dominant eye.

Drop—This is the vertical distance from the line of sight to the comb, Monte Carlo cheekpiece or heel of the stock.

- On rifles, drop is measured downward from a straight line extended from the top of the front sight through the top surface of the open rear sight adjacent to the notch. The drop on target rifles is usually measured from the centerline of the bore. On rifles having no sights, drop is measured from the top of the receiver.
- Drop measurements in shotguns are taken from an extension of a straight line drawn from the base of the front bead sight

Long Gun Stock Specifications

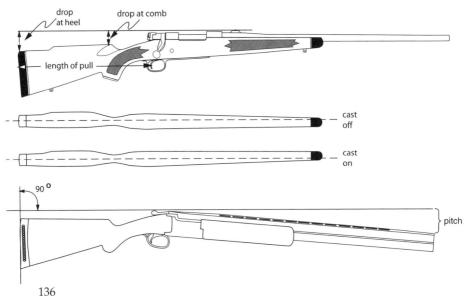

across the highest point on the frame or receiver. To give an indication of the angle or slant of the comb from horizontal, two drop measurements are often given: drop at comb and drop at heel. If these two measurements are the same, the stock has a straight comb. More often, on hunting rifles, the drop at heel will be larger than the drop at the comb, giving a comb that slants downward toward the butt.

Girth—This is the smallest circumferential dimension at the pistol grip.

Length of pull—This is the distance from the center of the trigger to the center of the buttplate or recoil pad. Taller or longer-armed shooters generally require a longer length of pull, while the reverse is true for the shorter-statured. Most standard factory rifles and shotguns have pull lengths of from 13½" to 14½". Many manufacturers offer rifles with stocks having pull lengths of about 12½" for youth shooters.

Pitch—A term normally reserved for shotguns stocks, this is the angle at which the buttplate or recoil pad slopes in relation to the bore axis. It is found by extending a line across the butt and drawing at right angles to this line an additional line through the highest point on the receiver or frame and measuring the distance from an extension of this line to a point at the base of the front sight bead. The pitch is said to be "down" if the described line is above the front sight bead, and "up" if below. The pitch is normally down.

Handguns

There are four main dimensions of importance relating to the stocks and grip frame of a handgun.

Grip circumference—The circumference of the grip frame area of a

Handgun Grip Specifications

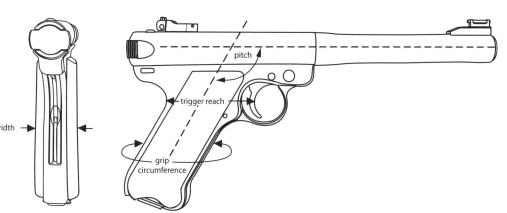

handgun with the stocks installed. On many guns, this measurement will vary at various points on the grip frame.

Pitch—The angle of the grip in relation to the axis of the bore. This measurement, in degrees, may determine how naturally a handgun points in a shooter's hand.

Trigger reach—The distance from the face of the trigger to the backstrap, on a line drawn directly rearward from the center of the trigger face. This dimension helps determine where a shooter's index finger will contact the trigger.

Width—The width of the grip area of the handgun at its widest point. This measurement is related to Grip Circumference, and thus affects how persons with different hand sizes will grip the gun. Additionally, Width may determine how well a personal protection handgun may conceal beneath clothing.

Chapter 8
BARRELS

A gun barrel is a metal tube through which hot, rapidly expanding propellant gases convert stored chemical energy to kinetic energy by accelerating a bullet, shot swarm or other mass to a velocity. While this may seem simple, modern gun barrels are the result of over 600 years of continuous technological development. Although little more than a tube with one end closed, a gun barrel represents a complex blend of chemistry, physics, metallurgy, engineering and ballistics.

In rifles and handguns, the barrel is the single most important factor in determining accuracy. In shotguns, the barrel controls the tightness and quality of the pattern.

Gun barrels also influence the physical characteristics of firearms such as overall length, weight and recoil, as well as handling qualities such as balance, swing and pointing.

Barrel Nomenclature

All gun barrels have a cylindrical hole running completely through them, known as the bore, in which the bullet or shot swarm travels as it is accelerated. In rifles and handguns, the bore has spiral lands and grooves called rifling. As the bullet travels down the bore, the lands grip the bullet by engraving its outer surface, causing it to spin on its axis so it will stabilize in flight. Rifling may be either left-hand twist or right-hand twist with the latter being the most common. Most shotguns have smooth bores with a constriction about 2" from the muzzle called the choke. At the rear end of the barrel is an enlarged area for the cartridge called the chamber. The tapered portion at the front of the chamber is called the leade or throat in a rifle and the forcing cone in a

Rifle Barrel Nomenclature

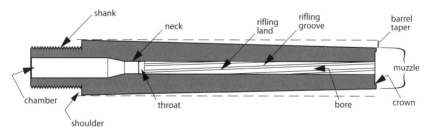

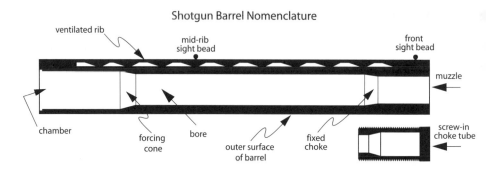

Shotgun Barrel Nomenclature

shotgun. Finally, the front end of the barrel is called the muzzle and the chamfered end of the bore is called the crown.

Rifling

Rifling takes the form of one or more lands and grooves of differing widths, profiles, arrangements and twist (turn) rates. The spiral depressions in the bore surface between the lands are called the grooves; the lands are projections on the bore surface between the grooves. Land diameter is taken as the diameter of the circle formed by the top of the lands, and groove diameter is taken as the diameter of the circle formed by the bottom of the grooves. The difference between these two dimensions is the groove depth. This is normally around .005" to .010". The groove depth selected depends upon the type of bullet to be fired in the barrel. For example, muzzleloading firearms and cartridge arms intended for lead bullets normally have deeper grooves than cartridge arms for jacketed bullets. Groove diameter is usually the same diameter as the bullet that is to be used (e.g., .308" diameter bullets are intended for a groove diameter of .308").

- **Width**—The width of the lands and grooves depends upon the preferences of the barrelmaker and/or customer. Normally, land width is less than groove width.

- **Number**—The number of lands and grooves may vary from one to 20 or more, depending on the preferences of the barrelmaker and customer. Most common are four, six or eight lands and grooves. Barrels with more than eight lands and grooves are sometimes called "multigroove" or "microgroove" types. An even or uneven number of lands or grooves may be used.

- **Profile**—Lands and grooves will be found with differing profiles or shapes. The most popular profile is the type with sharp corners on the shoulders of the lands and grooves. This type of profile is often called "conventional" rifling. However, other profiles such as polygon, sloped or ratchet-edged, semi-polygon and others will be encountered.

Rifling Profiles

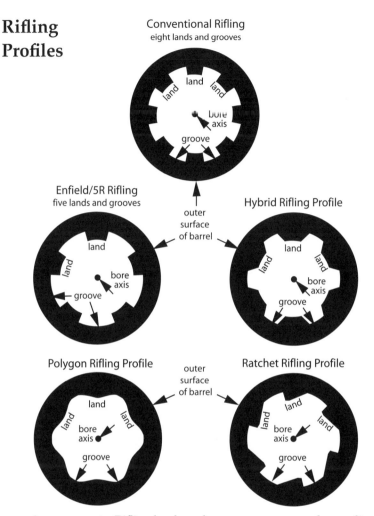

Conventional Rifling
eight lands and grooves

land / land / land / bore axis / groove

Enfield/5R Rifling
five lands and grooves

land / land / bore axis / groove

outer surface of barrel

Hybrid Rifling Profile

land / land / land / bore axis / groove

Polygon Rifling Profile

land / land / land / bore axis / groove

outer surface of barrel

Ratchet Rifling Profile

land / land / land / bore axis / groove

- **Arrangement**—Rifling lands and grooves are arranged according to the preference of the barrelmaker and customer. The most popular arrangement consists of an equal number of lands and grooves arranged so that a land is directly opposite a land. However, land and groove arrangements can consist of an unequal number of lands and grooves so that a land is opposite a groove. Such an arrangement is often called "Enfield" or "5R" rifling.

- **Twist**—Rifling is made with different twist rates or turn rates depending on the stabilization requirements of the bullets to be used. Most rifling is of constant twist rate, meaning the rate of turn is the same from the origin of the rifling to the muzzle. A second type of rifling is known as "gain twist" or variable twist.

143

In this type of rifling, the turn rate starts slowly at the origin of the rifling and increases in rate toward the muzzle. Gain twist is popular on some muzzleloading rifles and occasionally will be found on some cartridge firearms as well.

Barrel Profile

The external surface of most barrels is tapered with thicker walls around and just forward of the chamber, where pressure is highest, and thinner walls at the muzzle, where pressures are lowest. The degree of taper may be constant or variable with or without distinctive steps or shoulders. Heavy barrels for target rifles and handguns often called "bull barrels" have thick walls often with no taper at all. Barrelmakers commonly offer barrel profiles of different types ranging from ultra-thin lightweight shapes to heavy competition types.

The rear end of the barrel terminates in a "shank" that attaches the barrel to the receiver. In center-fire rifles and handguns, the shank is usually threaded, though most .22-rimfire designs utilize smooth shanks. Interchangeable pump- and semi-auto shotgun barrels often have an extension on the back end of the barrel to which the breechbolt locks.

Accessories

Barrels are commonly used to mount external accessories on firearms such as:

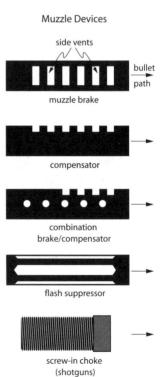

Muzzle Devices

side vents

bullet path

muzzle brake

compensator

combination brake/compensator

flash suppressor

screw-in choke (shotguns)

- iron and/or optical sights
- front sling swivel
- light
- fore-end hanger and latch
- gas-piston assembly
- bipod
- quick-change barrel latches
- vehicle mounts
- ventilated or solid rib
- perforated handguard or jacket.

Or muzzle devices such as a:

- muzzle brake
- compensator
- flash suppressor
- flash hider
- sound suppressor
- silencer
- recoil booster
- grenade launcher
- blank-firing adaptor
- bayonet.

Barrel Materials

Prior to 1880, alloys of brass or iron were commonly used to make gun barrels. However, these metals proved unsuitable for the new smokeless propellants introduced after 1885. To safely function with smokeless propellants, new metal alloys had to be developed. Today, various alloys of steel are universally preferred for gun barrels because they are:

- widely available
- relatively inexpensive
- easily machined
- superior in strength
- superior in toughness
- high hardness
- excellent heat and wear resistance
- resistant to shock.

Steel makers offer special "ordnance-grade" steel alloys for the manufacture of gun barrels. Ordnance-grade steel alloys are subjected to special handling, careful heat treatment and rigorous analysis to assure quality and consistency. The majority of barrels are monolithic—that is, the entire barrel is made out of a single piece of metal. Here, it should be noted that different rifling methods utilized by barrelmakers (see below) often work best with specific steel alloys and levels of hardness. Most barrel steels have a hardness of around 25 to 32 on the Rockwell C scale. Suitable metal alloys for monolithic gun barrels include:

Alloy steels

Suitable barrel alloys include types having varying amounts of chromium, molybdenum, vanadium, nickel and manganese as alloying metals. A popular example and perennial favorite in the U.S. is SAE 4140 chrome-molybdenum or "chrome-moly" steel. In Europe, vanadium and nickel-steel alloys are preferred. Most standard barrels are made with alloy steels, as they offer an excellent balance of strength and cost.

Stainless steels

Stainless steel barrels have been around since the 1930s. However, they have recently seen widespread use for two reasons:

- Their resistance to heat erosion is superior to chrome-moly barrels.
- Their resistance to rust nearly eliminates corrosion in humid environments.

For this reason, stainless steel barrels have become a popular choice for competition rifles, varmint rifles, all-weather rifles, combat handguns and marine shotguns. An especially popular stainless steel alloy used by many barrelmakers is 416R. Like all stainless steels, it contains a high percentage of chromium (about 10 percent) and small amounts of sulfur to aid machinability. Barrels made of stainless steel are more expensive than those made of alloy steel, as the cost of the raw material is higher.

Columbium

Columbium is an elemental metal with similar physical and strength characteristics to stainless steel but with superior resistance to heat erosion and corrosion. However, columbium is scarce and very expensive, making it a rare choice for a gun barrel.

New materials and manufacturing techniques have made possible several types of non-traditional, specialized barrels having composite or multi-component construction. Normally, such barrels have an alloy steel or stainless steel bore liner. Some of these materials include:

Aluminum

Although aluminum is very light, it lacks the strength and resistance to heat erosion found in steels. For this reason, aluminum barrels must have a steel liner. Aluminum-alloy sleeves around a steel barrel are common in some revolvers such as the Dan Wesson series.

Titanium

Titanium-cobalt alloys offer the strength of steel at approximately half the weight. However, titanium is very expensive and difficult to machine. In addition, titanium barrels and cylinders must have a steel liner inside. Popular applications include barrels, cylinders on some models of S&W and Taurus revolvers, as well as some models of bolt-action rifles, notably recent models from Remington.

Carbon fiber

Stainless steel is commonly used as a liner inside carbon-fiber barrels. The carbon-fiber outer shell may be molded on the steel liner or built up by winding around the liner tube. Although expensive, the carbon-fiber outer shell imparts high rigidity, natural vibration damping and excellent heat resistance at a fraction of the weight of metal barrels. For these reasons, carbon-fiber barrels are a popular choice for ultra-lightweight rifles.

Fiberglass

Glass fiber is very strong and resistant to heat. Like carbon fiber, it must be built up on a steel liner tube where its strength and light weight can be combined to best advantage. In addition, glass fiber is inexpensive and widely available. In the past, several models of repeating shotguns have been made with such barrels. Today, it has been all but replaced by carbon fiber for gun barrel reinforcement despite carbon fiber's high cost.

Other

Considerable opportunity remains in the technical development of gun barrels, making them stronger, lighter and more resistant to the effects of hot propellant gas erosion. New materials that promise to be very effective in such applications include metal-matrix composites, ceramics and metal alloys engineered at the atomic particle level.

Bore Coatings And Treatments

To improve resistance to erosion from hot propellant gases and to extend barrel life, various coatings, platings and inserts have been applied to bores and throats.

Some of these include:

Chrome plating

Chrome plating is a popular and effective method of extending barrel life of military firearms that may be fired until they are overheated (such as in machine guns) and/or with corrosively primed ammunition. However, because it is difficult to keep the thickness of the plating uniform from throat to muzzle, chrome plating is rarely used on barrels for match shooting. It is nearly unknown on sporting rifles and pistols, as most sporting ammunition has been loaded with non-corrosive primers for over 50 years. Many modern shotguns made in Europe and other countries have chrome-lined bores and chambers to prevent corrosion.

Gas-nitriding

This method of improving bore resistance to erosion from hot propellant gases involves heating the barrel and then introducing a hot, nitride-rich gas through the bore. The nitride bonds with the bore surface, forming a heat-resistant barrier.

Stellite liners

Stellite is a non-ferrous, cobalt-based metal alloy that is much more resistant to high-temperature erosion than normal steels. For many years, Stellite liners were used in the manufacture of U.S. military machine gun barrels. This practice was stopped on cost grounds.

Molybdenum disulphide

Molybdenum disulphide is a dry, high-temperature lubricant with a strong affinity for steel. Steels properly treated with moly disulphide exhibit significantly reduced wear. For these reasons, molybdenum disulphide has become a popular choice for lubricating rifle and handgun bores to reduce wear and metal fouling and ease cleaning. This is especially popular on match rifles and varmint rifles.

Cryogenic treatments

Various cryogenic treatments are available that claim to improve the life and accuracy of rifle and handgun barrels. All of these treatments have in common the immersion of the finished barrel in a super-cold cryogenic solution for a number of hours, followed by a gradual warming back to room temperature. This process involves no plating or chemicals and is not expensive. However, the results are economic only for match-grade competition barrels. Such treatments do not generally offer any advantage to hunting-rifle or service-pistol barrels.

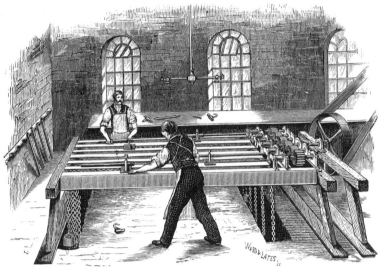

Gun-barrel boring at W. W. Greener's Factory.

Barrel Manufacture

Old Methods

The barrels of very early firearms were smoothbore. Longitudinal grooves in the bore appeared toward the end of the 15th century, but were straight instead of spiraled and had the sole purpose of giving powder and lead fouling a place to accumulate, thus reducing the amount and frequency of cleaning. Around 1520, spiral grooves appeared in some sporting arms. This development has been attributed to Koster of Nuremburg, Germany. However, rifled barrels were not used in military arms for another century, due perhaps to the lack of understanding of the mechanical principles and ballistic advantages of spin-stabilized projectiles.

Before the modern era of mass-production and alloy steel, barrels for small arms were usually made using a variety of hand-production methods. For example:

- Red-hot ribbons of steel ("skelps") about an inch wide and 1/4" thick were hammer-welded together at one end, wrapped in spirals around a mandrel smaller than bore size, then hammer-welded together the rest of their length. This produced a barrel of roughly octagonal shape with a hole in the center that was bored smooth. The rifling grooves were cut one groove at a time using crude, homemade rifling tools. The final octagonal shape was finished by hand filing or water-driven grinders.

- Folding a thick ribbon of steel lengthwise over a mandrel, the open seams were then hammer-welded together at the edges.

This welded joint was not particularly good and often split when heavy loads were fired.

- Bronze or iron was heated to its melting point and the hot liquid metal poured into a mold and allowed to cool. After the mold was broken open, the rough casting of the barrel was finished. This method was often used for cannon and mortar barrels.

Rifling machines were in wide use by the 1700s. Known as "rifling benches" because they were mounted on heavy wooden benches, these machines utilized a wooden rifling guide with an indexing head.

Until the early years of the 20th century, most shotgun barrels were made by twisting alternating ribbons of steel and iron together, wrapping the twisted strands around a mandrel, then hammer-welding the seams together. When properly made, these "Damascus" barrels functioned well with blackpowder loads, but are insufficiently strong for modern smokeless-powder loads.

Modern Methods

Most rifle and handgun barrels (except those intended for hammer forging, as noted below) start life as a cylindrical steel bar about 1" thick and 12 or more feet long, obtained from a steel mill. Each barrelmaker or gun manufacturer specifies the exact grade and composition of steel to be used in order to obtain the desired combination of physical properties. Often the steel bars are stress-relieved before leaving the steel mill. Many shotgun barrels begin as thick-walled, seamless steel tubing.

Initial Trueing—At the barrelmaker's, the bar is cut into lengths of 28" to 30", then turned on a lathe to face the ends off square and give the exterior a uniform roundness. If the steel was not stress-relieved at the mill, it may be given such treatment at this point by heating in a furnace to 600 degrees F. and then cooling over a period of hours.

Deep-Hole Drilling—Next, the trued, stress-relieved bar is drilled using a long drill with a hollow stem and a tungsten-carbide bit, having a single cutting tooth on only one side. Under high pressure, cutting oil is forced through the hollow stem to cool the cutting tooth and to flush chips away. Some drilling machines spin the drill, some the barrel, and some spin both in opposite directions. Drilling a 28"- or 30"-long hole that is uniform in diameter, smooth, and straight to within .0005" or so throughout its length is the most difficult part of the barrel-making operation. Most barrels that are to be button, broach or cut-rifled are drilled several thousandths under bore size.

Reaming—To bring the drilled hole to the proper diameter with a smooth interior surface finish, the drilled hole is now reamed. Care must be taken not to leave reamer marks on the bore surface in this step. Chatter marks from a dull or improperly used reamer are common defects.

Rifling—When the hole is straight and uniform, the next step is to put the rifling grooves in the bore using one of several methods. The most common methods of rifling a barrel include cut, broach or button rifling.

Air-Gauging—After rifling, the bore may be subjected to an air-gauge examination. An air gauge is a precision measuring instrument that uses a snug-fitting probe sensitive enough to detect extremely small inconsistencies in bore diameter as it travels through the barrel.

Straightening—At this point, the barrel may not be perfectly straight as a result of the stresses imposed by the various machining processes or from a change in pre-existing internal stresses. Barrels can be straightened by an experienced craftsman using a turret press.

Lapping—To remove the small inconsistencies remaining in the bore, barrels are lapped as a final step. The lapping process involves pouring a small amount of molten lead into the bore to create a plug that fills the bore perfectly. The plug is coated with lapping abrasive and run back and forth in the bore using a metal rod. Depending upon the fineness of the abrasive, the lapping process will eliminate tight spots and take the interior finish to a mirror-like polish. Lapping is often performed after final contouring, as bore diameter may grow slightly when metal is removed from the outside of the barrel. Lapping is a time-consuming process usually performed only on match-grade barrels. The bores of factory production barrels are rarely, if ever, lapped.

Stress Relief—As a final step, virtually all aftermarket barrel manufacturers and many commercial gunmakers stress-relieve finished barrels to remove internal stresses that can cause warping and wandering points of impact as the barrel heats up. Most stress-relieving methods utilize conventional heat treating at elevated temperatures, as described earlier. Cryogenic stress relief is also becoming popular, although some manufacturers feel it does little for certain types of steel.

The rifled cylindrical bar is called a barrel blank. It will undergo additional operations such as chambering, head spacing, crowning, threading and/or further contouring and polishing before it begins service as a barrel.

Note that the above sequence is a description of the procedure used to produce a cylindrical barrel for a bolt-action rifle, and may not be a complete description for all barrels. Many barrels for handguns and semi-automatic rifles, for example, have complex profiles for locking lugs, sights, gas blocks and so forth that require more than just lathe work. The basic steps in barrel production are still followed, however.

Barrel Rifling Methods

There are five barrel-rifling methods in general use: cut, button, broach, hammer forging and ECM (electrolytic cationic machining). All have their benefits.

Cut Rifling

Cut rifling is the oldest method of rifling a gun barrel. The cut-rifling method removes metal from the surface of the bore to create the grooves using a single-bladed, hook-type cutter of groove width that is pulled through the cold barrel. It is sometimes called "hook rifling" after the fishhook-shaped cutter used. Cutter depth is adjustable, so that it removes only a small amount of metal on a pass. Each groove must be cut individually with multiple passes of the cutter. The cutter is indexed to each groove in turn and positively rotated by the rifling machine using a sine bar.

Advantages:
- The shape and number of grooves and groove depth can be easily changed as necessary.
- Rifling twist rate may be easily changed as required.
- Rifling twist is consistent from one end to the other.
- Little or no additional stress is imposed on the barrel.
- Cut-rifled barrels may be contoured after rifling.
- Close tolerance can be held.

Disadvantages:
- The process is slow and not well adapted to mass production.
- Cut barrels normally cost more due to the slower manufacturing process.
- Some metal alloys can not be cut.
- A mistake or machine malfunction at the end of the process can prove wasteful.
- Cut-rifled barrels must be lapped.

Many target shooters prefer cut-rifled barrels for their uniformity and close tolerance. The cut-rifling method is normally used on prototype or test barrels where only a small number will be made to experimental purposes.

Button Rifling

Button rifling is a modern method that creates the grooves in the cold surface of a rifle bore by displacing metal utilizing a bullet-shaped, super-hard button of tungsten carbide. The rifling button has the reverse pattern of the groove profile ground into its surface. As the rifling button is pushed or pulled through the barrel, the groove pattern is ironed into the bore surface by displacement. There are several variations in button rifling procedure. Some barrelmakers prefer to pull the button through the bore while others prefer to push it through. In most cases, the button remains free to rotate during this process, dependent on the angle of the grooves in its surface to cause the desired degree of rifling twist. As variations in rifling twist may occur during this procedure, some barrelmakers affix the rifling button to a rod and positively rotate it with a sine bar.

Advantages:
- The procedure is fast and very economical, as only a single pass of the button is required to rifle a barrel.
- Button rifling is well suited to mass-production methods with high output.
- Button rifling leaves a smooth, bright finish inside the barrel that need not be lapped.
- Button-rifled barrels are very accurate.
- Bore and groove dimensions are very consistent.

Disadvantages:
- Button rifling creates stress in a barrel; high-quality button-rifled barrels must be stress-relieved after rifling.
- Buttons are expensive and difficult to make.
- Different groove configurations and different rifling twists require a new button.
- The button-rifling system is not flexible.

Button-rifled barrels can be extremely accurate; more bench-rest records are held by such barrels than by any other type. Button-rifled barrels are very common on modern center-fire and rimfire firearms.

Broach Rifling

Broach rifling is a modern, production-orientated variant of cut rifling that addresses some shortcomings of the cut-rifling process. While cut rifling utilizes a single-bladed cutter, a broach is a metal bar with sets of progressive cutting blades in its outer surface corresponding to the number of grooves. The cutting blades are fixed in spiraled succession, each blade cutting to slightly greater depth than the one in front of it. As the broach is pushed or pulled through the cold barrel, all the grooves are cut on a single pass. In some cases, a series of ever-larger broaches is run through the barrel until the desired groove depth is reached.

Advantages:
- Fast and well-suited to mass-production methods.
- Little or no stress is imposed on the barrel.
- Rifling twist is consistent from one end to the other.
- Broach-rifled barrels may be contoured after rifling.
- Adequate tolerances can be held.

Disadvantages:
- Broaches are expensive and hard to make.
- Different groove configurations and different rifling twists require a new broach.
- Broach-rifled barrels must be lapped.

- The broach-rifling system is not flexible.
- Match-grade barrels are not compatible with this system.

Because broach rifling was well suited to high-volume production, it was the rifling system of choice in making military rifles during the first half of the 20th century. In the second half of the 20th century, button rifling replaced broach rifling for the manufacture of rifle barrels with few exceptions. Today, broach rifling is commonly used to rifle some handgun barrels.

Hammer-Forged Rifling

Hammer forging is an ultra-modern method of rifling a gun barrel that is well suited to high-volume production by large manufacturers such as government arsenals and commercial corporations that can afford the sophisticated machinery. This method begins with a metal barrel blank about 12" long and 2" in diameter with a hole in its center honed to a fine finish. A tungsten carbide mandrel with the pattern of the rifling lands and grooves machined into its surface in reverse relief is then inserted into the hole of the blank. A forging machine with a series of radially opposed hammers is then used to compress the blank inward against the mandrel. As the hammers compress the outer surface, the blank is reduced in diameter and lengthened, simultaneously creating the bore and rifling. If needed, hammer forging can form the chamber and throat as well as a fully profiled outer surface. The spiral tracks of the hammers can often be seen on the outer surface of hammer-forged barrels. Some manufacturers turn the barrels to remove this surface, while others leave it in place.

Barrel blanks may be hammer forged cold or hot. Hot hammer forging reduces the amount of effort that the hammers must exert on the blank and can result in better grain structure and improved strength. However, hot hammer forging is more expensive and requires more sophisticated machinery. The cold hammer-forging process produces barrels of excellent quality.

Advantages:
- Hammer forging consistently produces high-quality barrels.
- It can form chamber, throat and outer profile
  if necessary.
- It does not remove metal—no waste or chips.
- It produces barrels with excellent grain structure and
  high strength.
- Hammer forging produces superb bore finish, no lapping needed.

Disadvantages:
- Machinery and mandrels are expensive.
- Inflexible; changes in rifling require new mandrel.
- Quality is very good, but not match grade.
- Hammer tracks are left on outer surface.
- Process introduces stress in the barrel; must be stress-relieved.

Hammer-forged barrels are very common on high-volume center-fire hunting rifles and pistols where their consistency and strength outweigh their accuracy capabilities. They are not common on match-grade or varmint barrels, as their accuracy is perceived to be inferior to cut- or button-rifling methods.

Cation Rifling

A recently developed method of rifling a gun barrel by removing metal using acid is called the cation system. In this system, the barrel blank is first drilled and reamed in a normal manner. Next, a rod with a series of groove-width wipes is pushed through the bore while being positively rotated at the desired twist rate. Each wipe deposits a groove-width trail of very strong acid that immediately begins eating into the surface of the bore. The strength and type of the acid and the dwell time it is allowed to remain on the bore can be varied to obtain the desired groove depth and to suit the metallurgy. When the acid has eaten into the surface the desired amount, a neutralizing liquid is flushed through the bore to stop the acid's action. In practice, very close tolerances can be held. This system works very well on metal alloys that cannot be easily cut, buttoned or hammer forged.

Advantages:
- uses no cutters, no buttons and no mandrels
- flexible system that can easily vary size and number of grooves and twist rate
- produces excellent bore finish
- does not impose stress on the barrel
- will rifle hard or exotic metal alloys that cannot be rifled by other methods.

Disadvantages:
- equipment expensive
- requires storage and handling of strong acids and neutralizers
- system not yet well known.

As its advantages become better known, the cation system may become more popular. The cation system may very well be the only way new metal alloys can be rifled.

Rifling Patterns, Forms and Twist Rates

Rifling lands and grooves can take a bewildering variety of patterns, forms and twist rates depending on customer requirements and the imagination of the barrelmaker. In addition, the relationship of the lands to the grooves can vary significantly.

Number of Grooves

The number of rifling grooves in a barrel may vary from one to as many as 16 or even more. However, four, six or eight grooves are the most common, with six being the most popular. Experience has shown that there is little difference in performance among barrels with two, four, six or eight grooves, all other aspects of barrel quality being equal. Some barrels with more than eight grooves ("microgroove" barrels) will not stabilize large-caliber, heavy bullets or lead bullets

Normally, the lands are wider than the grooves. However, the ratio of groove width to land width will vary according to the preferences of the barrelmaker. For example, groove width and land width may be equal.

The relationship of land position to groove position given an equal number of lands is normally a land opposite another land. However, an odd number of grooves will produce a different relationship of a land opposite a groove. Many manufacturers and shooters prefer this type of land/groove relationship. One popular groove/land relationship of this type consists of five grooves opposite five lands. This configuration is often called the "5R system." The five-land-and-groove arrangement will be found on many Enfield military rifles as well as on many modern Smith & Wesson handguns.

Groove Depth

Modern barrels intended for use with conventional lead and jacketed bullets normally have a groove depth from .0025" to .005". Many muzzleloading rifles (both original and modern) and early breechloading rifles have deeper rifling grooves more suited for their intended use with lead bullets. There are several reasons for the deeper grooves on these guns. First, they are normally fired with blackpowder. The deeper grooves give powder fouling a place to accumulate and reduce the amount of cleaning. Second, the deeper grooves grip the soft lead bullets better and avoid stripping.

Land/Groove Form

The form taken by the lands and grooves may also vary. There are forms that will be commonly encountered:

Conventional—In conventional rifling, the groove is cut into the bore with parallel sides and sharp corners at the bottom of the groove and top edges of the land. The top face of the lands may be flat or slightly curved.

Advantages:
- proven technology
- manufacture compatible with most types of rifling methods
- inexpensive
- appropriate for a broad range of applications.

Disadvantages:
- good overall type, but other forms may be better for specific applications
- sharp edges of lands tear bullet-jacket material
- poor sealing in corners of grooves
- metal fouling collects in bottom of grooves and top face of lands.

Polygonal—Polygonal rifling produces a series of curves that form a polygon having no sharp corners, distinct edges or parallel sides. The visual effect of polygonal rifling is very subtle. When viewed from the breech or muzzle, polygon-rifled barrels often appear to be smoothbore.

Advantages:
- better gas seal for slightly higher muzzle velocity
- lack of sharp edges makes it easier to remove mandrel after hammer forging
- reduced metal fouling due to absence of sharp edges
- excellent quality bore surface
- longer effective barrel life
- easier to clean.

Disadvantages:
- will not stabilize unjacketed lead bullets
- popular choice for pistols, but not for revolvers or rifles
- best suited to hammer-forging manufacture.

Today, polygon-rifled barrels are commonly found in pistols such as those made by H&K, Glock and other European manufacturers.

Metford—Sometimes called "ratchet rifling" the Metford form of rifling features a sloped land face with a full-height shoulder on the driving side of the land and a no shoulder on the trailing side. This type of rifling was used on early Lee-Metford military rifles but is uncommon today.

Hexagonal—This type of rifling was made famous by the Whitworth muzzleloading rifles made in Britain during the mid-19th century. For this form of rifling, the hexagonal (six-sided), elongated lead bullet was molded with a series of curving hexagonal surfaces that mated with spiral hexagonal surfaces inside the barrel. The bullet did not engrave, rather the hexagonal sides of the bullet rode the spiral hexagonal slots in the barrel to cause rotation.

Advantages:
- reduced effects of blackpowder fouling
- reduced effects of wear and corrosion in bore
- very easy to load bullet.

Disadvantages:
- unique bullet required, not compatible with standard Minié balls
- expensive to manufacture.

Hybrid—Hybrid rifling blends the best features of both conventional rifling and polygon rifling to overcome the deficiencies in both types. Hybrid rifling improves sealing in the corners of the grooves by using a wider angle in the corner where the land and groove meet. The top edge of the land is rounded to eliminate tearing of the bullet jacket. The result is a hybrid-rifling form with no sharp edges and better sealing that is compatible with lead bullets. This type of rifling offers reduced metal fouling, longer barrel life and higher muzzle velocity. Hybrid barrels are found in some models of Ruger M77 varmint rifles as well as in some benchrest barrels.

Rifling Twist Rate

Elongated bullets must spin on their axes as they travel through the air in order to maintain point-first flight and accuracy. This spin is imparted to the bullet by the twist rate or pitch of the rifling. For a given projectile, there is a range of rifling twists that will produce optimum bullet stabilization. Greenhill's Formula is a popular means of calculating the correct twist rate for a given bullet.

Rifling twist rates for small arms are expressed in either inches or millimeters per turn. In general, rifling twist rates for modern cartridge guns fall between one turn in 10"/254 mm and one turn in 20"/508 mm. Muzzleloading rifles and many blackpowder arms use much slower twist rates (1:24" to 1:48"). The optimum twist rate will provide best accuracy, while faster or slower twists may still stabilize the bullet but with reduced accuracy. A list of common calibers and their rifling twist rates will be found in *Chapter 17—Reference Data* of this book.

Bullets with a length-to-diameter ratio of about 1:5 can be stabilized by rifled barrels. Projectiles with length-to-diameter ratios exceeding about 1:5 must be fin stabilized.

For hunting and service use, the rifling twist rate must be suitable for most bullets at common muzzle velocities and ambient temperatures. Such a rifling twist rate must be a compromise that will provide acceptable stabilization under a wide range of bullet weight and conditions.

There are two types of rifling twist:

Constant-rate twist—In this type of rifling twist, the rate of twist remains constant from one end of the bore to the other. This is the most common type of rifling twist.

Gain twist—In this type of rifling, the rate of twist varies inside the bore beginning slowly and then increasing as it runs toward the muzzle. Gain-twist rifling is often found on muzzleloading rifles, but is comparatively rare in cartridge guns. Gain-twist barrels are harder to make than constant-twist barrels and are therefore more expensive.

Shotgun Barrels

Except for the lack of rifling, smoothbore shotgun barrels are at least outwardly similar in many respects to rifle or handgun barrels. There are some notable differences, however. Since shotgun shells operate at far lower pressures than current high-intensity rifle cartridges, the walls of a shotgun barrel can be considerably thinner than those of a rifle barrel. Furthermore, while the bore diameters of rifle barrels in a given caliber are usually consistent to within a half a thousandth or so, shotgun bores in a particular gauge may vary as much as .020" or more. Tighter bores generally give higher velocities as well as better groups with traditional slug loads, while more generous, "back-bored" barrels are often preferred for target shotguns for their recoil-reducing properties. Finally, unlike rifle and handgun barrels, whose bores, ideally, are consistent from chamber to muzzle, most shotgun tubes have a constriction or choke at the muzzle to control the tightness of the pellet pattern downrange (*see below*).

Shotgun barrels for lead shot are made of soft steel alloys that are easy to machine and allow a high-polish finish. However, such barrel steels are unsuited for use of steel shot ammunition, as the hard steel pellets can cause choke expansion and damage to the bore and forcing cone. For this reason, shotgun barrels intended for steel shot ammunition are normally made of high-strength steel alloys with thick sidewalls and heat-treated chokes to prevent choke expansion.

At the muzzle end of a shotgun barrel is the choke. The choke is a constriction in the last 2" or 2½" of the barrel that squeezes the shot column down to a lesser diameter by means of a tapered cone between two parallel surfaces. The choke may be fixed (swaged into the barrel itself), interchangeable (using screw-in choke tubes of different constrictions) or variable (a permanently mounted choke device that can be adjusted to different constrictions by twisting a collar).

Chokes greatly affect downrange patterning; very tight chokes produce small, dense patterns, while open-choke patterns are just the opposite. Shooters and hunters can thus match choke selection to the types of shots they anticipate, a practice that has become so popular that screw-in choke tubes are now standard equipment on most new shotguns. For example, one would opt for cylinder or skeet for close-flushing grouse in heavy cover, but switch to improved cylinder or modified for open-country pheasants. Sporting clays shooters routinely swap chokes during a tournament in response to varying target presentations. Choke constrictions are typically as follows:

Cylinder—no constriction, best for slugs and buckshot

Skeet —.005" constriction, best for skeet competition

Improved cylinder—.010" constriction, best for close-range bird hunting

Modified —.020" constriction, best all-around choice for bird and small-game hunting

Improved modified —.027" constriction, a popular choice for trap competition and waterfowl hunting with steel shot

Full—.036" constriction, occassionally used for upland bird and waterfowl hunting

Extra full—.040"+ constriction, specialized for turkey hunting

Shotgun Barrel Manufacture

Modern smoothbore shotgun barrels are usually made in one
of three ways:
- by drilling and reaming seamless steel tubing
- by drilling and reaming steel bar stock
- by hot or cold hammer forging

Some shotgun bores are tapered from forcing cone to muzzle,
often in several distinct stages. Immediately in front of the chamber is
the forcing cone that centers the shot charge or slug in the bore. The
American practice is to make forcing cones relatively short with a
steep angle, while European practice favors longer forcing cones with
shallower angles. Many European shotguns have chrome-lined bores
and chambers.

While the bores of smoothbore shotgun barrels may be polished, they
are not lapped or air-gauged. Although straightness and bore uniformity
of shotgun barrels remains important, shotgun barrels do not require the
same level of precision and uniformity as rifle barrels.

Rifled shotgun barrels designed exclusively for slug use are
manufactured in a manner similar to rifle barrels, although they
are rarely lapped. While all rifle barrels in a given caliber will have
standardized bore and groove diameters, bore dimensions and rifling
twist rates for rifled slug barrels are not yet standardized. Consequently,
accuracy and velocity with slugs in such barrels may vary markedly
among different gun brands.

Shotgun Barrel Construction

As most pump and semi-automatic shotguns have a non-stressed
receiver, the barrel can be quickly and easily removed for exchange,
maintenance or travel. In such shotguns, the bolt locks into a notch or
recess cut into a thick-walled extension on the back end of the barrel.
This allows the use of an aluminum alloy receiver with no loss of
strength or safety.

Today, barrels for break-action shotguns, whether side-by-side,
over-under, or single-barrel models, are mostly built on the monobloc
principle. In this type of construction, the barrels are silver-soldered into
a machined steel monobloc assembly containing the ejector cuts and the
solid projections under the breech end (called lumps) that fit into the
action. These projections are engaged by the locking mechanism to hold
the action shut. Monobloc construction is a simpler and easier mounting
system than the old method of producing barrels with forged integral
lumps.

Barrel Ribs

Most shotguns are fitted with a flat-top sighting rib to guide the
shooter's eye to the target. On side-by-side shotguns, the rib is mounted on
the center web between the barrels. On over-under shotguns, the sighting

A shotgun's rib is simply a metal rail affixed to its barrel, which creates a sighting plane for the shooter. Often the rib is attached by way of an upraised support system that helps isolate the rib from the heat of the barrel.

rib is on the top barrel. Sighting ribs may be solid or ventilated, full length or partial length, straight or tapered, and of steel or aluminum. Typically, sight ribs have a cross-hatched or grooved upper surface to reduce glare and reflections. Nearly all have a front sight bead, and many are equipped with a mid-rib bead as well. Sighting ribs are normally silver-soldered to the barrel on both the front and the rear ends with the intermediate ribs left free to flex as the barrel heats and cools. Sight ribs are found on some rifles as well, particularly heavy-caliber rifles for hunting dangerous game and rifles for fast shots at close range in dense cover.

Shotguns having two barrels must have their barrels regulated so that they produce patterns that hit at the same point of aim (usually at 40 yds.). Some high-grade over-under shotguns have devices that allow self-adjustment of barrel regulation.

Aspects of Barrel Quality

In any given caliber, some barrels will group shots more accurately than others, even if they are installed on the same action. There are many factors that determine rifle barrel accuracy. Here are some of the most common. Note that these factors can and do occur interactively as groups that can shift over time.

Steel quality—Inclusions, localized variations in hardness or composition, or other imperfections in the barrel steel can affect the smoothness and uniformity with which it is drilled, reamed, rifled and lapped. These, in turn, can have an adverse effect on accuracy.

Dimensional uniformity—The width and depth of the lands and grooves, diameter of the bore, and twist rate of the rifling should be as uniform as possible. Top-quality match barrels typically have around 0.0003" or less of variation in bore dimensions. A device known as an air gauge is often used to determine the uniformity of bore dimensions.

Chamber alignment—The chamber may be misaligned with the bore axis in two ways. First, it can be skewed, such that the axis of the chamber is angled to the axis of the bore. Alternately, the chamber axis may be parallel to the bore, but offset to it. Either defect will cause the bullet to enter the bore at an angle, leading to in-bore yaw and an increase in bullet dispersion. A chamber that is properly aligned but cut too generously will allow the cartridge to lay in the bottom where it becomes misaligned in relation to the bore, creating the same situation as occurs with a misaligned chamber. A perfectly aligned chamber is a critical factor in obtaining maximum accuracy from a rifle barrel.

Throat configuration—Throat diameter, throat length and throat angle all determine how the bullet travels from the case mouth into the rifling. Optimum accuracy is normally obtained with a throat length that puts the bullet lightly in contact with the rifling or just shy of such contact. With reloaded ammunition, the bullet can be seated to give an optimal relationship with the throat of a specific rifle. With factory ammunition, differences in throat configuration can sometimes produce significant accuracy differences.

Revolvers can be said to have two throats: The first is in the chambers of the cylinder just forward of the shoulder for the case mouth, and, second, the forcing cone in the barrel. The dimensions of both must work together. In the cylinder, a throat that is too small in relation to the bore yields an undersize bullet that will not grip the rifling. An overly generous throat can produce an oversize bullet that must be deformed excessively to fit in the bore. Many pistolsmiths feel that a gentle taper in the forcing cone guides the bullet into the bore without deforming it.

A perfect chamber and forcing cone may be compromised if one or more chambers in the cylinder is misaligned with the bore at the moment of ignition.

Muzzle crown—As the bullet exits the barrel, hot, expanding propellant gases flow out around the bullet's base at high pressure and velocity. A crown that is not exactly square to the axis of the bore will allow gas to escape around one side of the bullet first, potentially producing yaw which can decrease accuracy.

Bore finish—The better the finish in a bore, the more uniformly a bullet will move through it. Furthermore, a smooth bore finish has less of a tendency to pick up lead or jacket fouling than one that is rough. Although bores with different levels of surface finish may give the same initial level of accuracy, the bore that fouls more quickly will lose accuracy faster. Tests have shown, however, that a bore can be too smooth. In such a bore, bullet fouling is actually greater than in a slightly rougher bore.

Bore taper—The bore of many rifle barrels is slightly larger in diameter at one end than the other. In match-grade barrels, the amount of taper may be so small that it has no effect on accuracy. With production-grade barrels, however, the amount of taper may be enough to adversely effect accuracy, particularly if the bore is larger at the muzzle than at the chamber. Such reverse-taper barrels squeeze the bullet down to the smaller bore diameter at the chamber end, then allow the bullet to yaw as it travels through the larger diameter end. For this reason, whenever possible it is preferable to ream the chamber at the end of the barrel with the larger bore diameter.

Thread and shoulder alignment—Most rifle barrels thread into the receiver until stopped by a shoulder on the barrel that abuts the receiver face. For best accuracy, barrel threads must be cut so their axis aligns precisely with the axis of the bore and the shoulder must be machined square to the bore axis. In addition, the receiver threads and receiver face should be aligned with and squared to the bore axis.

Barrel Enhancement

Cryogenic Barrel Treatment

Recently, cryogenic rifle barrel treatments have received considerable attention as an accuracy-enhancing process. This treatment involves slowly cooling a barrel to approximately -300 degrees Fahrenheit, leaving the barrel "soak" at that temperature for several hours, then gradually returning it to room temperature. Proponents of cryogenic treatment claim that it removes stresses, changes the grain structure, stabilizes the barrel so that it will not warp as it heats up, increases accuracy, improves barrel life and reduces metal fouling. Proponents also note that the process is inexpensive.

Cryogenic treatment has been used for decades to remove stresses in various types of metals, however the steel alloys commonly used in rifle barrels must be stress-relieved in the normal way (using elevated temperatures) to fully remove the stresses created during manufacture. According to metallurgists, cryogenic treatment alone will remove only about 6 percent of these stresses. In addition, some barrel steels, such as the 416R stainless alloy used by many barrelmakers, seem unaffected by cryogenic treatment.

Tests performed by NRA Publications staffers indicate that cryogenic treatment produces a modest improvement in accuracy (10 percent or less) in some barrels and virtually none in others. Research by Sierra Bullets showed no accuracy improvement in match-grade barrels, though a slight increase in barrel life was observed.

Molybdenum Disulfide Treatment

Another barrel treatment process that has become popular in recent years is molybdenum disulfide treatment, known colloquially as "moly" coating. Proponents for this system claim higher muzzle velocities, reduced metal fouling, easier cleaning and increased barrel life.

In one method, the treatment is accomplished by shooting molybdenum disulphide-coated bullets through the barrel. Once the bore is thoroughly coated with the moly, the claimed benefits can be enjoyed. However, tests performed by several barrel makers and Sierra Bullets indicate that molybdenum disulphide does not increase barrel life or accuracy and can accumulate in the bore, creating its own type of fouling.

A second method of treatment, proposed by the Parsec Corp., soaks a clean bore in a supersaturated solution of passivated, virgin, weapons-grade molybdenum disulphide containing particles three-tenths of a micron in diameter. As molybdenum disulphide has a strong affinity for steel, these particles bond to the steel at the molecular level where they cannot be removed. This system does not depend on moly-coated bullets and in fact discourages their use. This treatment method is simple and inexpensive and duplicates the process used by the U.S. military on many ordnance items.

Molybdenum disulfide barrel treatments have won the endorsements of many top competitive shooters and varmint hunters.

Fire Lapping

Fire lapping is a barrel-lapping process that uses bullets impregnated with abrasive material fired through the barrel to lap the bore. Fire-lapping kits come in several forms: a set of abrasive compounds that must be embedded into the bullet jacket, fully impregnated bullets ready for loading and ammunition loaded with impregnated bullets. In most cases, a variety of abrasive grits is offered, allowing the shooter to lap the barrel of the gun with a grit as fine—or as coarse—as needed. Coarse grits are recommended for older, pitted or corroded bores followed by a series of shots impregnated with progressively finer grits.

Fire lapping is claimed to reduce metal fouling and improve accuracy. These benefits have been observed in corroded or worn bores and in some factory barrels with rough bores.

There is very little benefit to fire lapping match barrels, as such barrels are normally hand-lapped before leaving the factory. Many custom barrelmakers, in fact, specifically advise against fire lapping.

It is not uncommon to find a measurable lengthening of the throat after fire lapping. Aggressive fire lapping can also actually change bore dimensions. Thus, the fire-lapping process should be used with caution. Fire lapping is a treatment best restricted to older, worn barrels that have not responded to less drastic therapies such as cleaning, recrowning or a change in ammunition.

Barrel Fluting

Fluting—the machining of longitudinal grooves into the outside surface of a barrel—has long been used as a means to lighten a barrel or increase its length while maintaining its weight. By increasing surface area, fluting may improve barrel stiffness and cooling rates. Fluting can be done in any of a number of grooves, groove widths and groove depths. Six- and eight-flute groove patterns are the most popular.

There are two common misconceptions about barrel fluting:

- *The process of cutting the flutes in a barrel introduces new stress that will require heating for stress relief.* This is false. The consensus of barrelmakers is that properly cut barrel fluting will *not* introduce new stress into a barrel.
- *Fluting adversely effects accuracy.* Experience with both hunting and match-fluted barrels has shown this to be untrue.

Barrel Tuning

One way to improve the performance of a barrel showing lackluster accuracy is to cut a small amount from the muzzle—as little as 0.050" may suffice—and recrown it. Experience has shown the slight change in barrel length and fresh crown often "tunes" the vibratory patterns in the barrel for improved accuracy.

Another barrel-tuning device is Browning's Ballistic Optimizing Stablizing System (B.O.S.S.). This factory-installed device is threaded onto the muzzle and consists of a combined muzzle brake and tuning weight. By adjusting the B.O.S.S and noting any change in accuracy, the shooter can, by trial and error, determine an optimal setting for a particular load.

Many other barrel-tuning devices operate on the same general principle: a weight located at a particular location in relation to the muzzle.

Clearly, changes in barrel harmonics can improve accuracy significantly. In a sense, barrel-tuning devices make the barrel a better tuning fork.

Hummer Barrels

The term "hummer barrel" originated among benchrest shooters, and its use has spread into the general population of shooters. The term denotes a barrel giving unusually good accuracy.

Double-Rifle Barrels and Drillings

Rifles having two or more barrels are relatively common in Europe. Double-barrel side-by-side rifles are perhaps most familiar as the type preferred by British sportsmen for hunting dangerous game in Africa and India. Such rifles have double locks that allow each barrel to be fired as quickly as the double triggers can be pulled. Furthermore, a double rifle gives reliability unequalled by any other type of firearm. Although double rifles are commonly chambered for powerful, large-bore cartridges, they may also be found in smaller calibers suited to hunting lighter, thin-skinned game. Recently, over-under rifles based on shotgun actions in smaller calibers have become more popular.

On the European continent, combination guns with three or four barrels are popular because they are, in effect, several guns in one that can be used on mixed-bag hunts where both birds and larger game may be taken. Normally, these guns consist of side-by-side shotgun barrels with one or two center-fire rifle-caliber barrels beneath.

The main technical challenge with multi-barrel arms is that of barrel regulation—getting all the barrels to shoot to the same point of aim at some specified distance. Ideally, the groups produced

European drilling

by each barrel of a double rifle should overlap at 100 yds. This becomes especially difficult in multi-barreled arms with a single set of sights for all barrels. For this reason folding sights are a common feature on combination guns. Regulating the barrels requires patience, extensive shooting tests and considerable experience in the gunmaker's craft. Note, too, that the barrels are usually regulated for a single load or bullet weight. With used, older-model combination guns, the regulating loads may no longer be available, while a newer load using a different powder or slightly different bullet, but having the same nominal ballistics, will give two separate groups out of the two barrels.

Barrel Maintenance

Barrel Break-In

Competitive shooters, varmint hunters and law enforcement personnel seek maximum accuracy for an extended barrel life with minimum bore fouling. For this reason, such shooters often perform a procedure known as barrel break-in. Every barrel, no matter how smoothly the bore has been machined, still has surface imperfections created during the drilling, reaming and rifling processes. As a bullet passes through the bore, it will smooth or burnish away these surface imperfections. However, as the imperfections are smoothed down, small amounts of bullet-jacket material can become trapped beneath them leading to increase metal fouling. By initially cleaning between each shot and then between each group of two, three, five or more shots until the process is complete, the break-in process produces a smooth bore with no lead or jacket fouling embedded in the metal. This produces a barrel that will not foul as quickly between cleanings and can be cleaned more easily. Barrel break-in need be performed only on rifled bores.

There are several different procedures for breaking in a new barrel, although most use the same basic process. One popular method is to thoroughly clean the barrel between each of the first 15 to 25 shots, then between every two or three shots for the next 10 shots. Finally, several five- or 10-shot strings are fired with a complete cleaning between each. Barrel break-in is typically completed within 50 or fewer rounds and is usually signaled by a noticeable reduction in fouling during cleaning.

Barrel Cleaning

There are many acceptable procedures to clean a rifle, handgun or shotgun bore. All are basically similar in that they involve two separate processes: removing powder residue, and removing copper, lead or plastic fouling. Suitable gun-cleaning solvents are available to attack both problems.

For proper bore cleaning, you will need the following items:

- a steel cleaning rod with ball-bearing mounted handle (one-piece rod preferred)
- a bronze brush specific for caliber or gauge with brass wire core

- jag tips for the cleaning rod—one for each caliber or gauge
- cloth cleaning patches appropriate for caliber or gauge (cotton preferred)
- a bore cleaner specific to fouling type (i.e., a bore cleaner formulated for lead removal, copper, etc.)
- a preservative gun oil.

Shooters often follow a common cleaning procedure. Before beginning, *always* check to make certain the gun is unloaded and all ammunition has been removed from the immediate area. If necessary, disassemble the gun as needed. Whenever possible, clean the barrel from the breech end (not accessible on most lever- and pump-action and semi-auto rifles). With bolt-action rifles it is advisable to use a bore guide that fits into the receiver.

- Mount the jag tip on the cleaning rod, then attach a cleaning patch saturated with cleaning solvent on the jag tip.
- Push the saturated patch through the bore then out the muzzle (if possible) and remove; repeat this step as needed.
- Wipe the rod clean, then push a clean dry patch through the bore once and remove at the muzzle.
- Wipe the cleaning rod clean, and repeat Steps 1 and 2.
- Wipe rod clean, remove the jag tip and mount the cleaning brush.
- Saturate the cleaning brush with solvent, then scrub the bore using eight to 10 full strokes so the brush clears the muzzle each time.
- Wipe rod clean, dismount the brush then reinstall the jag tip.
- Push four or five clean, dry patches through the bore, one time each until they come out clean. Repeat this and all the previous steps as necessary.
- Use several clean, dry patches and the jag tip to clean the chamber.
- Place a clean patch saturated with preservative oil on the jag tip and push once through the barrel, then remove it at the muzzle.

Bore Cleaners

Bore cleaners fall into six general categories:
- Standard or **traditional liquid cleaners** formulated primarily to remove powder residue that have only a very limited effect on copper fouling and lead buildup. These solvents are normally grouped under the heading of nitro solvents and have been around for many years. They are proven, all-purpose, inexpensive solvents for normal cleaning chores.
- **Specialized liquid solvents** formulated to speedily remove heavy, stubborn cases of copper or lead fouling. These new and powerful solvents often contain ammonia as their active ingredient. They are more expensive than traditional solvents and many will attack bedding compounds and stock finishes, so they must be used carefully.

- **Abrasive pastes** containing very fine abrasive that, when applied properly, will mechanically remove copper and lead fouling without harming the bore.
- **Mechanical removal systems** (mainly lead fouling) that rely on some type of mechanical device such as fine screen mesh to remove lead fouling when pushed through the bore.
- **Modern electrical cleaning systems** use a very low-voltage, reverse-plating process with a liquid electrolyte of lead or copper acetate to electronically strip metal fouling from the bore and deposit it on a stainless steel rod inserted in the barrel.
- **Modern ultrasonic cleaning systems** employ ultrasound broadcast through a liquid solvent to remove residue from firearms barrels. The sound waves loosen the residue and the liquid floats the particles away.

Fouling Shots

After a thorough cleaning, it is accepted practice to fire one to five fouling shots through the barrel. Essentially, these shots lay down a fresh layer of copper fouling in the bore. Subsequent shots will not change the amount of deposited copper very much, so the bore surface remains consistent for the best grouping. After a certain number of shots—as few as 15 and as many as 50 or more—the accumulated fouling in the bore begins to degrade accuracy once again, making another cleaning necessary.

Chapter 9
TRIGGERS

The trigger is the heart of the gun's fire-control mechanism. When the shooter's finger presses the trigger, a complex chain of events begins that causes the gun to fire. While this may sound straightforward, there are many types of triggers.

Bolt-Action Rifle Triggers

Two types of trigger systems are employed on bolt-action rifles:

Two-stage trigger

This type is used predominantly on early military bolt-action rifles such as the Mauser 98. Double-draw triggers are simple, robust, safe and relatively unaffected by exposure to dirt, grit, harsh conditions, poor maintenance and rough handling. However, military-style double-draw triggers do not offer a crisp, light release preferred for accurate shooting and are not readily adjustable.

Single-stage trigger

This type is popular on modern sporting rifles as it offers a crisp, light and safe pull. Many single (or override) triggers are adjustable. Most have two levers, but three- and four-lever models are also common.

Revolver Triggers

There are three basic types of revolver trigger systems:

Single-action-only (SA)

This type is oldest of the two systems and requires that the hammer be manually cocked by the shooter for each shot. While slow, it offers a light trigger pull that is conducive to accuracy.

Single-action revolvers such as the Colt Single Action Army were popular in the American West and remain popular today among cowboy action competitors and traditionalists.

Double-action/single-action (DA/SA)

This system is so named because pulling the trigger will cock and release the hammer. Most double-action revolvers can also be fired in the single-action mode as well. When fired in the double-action mode, most revolvers offer a long, heavy trigger pull that is not conducive to accuracy. For this reason, most double-action shooting is done at close ranges in self-defense scenarios.

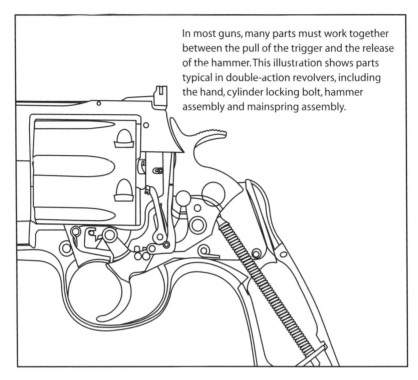

In most guns, many parts must work together between the pull of the trigger and the release of the hammer. This illustration shows parts typical in double-action revolvers, including the hand, cylinder locking bolt, hammer assembly and mainspring assembly.

Most modern revolvers are of double-action/single-action design such as the Colt Python, Ruger SP100 and S&W Model 29. This includes even large-bore models that will seldom, if ever, be fired in the double-action mode.

Double-action-only (DAO)

In this system, pulling the trigger cocks and releases the hammer. There is no provision for single-action operation. This system is found commonly on small revolvers intended mainly for concealed carry. Most examples have the hammer spur removed for added concealability, while others employ an integral hammer.

Self-Loading Pistol Triggers

In a similar manner to revolvers, modern semi-automatic pistols can be divided into categories by the manner in which their triggers operate:

Single-action (SA)

This system offers the same short, crisp trigger pull for each shot. In order to fire the first shot quickly, single-action pistols must be carried with a round in the chamber, the hammer cocked and the manual safety engaged (the so-called "cocked-and-locked" condition). Although not comfortable to all shooters, this is currently being taught in most schools as a safe mode of carry. Nearly all single-action pistols are equipped with an exposed hammer.

Double-action/single-action (DA/SA)

In this type of fire-control mechanism, the first shot is fired in a double-action mode using a long, heavy trigger pull to cock and release the hammer. Subsequent shots are fired in a single-action mode. This system allows the pistol to be carried safely with a round in the chamber and the hammer lowered, while still allowing a rapid first shot. However, the different modes of trigger operation involve different grip positions, thus consistent accuracy is difficult to maintain. Most double-action pistols have an exposed hammer and a decocking lever that provides a fast, easy and secure system to lower the hammer on a loaded chamber.

Double-action-only (DAO)

The double-action-only trigger system is preferred by many law enforcement agencies as it is felt to be safer and "defensive" in nature. However, the long, heavy trigger pull of most double-action-only systems is not conducive to accuracy. This led pistol manufacturers to devise various ways of reducing the DAO trigger pull without sacrificing the inherent safety and perceived defensive nature of the system.

Such systems are now common and essentially operate by partially pre-cocking the striker to reduce the heavy double-action trigger pull and reducing trigger travel.

Most double-action-only pistols are hammerless with a striker firing pin system.

Self-Loading and Pump-Action Rifle and Shotgun Triggers

Nearly all contemporary semi-automatic and pump-action sporting rifles have an underride trigger with an internal hammer cocked by rearward motion of the bolt or bolt carrier. A notch or shelf on the hammer is engaged by the sear to retain it in the cocked condition. Pulling the trigger disengages the sear from the hammer, allowing it to fly forward to hit the firing pin and fire the gun.

Most fire-control assemblies for semi-automatic and pump-action rifles are held in the receiver by pins, screws or levers. The trigger is not readily adjustable.

Typically, semi-automatic and pump-action shotguns also have an internal hammer cocked by the rearward motion of the bolt or bolt carrier. A non-adjustable underride trigger system pinned inside the receiver retains the hammer in the cocked position by sear engagement on a notch in the hammer. Pulling the trigger disengages the sear from the hammer, allowing it to fly forward to strike the firing pin.

In addition to fire control, the trigger mechanisms for semi-automatic and pump-action shotguns must also perform several functions related to shotshell feeding. When the gun is fired and the bolt and bolt carrier move rearward, the fire-control system pivots the shell carrier downward and depresses the shell latch on the magazine tube to release the next shell onto the shell carrier. On the bolt's return trip forward, the shell carrier pivots upward, positioning a fresh shell directly in front of the chamber. As the bolt goes into battery, the fresh shell is chambered and the action's locking block or locking lugs engage the receiver or barrel extension.

An important part of the fire-control mechanism of any semi-automatic or pump-action firearm is the disconnector. After a shot has been fired, the shooter's finger may still be on the trigger as the action cycles to cock the hammer or firing pin. The disconnector prevents the cocked hammer or firing pin from falling unless the trigger is first released, then pressed again.

The disconnector can be a separate part or it may be designed into the trigger bar, sear or other components of the fire-control system.

Break-Action Triggers

There are two types of break-action firearm fire-control systems:

Mechanical

In this type of trigger system, the sear or sear-selector mechanically switches to the second barrel after the first barrel is fired. If the first barrel fails to fire, the sear or sear selector will still switch to the second barrel. Mechanical systems are reliable but more expensive and for this reason are found on many modern, high-grade double-barrel guns.

Inertial

This type of trigger system depends on the inertia from recoil forces to reset the sear for the second barrel. Should the first barrel fail to fire or the shooter hold the gun too loosely, the sear or sear selector may fail to reset the second barrel. Inertia systems are very popular, and may be found on many double-barrel guns.

Double-Barrel Triggers

A primary function of any trigger system on a double-barrel gun is to prevent doubling or both barrels firing at once. Mechanical trigger systems do this by mechanically resetting the sear while inertia systems use recoil forces to reset the sear.

Nearly all trigger systems on double-barrel guns have internal or external hammers. Very few have strikers.

Double-barrel break-action guns will have either a single trigger or double triggers.

- Double-trigger systems are an older design and more traditional. They are also relatively simple and cheaper to manufacture. In the past, double-trigger systems were felt to be more reliable, however, this is not true today. As a result, most modern shooters prefer single-trigger systems and double-triggers are much less popular except for double-barrel side-by-side rifles for dangerous game where the utmost reliability is required.

In a double-trigger system, each barrel is controlled by a dedicated trigger that cannot be switched. The shooter can easily change the sequence in which the triggers are pulled.

- Single-trigger systems may be one of two types:

  Non-selective—In this type of single-trigger system, the firing sequence of the barrels is fixed and cannot easily be changed. Generally, such systems are set to fire the lower barrel first in over-unders. This system is sometimes used on cheaper models with fixed chokes that are designed for one specific purpose, i.e., to shoot driven game.

  Selective—A single-selective trigger system will fire each barrel in a selectable sequence with a separate pull of the trigger. In other words, pulling the trigger twice will fire each barrel in turn and the sequence can be changed quickly and easily by means of a button or switch on the tang. A single-selective trigger is by far the most popular and flexible type of trigger in use today on modern double-barrel shotguns. When a single-selective trigger is combined with interchangeable choke tubes, a gun so-equipped becomes very flexible indeed.

Other Shotgun Triggers

Twin-single trigger

This type of system employs two triggers. Each trigger is dedicated non-selectively to fire a separate barrel on the first shot and then will fire the remaining barrel with a second pull. Some shooters feel this system combines the best of both single- and double-trigger systems with very fast barrel selection. Such systems have not proven popular, however.

Single-double trigger

This system also employs two triggers. The forward trigger offers single-non-selective operation and will fire both barrels in fixed sequence with successive pulls. The rear trigger fires only one barrel, normally the lower barrel or the one with the tightest choke.

Release trigger

While a typical trigger operates by pulling the bow rearward, a release trigger operates in the opposite manner. Release triggers must first be pulled and will not fire until released. Such triggers are normally aftermarket items that are not sold, installed or approved by firearms manufacturers. The purpose of a release trigger is to counteract flinching. Such triggers are geared for target shooting competition and are rarely used for hunting.

Trigger Pull

Most triggers are judged on their pull or let-off weight. This varies according to the type and use of the gun. For example, many benchrest rifles have a 0.5-oz. let-off weight which is too light for other applications. Hunting rifles generally have a trigger let-off weight of three to seven pounds, while a double-action handgun may have a let-off weight of 10 pounds or more. In addition, shooters judge trigger performance in terms of slack, take up, stacking and overtravel.

Chapter 10
SIGHTS & OPTICS

Afirearm cannot be used effectively without some system for pointing or aiming it precisely and repeatably. Such a system constitutes the firearm's sights, which may take the form of either metal ("iron") sights or optical sights. In addition, accessory optical devices such as binoculars, spotting scopes and rangefinders are often used by hunters, target shooters, police officers and military personnel in conjunction with firearms sights for target acquisition, spotting shots, zeroing-in and determining range.

Sights

Commonly seen open, iron or metallic sights provide the oldest method used to aim firearms. Rudimentary sights, often consisting of no more than a line painted on the barrel, were common on even the earliest small arms. Today, iron sights take many forms, depending on the firearm and the type of shooting in which they will be employed.

On rifles, handguns and some shotguns, iron sights normally consist of a front sight and a rear sight. Both are mounted on the upper surface of the firearm parallel to the axis of the bore. In use, the sights are aligned with the target by the shooter's eye to produce repeatable hits.

Iron-Sight Systems

There are six general types of iron sights:

Aperture or Peep Sight

In this sighting system, the rear sight consists of a small disk with a centerhole through which the shooter views the front sight and the target. The front sight may be a post, bead or another aperture. Such sights make use of the natural tendency of the eye to center objects viewed through the aperture. Most aperture sights are adjustable for both windage and elevation. A variation uses two apertures on an L-shaped rear hinged to the sight body at the junction of the two arms. One aperture is set for one range and the second for a different range.

The accuracy obtainable with a quality, micrometer peep sight rivals that achieved with telescopic sights. For this reason, aperture sights are preferred for iron-sighted target rifles. Aperture size is critical. In general, smaller apertures offer greater sighting precision, but at the cost of reduced light transmission. For this reason, apertures with adjustable irises are a popular choice.

Because of their simplicity and accuracy, aperture sights have often been found on military rifles. Normally, such sights have protruding ears on both sides to protect the front post and rear aperture from damage.

The "ghost-ring" sight is a special variation of peep sight. This sighting system employs a rear sight with a large-diameter aperture through which the front sight is viewed. When the shooter's eye is focused on the front sight, the rear sight appears as an indistinct, ghostly ring surrounding it. Ghost-ring sights work on the principle that the eye will automatically center any object seen through the ring. This provides a reasonable level of accuracy, but not to the level of conventional aperture sights. On the positive side, the large ring blocks little of the shooter's view while allowing fast target acquisition. This is the reason ghost-ring sights are popular on shotguns and carbines used for military, law enforcement and defensive use.

Post-and-Notch Sight

This type of sight consists of a vertical rear sighting blade with a square notch cut in the center teamed with a front post with parallel sides and a flat top. In use, the post is centered in the notch, with equal amounts of daylight on either side, and the top of the post is aligned with the top of the rear blade. On handguns, this type of sighting system is known as a Patridge sight.

This type of sight is extremely accurate, although the rear blade may obscure part of the target. For precise target work, a thick front post that leaves only a thin sliver of daylight visible on either side of the notch is preferred while faster combat shooting usually calls for a thinner post.

In low-light situations or against a dark target, the flat black blade and matching notch may be difficult to see. For such situations, post-and-notch sights are often enhanced with high-visibility contrasting colors such as a white outline around the rear notch, a spot of fluorescent red or orange on the front sight, or three white dots, two on the rear blade flanking the notch and one on the front post.

The advantages of three-dot sighting systems are offered in night

Iron Sight Types

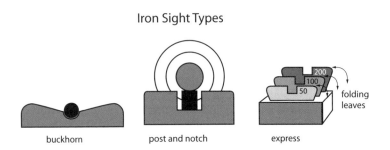

buckhorn   post and notch   express   folding leaves

sights. Such sights employ small glass ampules of self-luminous tritium set into the front and rear sights to form round dots that are visible even in complete darkness. Also popular is the "bar and dot" pattern, in which a tritium ampule is set sideways under the rear notch. Sighting alignment consists of centering the front dot over the rear bar. Many tritium inserts have a pale green color, though other colors may be encountered. Luminous sights may also be used in peep or post-and-notch sights on carbines or shotguns for defensive, police or military uses and they have become more common on hunting arms in recent years.

Buckhorn Sights

Buckhorn rear sights are used on many factory hunting rifles as they are simple, rugged and easy to use, though not capable of the same precision as a target-style peep sight. The rear sight blade has a nearly closed V-shaped notch, often with a small circular or U-shaped cutout at the bottom. Sight alignment consists of placing the front post bead squarely in the bottom of the cutout in the notch. Windage adjustment is accomplished by drifting the front or rear sight units laterally in their dovetails. On many buckhorn sights, the rear sight blade rides on a stepped elevator that allows coarse elevation changes.

Express Sights

Express sights are similar to buckhorn sights in that they have a front bead on a post and rear blades with shallow U-shaped notches. Instead of a stepped elevator for rear sight elevation changes, express sights employ one or more flip-up blades of different heights marked for different ranges. This system allows quick, one-handed elevation adjustment. When several sight blades are used, this type of sight is sometimes also called a multiple leaf sight. Express sights are most often used on large-caliber rifles intended for hunting dangerous game.

The major drawback of express sights is that they must be factory-regulated for a specific load and bullet weight. This restricts the rifle to a specific loading and is time consuming and expensive.

Shotgun Sights

Either of two types of sights may be found on shotguns:

Bead sights—Shotguns designed for wingshooting or for clay target competition are pointed rather than aimed. Such shotguns have a front bead, and sometimes an additional mid-rib bead, that serve as visual reference points when firing at rapidly moving targets. The bead(s) are mounted in the barrel's sighting plane or on a ventilated rib. Such ribs are mounted on the barrel where they serve as a sighting plane to guide the shooter's eye toward the target. Most ribs have a series of crosswise grooves or cross-hatching machined into the upper surface to reduce light reflection.

Front beads are typically made of brass, white plastic or metal often with a high-visibility orange or red insert. Mid-rib beads are almost always brass and of substantially smaller diameter than front beads.

Iron sights or optical sights—Shotguns used for hunting game such as deer, bear and turkey, often have rifle-type iron sights or optical sights, as these shotguns are aimed rather than pointed. Similar sights may be used on shotguns intended for defensive, police or military use. Ghost-ring sights are another popular choice for these shotguns.

Fiber-Optic Sights

Fiber-optic materials, usually in the shape of a small plastic rod or cylinder, are able to take in light from a variety of angles and redirect it along their axis. Seen end-on, fiber-optic units appear to be glowing dots.

Increasingly, fiber-optic units are being incorporated into front and rear sights for handguns, shotguns and rifles. When used in sunlit conditions, fiber-optic units offer enhanced visibility and contrast. This feature is greatly appreciated by shooters with poor eyesight or visual impairments. At dusk, dawn or under poor light conditions, fiber-optic sights are considerably easier to see than conventional iron sights.

Bullet Impact Movement

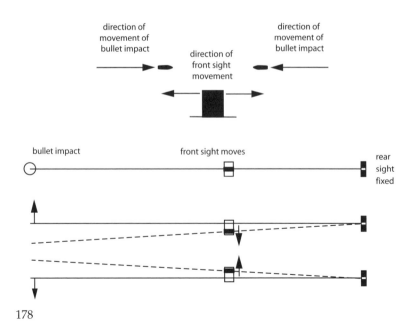

Fiber-optic sights may have either a single front sight unit paired with a conventional rear sight or front and rear sight units presenting the fiber-optics in a three-dot pattern. Fiber-optic rods come in a variety of colors, including green, red, orange and yellow.

Adjustments

Iron sights are either fixed or adjustable.

Fixed sights—This term is somewhat misleading as most fixed sights can be regulated to change point of impact. Fixed-sight units mounted on the slide, receiver or barrel using a dovetail can be drifted using a small hammer to effect horizontal changes in the point of impact. Normally, this is done to the rear sight as many front sights are permanently attached by staking, silver-soldering or with adhesives. Front sights that are dovetailed in the slide or barrel can also be drifted. Changes in elevation can be made by removing or adding material to the front or rear sight. The effect on point of impact will be opposite depending on which sight is altered. To move point of impact downward, one should either add material to the front sight or remove material from the rear sight. Conversely, adding material to the rear sight or removing it from the front sight moves the point of impact upward.

Getting the gun to shoot to point of aim can be calculated by

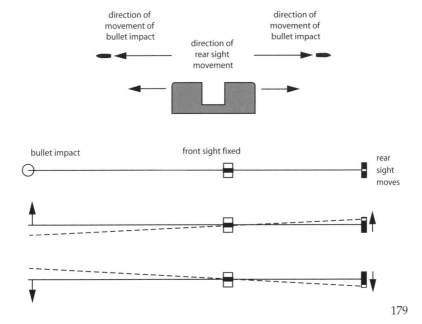

using the following formula that gives the change in sight height or windage to move bullet impacts to the point of aim at a given range:

$$\frac{X}{\text{sight radius in inches}} = \frac{\text{desired change in bullet impact in inches}}{\text{distance to target in inches}}$$

X is the amount of change in sight height or sight windage in inches needed to bring bullet impact to the point of aim.

Adjustable sights—Adjustable-sight units frequently utilize screw mechanisms mounted horizontally and vertically in the sight body to cause the sight blade or aperture to move laterally and/or vertically. Some screw-adjustment mechanisms have audible clicks while others do not. Nearly all have graduations inscribed or painted on the sight body and an indicator on the adjustment screw or knob. On some hunting rifles, vertical adjustment of the rear sight is made by movement of a stepped piece called an elevator, or a sight block, that slides on an inclined dovetail. Many military rifles utilize a ladder rear sight, in which sliding the rear sight block along a hinged, folding, ladder-like piece elevates the sight to varying degrees. Usually the ladder has ranges inscribed on it, so that positioning the sight on a given point on the ladder gives the required degree of elevation for the range indicated.

Regardless of the mechanism for adjustment, the process is the same: The rear sight is moved in the same direction as the desired change in bullet impact. Thus, to move bullet impact to the right, the rear sight must be moved to the right. With an adjustable front sight, the sight is moved in the direction opposite to the desired change in impact.

Sight Radius

The distance between front and rear iron sights is called the sight radius. A longer sight radius offers greater theoretical precision. For this reason, many iron-sighted target guns have features to increase the sight radius, such as front sight extenders on target pistols and "bloop" tubes on the end of rifle barrels. Tang rear sights mounted on the stocks were used for the same purpose in the 19th century.

Sight radius also affects iron-sight adjustments. A typical match-type micrometer rear sight offering 1/4-m.o.a. clicks moves the aperture 0.002" with each click. With a 30" sight radius, this changes bullet impact 0.24" per click at 100 yds., very close to the advertised value. Shorten the sight radius to 24" and the change in bullet impact per click is 0.30". This is not significant at 100 yds., but in a 1,000-yd. match each click will move the strike of the bullet 3".

Sight Alignment and Sight Picture

Sight alignment and sight picture are two critical and related concepts regarding iron sight use. Sight alignment refers to the proper visual relationship between the front and rear sights. For example, the front post should be sitting squarely and evenly in the rear notch. Sight alignment is critical to accuracy as small errors in sight alignment produce greater bullet dispersion as the range increases.

Sight picture refers to the relationship of the correctly aligned sights with the target. Small errors in sight picture produce small deviations in bullet impact at the target. Though aiming is normally a deliberate action, in practical shooting competition or in defensive shooting situations the process of aligning the sights with the target must be compressed into an instant. Under these conditions, the shooter must use a flash sight picture, that is, rapidly covering the target with the front sight, and concentrate on the front sight.

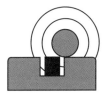 

correct sight alignment incorrect sight picture   correct sight alignment correct sight picture   incorrect sight alignment correct sight picture

Hold

Hold refers to the part or area of the target on which the sights are aligned during aiming. For example, many shooters use a six o'clock hold in which the front sight is held at the bottom of the round bullseye on the target. Other shooters prefer to hold the front sight in the center of the target at the point where the bullet impact is desired. Under conditions of strong cross-, head- or tailwinds, a shooter may hold off to one side of the target or another to compensate for wind deflection. Such "guesstimated" compensation is called "Kentucky windage."

Dominant Eye

Almost everyone has a dominant eye. This is the "master" eye whose visual signals have dominance in the brain over the signals from the non-dominant eye. Under most conditions, a person will not be aware of this phenomenon. However, when aiming a firearm, the issue of which eye is dominant becomes important. Attempting to aim a firearm using the non-dominant eye will be difficult if not impossible.

For most people, the dominant eye is on the same side as the dominant or strong hand. Thus, most right-handed people are also right-eye dominant. A minority will be cross-dominant (e.g., left-handed, but right-eye dominant). Cross-dominant persons must learn to shoot with their non-dominant hand, or (on long guns) utilize a stock with extreme cast-off to place the gun in front of their dominant eye when the rifle is shouldered on the non-dominant side.

Which eye is dominant can be determined quickly and easily with a simple test. The subject focuses both eyes on a small, distant object and fully extends his arms with the hands joined so that a small opening remains. While maintaining his view of the object through the opening, the subject slowly brings his hands rearward until they are almost touching his face. The opening between the hands will be in front of the dominant eye.

Visual Focus

Proper sight alignment and sight picture require that the target, the front sight and the rear sight all be kept in focus simultaneously. However, the human eye cannot focus on three objects at different distances with equal clarity. Thus, the recommended technique is to focus on the front sight, leaving the target and the rear sight slightly blurred. The trick is to maintain accurate sight alignment and sight picture while doing so.

Most shooters find the best way to do this is to shift the focus quickly between the sights and the target while refining the sight picture. Older shooters and those with poor eyesight or visual impairment frequently have difficulty using iron sights effectively. In many cases the visual acuity of such shooters can be improved by using a small-diameter aperture device that attaches to a pair of shooting glasses. Such aperture devices make use of the optical phenomenon in which objects viewed through a small pinhole are seen in sharper focus. Such devices are often adjustable for aperture size.

Optical Sights

Although telescopes have been in use for centuries, wide acceptance of optical sights by hunters and shooters occurred only over the past 50 years as their reliability, durability and precision have improved. The attributes of an optical sight include:

- The reticle of an optical sight is presented in a single sighting plane. This eliminates the need to focus on the front and rear iron sights and the target at the same time.
- Optical sights often magnify the target image thereby aiding positive target idenification and precise shot placement. Reading wind/mirage is also made easier.

- Optical sights are easy to use for a wide range of shooters.

- Good quality optical sights are widely available and affordably priced.

- Most firearms are now designed and equipped to mount optical sights.

Such is the popularity of optical sights today that about 90 percent of new factory rifles are subsequently equipped with a scope.

Basic Principles of Optical Sights

Light is a form of electromagnetic energy that travels in the form of waves. The light spectrum that is visible to the human eye falls between the wavelengths of 350 and 700 nanometers. As one nanometer equals one-billionth of an inch, light waves are very short indeed. Different wavelengths within this range correspond to the different colors perceived by the eye, with the shortest wavelengths in the violet range and the longest at the red end of the spectrum.

The operating principle of an optical sight is simple. A biconvex lens, with an outward curvature on both sides, magnifies the image. A second lens, placed at an appropriate distance from the first and optically aligned, in turn magnifies the image of the first. The image is also upside-down and reversed, thus an erector lens or a prism must be inserted into the system to put the image in its proper orientation. Although this may seem simple in description and principle, optical systems are complex compromises that achieve a balance among various optical properties.

Optical sights must contend with the fact that the speed of light varies in different media. When light waves travel from air to glass or glass to air, their velocity changes. In air, light travels at 186,000 miles per second, but slows to between 95,000 and 127,000 miles per second in glass depending upon density. Additionally, when light waves cross from one medium to another at an angle to the interface, they change direction. This bending of the light waves' path in passing from one medium to another is called refraction. The amount that light is refracted can be calculated from the angle at which it strikes the interface (called the angle of incidence) and the optical density of the medium (called the index of refraction). The index of refraction is 1 for air and from 1.5 to 1.96 for optical glass. These basic phenomena allow optical engineers to design lens systems able to clearly focus and magnify images of distant objects.

Describing a Riflescope

Riflescopes are typically labeled by a series of numbers that provide a basic description of the lens system and magnification. The first number(s) are the power, or magnification, of the scope lens system. A single number denotes that the scope is a fixed-power model, while two-number sets separated by a dash denote the magnification boundaries of a variable-power scope. For example, a fixed-power scope may be described as being 2.5X or 2.5 power, while a variable may be described as being 2.5-10X.

A second number after the magnification number set is the objective lens diameter expressed in millimeters. Thus a 2.5X-34 mm is a fixed-power scope with a magnification of 2.5X and a 34 mm objective lens diameter. A 2.5-10X-44 mm is a 2.5- to 10-power variable scope equipped with a 44 mm-diameter objective lens.

Most scope makers append a suffix of letters or words after the numerical description to describe additional features such as LER (long eye relief), AO (adjustable objective), IR (illuminated reticle) or PLEX (a reticle configuration). Scope makers may also append a word denoting the intended use of a particular scope such as "varmint," "handgun silhouette" or "benchrest."

Nomenclature of a Riflescope

Optical sights used on rifles, handguns and shotguns all share similar design and construction features. The scope body, or tube, is essentially a place for mounting various lens elements and other devices in proper relation to one another. A typical riflescope consists of the following parts:

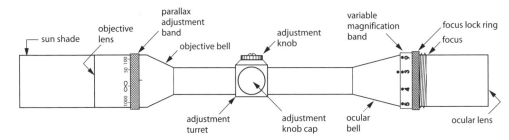

Main tube body—The main body of the scope is typically made of alloys of aircraft aluminum, steel or titanium. The main tube is normally formed from a single extrusion with the bell housings formed in a secondary operation. However, some tubes and bell housings are machined. Tube diameters range from 19 mm/0.75" to 34 mm/1.33" with 25.4 mm/1" and 30 mm/1.18" diameters being the two most popular sizes. In general, the larger main tubes are stiffer, pass more light and offer greater ranges of windage and elevation adjustment.

Objective lens—The front lens is called the objective lens. It is mounted securely in the objective bell or front of the scope tube that is normally expanded to a larger diameter than the main tube. Objective lens diameters may vary from 20 mm to 72 mm with 32 to 40 mm being most common. Larger-diameter objective lenses gather more light and that can be advantageous at dusk, dawn or conditions of poor visibility. Some objective lens bells are adjustable for parallax *(see pg. 188).*

Ocular lens—At the rear of the main tube in the rear bell housing is a second lens called the ocular lens. The ocular housing is threaded onto the main tube to allow focusing and normally has a lock ring to maintain the focus setting.

Magnification adjustment ring—On the rear of the main tube of a variable-power scope is the magnification adjustment ring. Turning the ring clockwise increases the magnification while counter-clockwise rotation decreases magnification. Note the field of view decreases as the magnification increases.

Turrets—A typical riflescope has two turrets in a housing on the main tube between the bell housings. Inside the housing under the turrets are a number of key elements:

- an erector lens system that puts the image right-side up
- a reticle (crosshairs) for aiming
- windage and elevation adjustment mechanisms
- reticle illumination devices (some models only)
- rangefinding devices (on scopes so equipped).

Recently, scopes bearing a third turret for quick focusing or parallax adjustment have become more prevalent.

Adjustments

Windage and elevation adjustments in riflescopes are made with either internal or external adjustment systems.

Internal—Most modern telescopic sights have internal adjustment systems using threaded, cylindrical knobs or screws in the turrets. The adjustment screws move the reticle assembly in the optical axis inside the main tube against spring pressure. The adjustment screws have clearly marked graduations around their circumference and many have a ball-detent system that clicks as the adjustment screws are turned. Each graduation or click represents a change in reticle position that moves the bullet strike at the target. This is expressed in minutes of angle (m.o.a.) and normally has a value of 1/2, 1/4 or 1/8 m.o.a. per click.

External—Many older scopes have an external-adjustment system built into the mounts and rings. Such scopes remain popular today for some types of target competition. In this type of scope, the reticle remains stationary within the main tube and the point of the bullet strike is adjusted by mounts having micrometer windage and elevation mechanisms that move the entire scope laterally and/or vertically. These mounts often allow the scope to slide fore and aft to reduce recoil. An advantage of external-adjustment scopes is that the user is always sighting through the optical center of the tube.

As internal-adjustment systems became more reliable and more accurate, the popularity of external-adjustment scopes faded. Today, external-adjustment models are still offered, however the use of such scopes are now generally limited to a few specialized disciplines of rifle competition.

It is important to note that some scope-mounting systems designed for internal-adjustment scopes still incorporate the ability to accommodate some coarse external windage adjustment.

Variable Power

Variable-power riflescopes have an internal mechanism to change the amount of magnification within design limits. This consists of an additional set of lenses mounted in an internal tube that slides forward and rearward under the control of a cam attached to the magnification ring. The design of the lens system and its position in the tube controls the amount of magnification.

The popularity of variable-power riflescopes rests squarely on their flexibility. Variable magnification enables the shooter to adjust the power to suit a wide variety of conditions ranging from lower power with a wide field of view for fast shots at close range to higher power for greater precision at long range. Once considered expensive and unreliable, variable-power riflescopes have become the most popular type as their design has matured and prices have dropped. Today, the single most popular riflescope is the 3-9X-40 mm which has become the jack-of-all-trades. Smaller variables such as 2-7X-32 mm remain popular for smaller-caliber rifles while 4.5-12X-50 mm and bigger models are favored for long-range shooting. Despite their flexibility, no one variable fits all applications and that is why there are so many different models.

Despite their popularity, variable-power riflescopes may suffer from certain drawbacks:

- The variable magnification system introduces another level of mechanical complexity and another source for optical error, potentially decreasing reliability.
- The movement of the internal components of a variable scope can produce changes in zero as the scope power is increased or decreased.
- Variable-power scopes are harder to seal than fixed-power scopes by virtue of the magnification-adjustment ring.
- As the magnification increases, the field of view and image brightness decrease, often substantially.
- Variable-magnification scopes are substantially heavier than fixed-power scopes.
- Variable-power scopes are more expensive than fixed-power scopes.

Reticles

The scope's reticle is the visible reference used as an aiming point to align the gun with the target. There are many reticle patterns ranging from simple to complex. The most popular remains the general-purpose crosshair. However, even the simple crosshair offers choices, such as tapered, ultra thin, duplex, mil-dot, ballistic compensating, range-finding, center dot, center ring and post, just to name a few. Each configuration is intended for a specific type of use and there are multiple versions of all. For example, tapered crosshairs are a popular choice for varmint hunting and duplex crosshairs are a common choice for big-game hunting. There seems no limit to new reticle designs being offered, and most makers offer at least six or more types. Your best bet is to try out several at a local gun store then consult with experienced hunters or competitors before making a final selection.

Reticles may be illuminated electronically, with tritium or with fiber optics to enhance their contrast against dark backgrounds, especially at dusk or dawn or during heavy overcast conditions. Illumination remains an expensive option that may not work well in very cold conditions and has limited usefulness. Still, it has proven a popular addition to many scopes.

The reticle itself may be located inside the scope at the first, or front, focal plane or the second, or rear, focal plane. The location is an issue only in variable-power scopes. Reticles located in the first focal plane in a variable-power scope will increase or decrease in size as the magnification is changed while those located in the second focal plane do not change size when the power is adjusted. For this reason, the latter location has become the most popular.

One situation in which a front-focal-plane reticle is clearly advantageous is in scopes with a mil-dot ranging system. This type of reticle employs dots spaced one milliradian apart on the crosshair. (A milliradian is the angle subtended by three feet at 1,000 yds.) An

Common Reticle Types

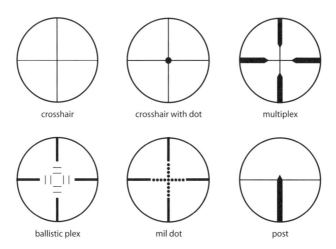

| crosshair | crosshair with dot | multiplex |

| ballistic plex | mil dot | post |

object of known size is bracketed between the dots, and a table is used to determine the range based on the number of dots the object measures. With a rear-focal-plane reticle variable, the mil-dot system is only accurate at one power setting. A front-focal-plane location maintains the same relationship to the target throughout the range of magnification, thus enabling mil-dots to be used accurately at any power.

A second benefit of placement in front of the variable-magnification lens system is that the reticle remains unaffected by tolerances or misalignment of the erector tube during power changes. With a rear-focal-plane location, these tolerances may shift point of impact as the power level changes.

In the past, many scope reticles were not constantly centered, meaning that they moved off to the side when windage or elevation adjustments were made. Many shooters found this annoying. Today, nearly all riflescopes have constantly centered reticles that do not change position when adjustments are made.

Crosshairs or other reticle patterns are created by laser etching on optical glass or by ultra-thin platinum wires. Some early scope reticles used strands of hair, hence the name crosshairs.

Parallax

Many riflescopes suffer from a condition that stems from the inability of a scope to remain focused at all ranges. The compromise solution for most scopes is to design them to focus at infinity or one specific range. This serves most purposes and simplifies scope design. When a scope is properly focused at the chosen zero range, parallax will be minimal.

However, this is not acceptable for some applications, such as varmint shooting and hunting at long ranges. Under such conditions, parallax becomes a problem that must be addressed. Scope makers solve this problem by offering models with adjustable objective (AO) lenses. AO models incorporate adjustable objective bell housings with graduations marked on the traveling edge that allow quick and easy adjustment to remove parallax at any range. Alternately, some models locate the parallax adjustment in a third turret on the main tube for more convenience. Although AO and side-focus models cost more, shooters demanding enhanced accuracy often feel they are worth the asking price.

Sealing

Most quality scopes are sealed. This means the outer lenses and adjustment systems must be sealed against ingress of water, dust and dirt. This is very important, as dust or dirt inside the tube will degrade the image in several ways, mainly by appearing as black spots within the field of view. Dirt inside the tube can also jam the delicate adjustment system. Moisture inside the tube can cause fogging so that the shooter cannot see through it. Moisture can also cause corrosion of inner parts and surfaces.

Scopes are sealed at the factory by first attaching them to a vacuum pump that removes all air from inside the tube. The tube is then filled with dry nitrogen gas to prevent fogging and then subsequently sealed. Of course, if you remove a turret or the ocular bell housing, the nitrogen gas may escape, thus compromising your scope's anti-fogging capability.

Many high-quality scopes have double seals to ensure gas-tight integrity. However, no scope is permanently waterproof despite advertising claims to the contrary. Wear, tear, impacts and age all conspire against the tube holding the nitrogen gas. For this reason, most scope manufacturers will reseal and refill a scope at modest cost.

Want to check your scope for leaks? Try this simple test: Fill a sink or wash basin with warm water. Immerse your scope in the water for five minutes and check for bubbles coming from the tube. Bubbles mean leakage and such scopes should be sent back to the manufacturer for resealing and refilling.

Shock and Recoil

Newtonian physics are not kind to riflescopes. In addition to maintaining their accuracy, reliability and water-tight integrity, scopes must withstand the considerable shock of repeated recoil many times the force of gravity. The delicate adjustment mechanisms and lens mounts are particularly susceptible to high G loads and must be designed accordingly. Scope makers are well aware of this and have designed shock resistance into their products. They have been so successful, that shock resistance is now taken for granted by shooters and manufacturers alike.

Air rifles are a special case. Be careful when using conventional riflescopes on a spring-piston air rifle. If you do so, the lenses may come loose, sometimes within a few shots, and your scope could be damaged or ruined. The reason is that spring-piston air rifles recoil in both rearward and then forward directions while a conventional rifle recoils only rearward. Thus, a riflescope for a conventional firearm need resist G forces in only one direction—rearward. Air rifle scopes must resist G forces in both directions. This requires a special scope designed for the purpose.

Lens Coatings

In any optical system, some light is lost through reflection each time the light passes through a glass-to-air surface. The light loss can be significant in multi-element riflescopes; as much as 50 percent of the light may be lost to reflection as it passes through an uncoated lens system.

In the 1940s, it was discovered that magnesium fluoride coatings on lenses would increase light transmission, color fidelity and image brightness considerably. Today, nearly all modern scopes have coated lenses that transmit from 95 percent to 99 percent of the light that enters the objective lens.

Coatings such as zinc sulfide and zirconium oxide are used, often in combination with magnesium fluoride. A coated lens will appear tinted when viewed from the side. The exact color may vary from blue, green, purple, red or gold. Abrasion-resistant coatings have been developed for the exterior lens surfaces of modern riflescopes. Water-shedding coatings have also been developed.

Various levels of coating can be applied to lenses ranging from a single layer of magnesium fluoride on the exterior objective and ocular surfaces, to as many as 15 layers or more on every surface of every lens. Typically, coating layers are only a few ten-thousandths of an inch thick.

- The term "fully coated" when applied to a riflescope usually means that all lens-to-air surfaces have at least one coating layer. This includes the interior lens systems as well as the exterior.

- The term "multi-coated" or "multiple-layer coated" signifies that multiple coating layers have been applied to some, but not all, lens surfaces. Normally, this means that only the outer lens surfaces have been multi-coated. "Fully multi-coated" signifies multiple coatings on all lens-to-air surfaces.

Lower-priced scopes may have from one to five lens-coating layers while more expensive scopes may have as many as 15 or even more. In lower-priced scopes, only the outside surface of the objective (front) and ocular (rear) lenses are coated. Higher-quality scopes have all internal and external lens surfaces multi-coated.

How many layers are enough? That depends on the quality of the lens system and the intended purpose of the scope. Adding more layers of coating rapidly reaches the point of diminishing returns, but on a high-quality scope where maximum light transmission and image fidelity are necessary, 15 layers of coating can be easily justified.

Common Optical Terms

Aberration

Any difference between the image of an object viewed through the riflescope and the ideal image of that object is called aberration. Some of the more common types of aberration are:

- **Chromatic aberration**
  This is a color flare or color fringe along the edges of objects in the image.

- **Spherical aberration**
  This occurs when light rays passing through the center of the lens do not focus at the same point as rays of light passing through the lens edges. The result is a low-contrast, soft-focus image.

- **Pincushion and barrel distortion**
  This is the tendency of straight lines to bow in or bow out from the center of the image to its edges.

- **Astigmatism**
  This is the inability to focus the image due to imperfections in the lens system.

- **Curvature of field**
  The image is not flat. Straight lines appear to be bent.

It is important to recognize that no optical system can be completely free of aberration. All optical systems are a design compromise that minimizes some types of aberration while necessarily allowing others. Many of the lens elements in a riflescope are included for the purpose of correcting various types of aberration.

Aberration is not simply the result of imperfect lens grinding or improper design; some types of aberration are basically inevitable, due to the fact that different wavelengths of light focus at different points. Also, some types of aberration result from the characteristics of spherical lenses (lenses whose curved surfaces are ground with an equal-radius curvature). Some forms of aberration can be eliminated by the use of aspherical lenses.

Contrast
    The ability of an optical system to distinguish clearly and crisply between areas of light and dark is called contrast. For shooting purposes, always select the riflescope with the highest contrast.

Exit Pupil
    Exit pupil is the diameter in millimeters of the beam of focused light transmitted by the ocular lens. The exit pupil can be calculated by dividing the diameter of the objective lens by the power, or magnification, of the scope. An exit pupil of about 5 mm or larger in diameter is preferable. A large exit pupil provides a brighter image with greater contrast and a wide field of view for easy target acquisition. Exit pupils smaller than 5 mm in diameter offer darker images with lower contrast and progressively narrower fields of view.

Eye Relief
    Eye relief is the distance of the eye from the ocular lens when the image fully fills the lens and is not vignetted. Normally, eye relief figures are given as a distance range, for example 3.2-3.8", due to differences in individual visual acuity. On a variable-power scope, eye relief typically changes with scope power. Too little eye relief is undesirable, particularly on a scope mounted on a hard-kicking magnum rifle, where it may contribute to a scope cut on the eyebrow. For this reason, most center-fire riflescopes have a minimum eye relief of 3.0 to 4". A riflescope with an eye relief of less than 3.0" should only be used on a small-caliber rifle with low recoil.

Most riflescopes and shotgun scopes are designed to be mounted on the receiver, close to the eye, and thus have relatively short eye relief. Scopes to be mounted on handguns and on the barrels of long guns are classed as long eye relief (LER) or extended eye relief (EER) scopes. Some models provide as much as 18-20 inches of eye relief, enabling scope use on a handgun extended at arm's length. Other models may offer an eye relief of 12 inches or less for scope mounting on a scout rifle. Note that the higher the magnification, the shorter the eye relief of such scopes.

Field of View

Field of view is the width of the area that can be seen in the image at a given distance. Normally, field of view is expressed as the number of feet in the image at 1,000 yds., for example 322 feet at 1,000 yds. Field of view decreases dramatically with increasing magnification. A narrow field of view makes it difficult to find the target and then to hold it in the image. For this reason, a wide field of view may be more important than high scope magnification.

When looking through a scope with a 100-ft. field of view at 1,000 yds., a 100-ft.-wide object viewed at that distance will just fill the visual field

Focal Plane

The focal plane is the plane or distance from the objective lens at which light rays from an object converge to form a focused image inside the main tube. Objects in the same focal plane appear to the eye to be at the same distance, and therefore can be seen with equal clarity without the need to refocus the eye. One of the advantages of optical sights is that the target and the reticle are in the same focal plane. This eliminates trying to focus on both iron sights and the target at the same time. This is why riflescopes are so popular with shooters having less than perfect eyesight.

There are two focal planes in a typical riflescope—the first behind the objective lens and the second behind the erector lens set.

Magnification

The magnification, or power, of a riflescope is expressed as a number corresponding to the size of an object viewed at a specified distance through the scope, relative to its size as seen with the naked eye. Put another way, an object at 100 yds. distant viewed through a 10X scope will appear to be the same size as if it were viewed with the naked eye from 10 yds. away.

Different scope magnifications are used for specific shooting activities.

- High-magnification riflescopes from 15X to 50X with objective lens diameters of 40-50 mm or more with adjustable objective-lens systems are popular for various types of center-fire rifle competitions such as benchrest and 1,000-yd. shooting.

- Varmint shooters normally prefer a scope with magnification levels of 12X to 24X and adjustable objective lens diameters of 44-50 mm for their precision work.

- Long-range big-game hunting demands a scope with an adjustable objective lens system of approximately 40 mm diameter with power levels up to 15X that enable the hunter to judge game and wind conditions at extreme distances.

- At dawn, dusk or during poor light conditions, scopes with large objective lenses of 50 mm and above that gather all existing light are preferred, with powers between 6X and 12X. Illuminated reticles are a popular option on these scopes.

- Low-power scopes of 1.1X to 4X with a wide field of view and fixed objective are well-suited for hunting in woods or brush at close range.

- For general-purpose hunting, most sportsmen are well served by a 3-9X-40 mm variable scope with fixed objective which is a good compromise between a wide field of view for close shots (at 3X) and added magnification (at 9X) for distant shots.

As magnification levels increase, the field of view decreases, which makes target acquisition increasingly difficult. Increasing magnification also magnifies movement, making the reticle appear less steady and thus hampering the ability of many shooters to hold their point of aim. These factors conspire to make most scopes over 8X very difficult to use without a solid rest. When shooting from a rest on a bench, a narrow field of view and high magnification are less of a problem.

Objective Lens

The objective lens is the light-gathering lens at the front of the scope. The larger the diameter of the objective lens, the more light will be admitted into the scope. This results in a larger exit pupil with a brighter image.

Most riflescopes have objective lens diameters from 32 mm to 44 mm. These provide a good balance between light-gathering capability, cost and image quality. Such riflescopes are relatively lightweight and easy to mount on most rifles. For many hunting applications, such riflescopes are an excellent choice.

For hunting at dusk, dawn or in very low light conditions, the increased light-gathering capability of a larger objective lens may be a better choice. For such conditions, most scope manufacturers offer models with 50 mm to 56 mm objective lenses. However, there is a penalty to be paid for this increased performance in the form of substantially increased weight, higher cost and difficulty in mounting a scope with such a large objective.

Varmint hunters and some target shooters prefer riflescopes with large 50 mm or greater objective lenses for a different reason. They want a high-power scope of 12X or more with a clear, crisp, flat image with excellent contrast and an adjustable objective to remove parallax. The image quality reduces eyestrain and enables them to clearly see small targets at long ranges and to judge wind and mirage precisely. They also spend considerable time looking through the scope with the rifle held on a solid rest, so unsteadiness from high magnification and a narrow field of view is less important.

Ocular Lens

The ocular lens is positioned at the rear of a riflescope, closest to the shooter's eye. Normally, the ocular lens is smaller in diameter than the front or objective lens. The ocular lens assembly is frequently threaded onto the main tube with a lock ring so that it can be used to adjust focus by turning the entire assembly in or out. This enables the scope to accommodate individual visual preferences and reduces parallax at the given distance at which the scope is focused.

When the ocular lens is used for adjusting focus, users can set focus for appropriate given distances by using paper targets placed downrange. Typically shooters select 50 yds. for rimfire rifles and 100 or 200 yds. for center-fire rifles. With the rifle secured in a solid rest, release the lock ring and turn it forward. Then turn the ocular assembly focus ring until a clear, crisp image of the paper target appears. Keep going past the clear focus point until the target becomes blurred. Now reverse directions and go back just until the image is clear and crisp. Countertighten the lock ring to hold the assembly securely in position.

Parallax

Parallax occurs when the image of the target is not focused precisely on the plane of the reticle. This can be easily checked by placing your rifle in a solid rest, then moving your head up and down, then back and forth as you view the image in the scope. If the position of the crosshairs appear to move on the target, parallax is present. If no parallax is present, the crosshairs will appear to remain stationary on the target. In a scope with parallax, the apparent point of aim changes with head position making accurate shooting difficult. For this reason, it is desirable to eliminate as much parallax as possible.

Parallax can be completely eliminated only at one specific distance. This is why adjustable-objective scopes are popular with many shooters. Most hunting scopes, particularly less expensive models, have their parallax correction fixed at 100 or 150 yds. This compromise distance results in minimal parallax error at hunting ranges to 250 yds. Shotgun scopes are normally set for parallax correction at 50 yds.

Parallax remains one of the most common problems with

riflescopes. Many new and used scopes exhibit excessive parallax, so always check a scope for parallax before you buy it.

Relative Brightness

This is a numerical measure of the potential brightness of an optical system. It is calculated by squaring the diameter (in millimeters) of the exit pupil. This number can then be compared with an actual reading taken from the exit pupil by a light measuring device.

Resolution

Resolution, or resolving power, refers to the ability of the lens system to distinguish detail. Most scope manufacturers check this by mounting the scope in a rest and viewing a series of horizontal and vertical line patterns at an exactly measured distance.

Resolving power is often expressed in lines per millimeter which indicates the greatest number of finely spaced black and white lines per millimeter that can clearly be distinguished at a given distance, normally 100 yds. In colloquial terms, resolving power is roughly synonymous with sharpness.

Twilight Factor

Twilight factor is a calculated number measuring low-light optical performance. It is obtained by multiplying the magnification of the optical system by the diameter of the objective lens in millimeters and taking the square root of the product. In general, the higher the twilight factor number, the better the potential performance.

Red-Dot Sights

Red-dot sights consist of a short, large-diameter (25 to 60 mm) tube or a single lens through which the target is viewed. Inside the sight, a small light-emitting diode (LED) of adjustable brightness is reflected off the lens surface. This projects a glowing dot of light into the shooter's field of view. The sight can be adjusted to bring the dot onto the point of bullet impact. Depending upon the design, windage and elevation can be set using screws in the sight that change the angle of the lens in the housing, the position of the LED or the position of an inner tube that houses both lens and LED.

Regardless of the mechanism involved, the adjustment alters the apparent location of the dot on the target.

Red-dot sights typically have a rheostat to control dot brightness. Also, most units are available with dots of different sizes, ranging from 2 to 20 m.o.a. Sights with small dots can be used on rifles and carbines for medium-range work, while larger dot sizes are more appropriate for pistol use.

Among the advantages of such sights are fast target acquisition, virtually unlimited eye relief and a relatively unobstructed field of view. Red-dot sights generally have either no magnification or low (2X to 4X) magnification. Their main advantage is that they place the dot and the target in the same focal plane.

Ranging Riflescopes

A number of different optical-sighting systems in riflescopes
have been devised to facilitate first-round hits at unknown ranges.
Accomplishing this involves two separate problems:

Determining the range to the target by means of:

- stadia lines with different spacing
- indicator marks or mil-dots
- split-image focus matching
- laser ranging (internal or separate).

Making appropriate elevation adjustments based on the trajectory of
the cartridge by:

- reference marks on the vertical crosshair
- range marks on the elevation turret
- a calibrated elevation cam on the scope mount
- previous experience and knowledge of actual bullet path and
  adjustments.

It is important to note that only a few systems make provision for
compensating for crosswind or mirage. Such corrections must then be
made by the shooter based on his judgement and experience.

A very high percentage of missed shots are caused by inaccurate
range determination and bullet trajectory adjustment. For this reason,
eliminating or reducing these two problems will show excellent results.

Modern technology has responded by combining a microcomputer
and a laser rangefinder with a riflescope to build a system offering a
near-complete ballistic solution. This system functions by first using
the laser to determine the exact distance to the target. This information
is then fed to the microcomputer that has the load trajectory stored in
its memory. The computer uses the target distance and load trajectory
data to automatically adjust the reticle to achieve a first round hit on
the target. Second-generation systems are even more sophisticated
and incorporate wind direction, wind speed, air temperature,
barometric pressure, gun tilt and barrel temperature to calculate reticle
compensation. At present, such scopes are beyond the reach of the
average sportsmen on cost and availability grounds.

Note that ranging and trajectory-compensation aiming systems are, of
necessity, based on a cartridge/load of known trajectory. Most computer/
laser systems today are based on the ballistics of either the 5.56x45 mm
NATO or 7.62x51 mm NATO rounds as their primary use is military.

Rangefinders

There are two types of commonly available rangefinders—optical
and laser.

Optical Rangefinders

The optical rangefinder is the oldest type, having first been developed by Archibald Barr and William Stroud around 1889. These devices utilize two parallel optical systems separated by a known distance, typically from three feet to 45 feet or more. To determine range, the operator looks through an optical device that provides a split image of the target as viewed by the two optical systems. To find the range, the operator simply brings both images of the target into clear focus. The divergence angle of the optical paths of the two systems is then determined and converted by simple geometry into a distance. In practice, the operator need not know mathematics. When the images come into perfect coincidence (focus), the range is read off a dial. Some optical rangefinders work on the coincidence principle with one image upside down and reversed on the other while others rely on stereoscopic images that are side-by-side.

Though simple in principle, effective use of optical rangefinders requires training, experience and excellent visual acuity. They work best in clear, well-lit conditions where the target can be seen easily and remains in position. The accuracy of any optical rangefinding system depends to a large extent on the base distance between the two lenses. Generally speaking, the greater the base distance between the lenses, the more accurate the system. For example, the theoretical minimum error for a Swiss, 80-cm base optical rangefinder is about 5.4 yds. at 1,000 yds.

Laser Rangefinders

Laser rangefinders have supplanted optical rangefinders because they are compact, light, inexpensive and extremely accurate (to within plus or minus one yard at most ranges).

Laser rangefinders operate on the echo principle. The user centers the target in the viewfinder and depresses a button that causes a pulse of laser light to be sent to the target. The button also starts a high-speed electronic clock. Light reflected from the target is picked up by a sensor which then stops the clock. Internal circuitry measures the elapsed time on the electronic clock and calculates the distance based on the speed of light through air (186,000 miles per second).

Though extremely accurate, laser rangefinders do have limitations. Very small targets and targets having low contrast with their surrounding terrain are difficult to range. Climactic conditions such as fog, smoke, rain or snow can also impair their function. Many modern laser rangefinders have special operational modes with filter systems designed to increase their sensitivity and accuracy under such conditions.

Binoculars and Spotting Scopes

Modern shooters have become heavy users of binoculars and spotting scopes. The basic optical principles that govern the design and construction of telescopic sights also generally apply to these essential shooting tools.

Binocular and Spotting Scope Optics

Binoculars and spotting scopes consist of three elements: an objective lens system, an internal prism system and an ocular lens system. The objective and ocular lens systems in a spotting scope or binocular serve the same purpose as in a riflescope. The prism system performs two functions. First, in similar manner to a riflescope, the reversed and upside-down image from the objective is turned right-side-up and reversed. Second, the prism system also folds the path of light within the optical device, allowing a longer focal length in a shorter tube.

Binocular Design

There are two main types of binocular designs in common use—roof prism and porro prism.

- Roof prism binoculars have objective lenses and ocular lenses mounted on the same axis as the straight tubes. Roof prism binoculars may be easily identified by their straight tubes.

- Porro prism binoculars have objective lenses and ocular lenses offset from the axis of the tubes. Porro prism binoculars may be readily identified by their offset or zig-zag tubes.

Both designs can be made to similar levels of optical quality, and thereby binocular choice often hinges on other factors.

Most binoculars have a focus wheel in the center between the barrels and a fine diopter adjustment on the right eyepiece. The barrels are mounted on a center pin which holds them in alignment. A common problem is misalignment of the barrels after the unit has been dropped or struck. Multicoated optics are common, but binoculars are often not waterproof or shock-resistant.

Common magnification powers are 7X or 8X with 36 mm objective lenses. For low light conditions, many users prefer 7x50 mm units. For the ultimate in performance, some shooters select 8X, 10X or 12X units with 60 mm or 80 mm objective lenses. However, such binoculars are heavy and can be very expensive. Binoculars providing magnifications greater than 10X become more difficult to hold steady.

Spotting Scope Design

Spotting scopes are commonly used to spot bullet holes in paper targets by shooters and coaches. To accomplish this, the spotting scope must be able to resolve the bullet hole or mark at the distances being shot. For example, spotting scopes used in benchrest competition must be able to resolve a .22-caliber bullet hole to a maximum of 200 yards while a spotting scope for use in long-range competition must resolve a .22-caliber bullet hole at 1,000 yds. Hunters also use spotting scopes to judge game at long ranges before starting a stalk. Spotting scopes for this purpose are generally used from a fixed position or base camp and are not used for judging range.

For these reasons, spotting scopes are made in a wide variety of sizes and capabilities. In general, magnification, fully coated optics, resolving power, image brightness and light-gathering capability are very important. Light weight, size and tube sealing are not key considerations.

Most spotting scopes offer variable magnification from 20X to 80X with an objective lens diameter of 60 mm to 80 mm. Lower-priced spotting scopes often have smaller objective lenses and are designed to be mounted on small, lightweight stands that rest on the shooting bench where they can be viewed straight-on through the tube. Higher-quality spotting scopes often have large objective lenses and are designed to be mounted on tripods. These scopes may offer a variety of interchangeable fixed-power and variable-power eyepieces that allow straight-on or offset use.

For most purposes, a spotting scope with an objective lens diameter of about 60 mm with multicoating and variable magnification of 20X-60X will offer satisfactory service.

Night-Vision Optics

Night-vision devices that enable the user to see objects in low-light and no-light conditions have come into widespread use in military and law-enforcement applications.

Most modern night-vision devices work in essentially the same way. Photons or packets of light energy entering the objective lens are directed into an electronic image intensifier tube. There, the photons impact on a photo cathode. These impacts produce electrons that go through a microchannel plate made of a glass disk perforated by millions of tiny holes from front to back. The microchannel plate has electrodes on both sides that accelerate the electrons passing through the plate. As the electrons pass through the holes in the microchannel plate, they knock additional electrons off the walls of the plate, which in turn release more electrons in a cascade effect. Thus, many electrons exit a hole in the microchannel plate where only few entered, effectively amplifying the original signal. After passing through the microchannel plate, the electrons strike a phosphor screen that glows where the electrons hit. Since the holes in the microchannel plate maintain the electrons in the same alignment they had when they left the photo cathode, the electrons produce an image on the phosphor screen that is an exact copy of the image created by the pattern of photons that entered the objective. In most night-vision devices, the image on the phosphor screen is viewed directly through the ocular lens. Current night-vision optics produce a monochromatic image having a grainy, green color.

Night-vision devices are classed as Generation 0, Generation I, Generation II, Generation III and Generation IV, with the resolution and degree of light amplification increasing with each successive generation. Generation 0 devices used active infrared light emissions to illuminate the subject; these were abandoned because they were easily detected by infrared-sensing optical devices. Generation I units, first used in the Vietnam war, were known as "starlight scopes." These units amplified ambient visible and near-infrared light, and are now generally considered obsolete for military use. Current military forces utilize Generation II, III and IV units. The level of light amplification varies from 500 to 1,000X for Generation I units to 20,000X for Generation II models and 30,000X to 70,000X for Generation III units.

Night-vision devices are sensitive to light in regions of the spectrum beyond the detection ability of the human eye. This makes them able to "see" in no-light conditions. The human eye can see light with wavelengths from 400 to 700 nanometers, while the Generation II and III night-vision devices are sensitive to light with wavelengths as long as 900 nanometers which is well into the near-infrared region.

Thermal imaging is a separate type of passive low-light imaging technology that uses a phased array of infrared detectors to pick up the heat energy emitted by objects. Such energy is typically emitted in infrared wavelengths from 1,000 to 100,000 nanometers. This is a much broader light spectrum than that detected by night-vision devices, which makes thermal imagers especially good at detecting heat-emitting objects such as an engine, hot gun barrel or a living organism.

Chapter 11
MATERIALS

In contemporary firearms manufacture, major components are commonly produced from alloys of steel, aluminum, brass or titanium, with a number of additional metals used as alloying agents or for specialized parts fabrication.

Metals comprise more than 80 elements in the periodic table. Metals conduct heat and electricity well. They can also be formed at room temperature and, in their solid state, typically have a shiny surface appearance. A few materials, such as carbon, silicon, phosphorus and sulfur, are known as "metalloids" because they sometimes, but not always, exhibit metallic properties. The term "metal" is often improperly used to include metal alloys, which are combinations of one or more metal elements with one or more metallic or non-metallic elements. Iron and iron-based alloys are classed as ferrous; all other metals and alloys having little or no iron are classed as non-ferrous.

Metals are normally found in nature in an oxidized form in minerals known as ores. Extraction of metal from ore is typically accomplished through smelting, a process that uses heat to separate the metal from the other constituents. In chemical terms, the heat removes the oxygen from the oxidized metal by combining it with carbon in a reduction reaction. Additional processes further refine the metal or produce it in forms for other purposes such as casting, machining, etc.

Metal Properties and Terms

Metals and their alloys have a number of properties, but only a few are relevant to the manufacture and use of firearms.

Abrasion Resistance (see Hardness)

Brittleness

Brittleness is the tendency of a material to fracture with relatively little prior deformation. In technical terms, a brittle metal or alloy is one that tends to break catastrophically when its elastic limit is reached or exceeded. Brittleness often increases with hardening, thus requiring tempering (*see Heat Treating, pg. 211*). A good example of a brittle metal is cast iron.

Corrosion Resistance

Corrosion is the reaction between a metal and its environment that degrades the metal and its properties. Corrosion is primarily an electro-chemical process that can be produced in a variety of ways. The most common type of corrosion is oxidation, produced by exposure to water or solutions containing water. Oxidation can adversely affect metals including aluminum, brass, copper and steel (in the form of iron oxide or rust). In some metals such as aluminum, a layer of metal oxide forms on the surface that inhibits further corrosion. Other types of corrosion can be caused by exposure to chemicals such as salts, acids and solvents as found in tanned leather and in human perspiration.

Because of the chemical reactivity of iron, ferrous metals such as steel are particularly susceptible to corrosion. A common method of inhibiting corrosion in ferrous metals is by surface treatment such as bluing, Parkerizing, Teflon coating and chrome- or nickel-plating.

Stainless steel alloys are less vulnerable to corrosion by virtue of their high nickel content. It is important to note that stainless steels will corrode, although they are more resistant to corrosion than many other steel alloys. Corrosion can adversely affect non-ferrous metals, producing effects ranging from a surface discoloration to more severe pitting.

Ductility

Ductility is the property of a metal allowing it to be stretched or elongated into a new shape without breaking.

Elasticity

Elasticity is a measure of a metal's ability to return to its original shape after deformation. The elastic limit is the maximum stress that can be applied to a metal without permanently deforming it.

Erosion Resistance

Erosion is the enlargement or degradation of a metal surface by abrasion. The process involves interrelated mechanical, chemical and thermal effects. In firearms, gases and residues generated by burning propellant and driven at high velocity can cause erosion to the barrel throat and bore. High heat accelerates the erosion process.

Fatigue Resistance

Metal fatigue occurs when a metal weakens or breaks as the result of a number of cycles of flexing, stress or vibration. Metals and alloys that are less susceptible to this type of damage are said to be fatigue-resistant.

Hardness

Hardness of a metal or alloy can be defined in terms of its resistance to deformation. Resistance to indentation is the definition upon which existing hardness tests are based.

Indentation methods used to measure metal hardness include the Brinell, Rockwell A to D, Shore, Knoop and Vickers systems. Normally, the hardness of metals used in firearms is measured on the Brinell or Rockwell scales.

In the Brinell system, the metal sample is placed beneath a hardened sphere—a 10 mm-diameter steel ball is the standard—which is then subjected to a load of 500, 1,500 or 3,000 kilograms, depending on the hardness of the metal being tested. The Brinell hardness number (BHN) is determined by dividing the load used, in kilograms, by the actual surface area of the indentation, in square millimeters.

The Rockwell system is a two-stage penetration test using a preliminary load followed by a heavier load. The Rockwell B scale commonly used for firearms is based on the deformation produced by a 1/16"-diameter hardened steel ball under a load of 100 kilograms (220 lbs.) The Rockwell C scale used for harder metals such as steel alloys employed for firearm receivers, bolts and barrels is based on the indentation of a diamond-tipped cone under a 150-kilogram (330-lb.) load. On all hardness scales, the higher the number, the greater the hardness.

In steel, hardenability refers to the property that governs the depth and distribution of hardness produced by heat hardening followed by quenching. Steel alloys differ in their hardenability. In general, the greater the carbon content of a steel alloy, the greater the potential hardness. However, some steels—such as 300-series stainless steels—are not heat-treatable. Likewise, some alloys of aluminum are more amenable to heat-treatment than others.

Heat Resistance

At high temperatures, such as might be produced in a gun barrel by prolonged rapid fire, many alloys vary in their ability to resist deterioration in hardness, strength and other properties.

Impact Resistance

Impact resistance may be defined as the ability of a metal or alloy to withstand the imposition of a sudden stress or shock without fracture.

Lubricity

Lubricity is the smoothness, slipperiness or freedom from friction of a given metal or alloy. This is an especially important property of metals or alloys that must slide against each other.

Machinability

Machinability is the relative ease with which a metal can be cut or shaped by typical machining processes. Machinability is related primarily to two factors: hardness and composition. In general, the harder a metal or alloy, the less machinable it is. There is also a hardness limit below which machinability decreases. Composition affects machinability as well. For example, stainless steels are generally less machineable while steel alloys containing sulfur and lead are known as "free cutting" steels for the ease with which they can be turned, milled, drilled and so forth.

Malleability
This is the property of a metal to be deformed under compression without cracking or breaking.

Shock Resistance (see Impact Resistance)

Strain
The dimensional change, whether plastic (permanent) or elastic (non-permanent), resulting from a stress.

Stress
The load or force applied to a metal sample or part.

Thermal Stability
Most metals and alloys exhibit dimensional change corresponding to changes in temperature. This is called the coefficient of thermal expansion. This number reflects the magnitude of change per degree of temperature, compared to the material at room temperature. In general, a low coefficient of expansion is desirable.

Toughness
Toughness is very important in metals used in firearms construction. Toughness is the ability of a metal to withstand a suddenly applied load. Toughness is also a metal's ability to resist breakage when its elastic limit has been exceeded, as well as ability to undergo some degree of deformation prior to failure.

Ultimate Tensile Strength
This is the maximum tensile strength sustained by a specimen before breaking, divided by the specimen's original cross-sectional area.

Yield Strength
This is the maximum load sustained by a specimen without permanent deformation (*see Elasticity*).

The "Bronze Age" of Firearms
A defining point in the history of mankind occurred when our ancestors discovered how to extract metal from ore and then learned to fabricate that metal into useful objects. Tools, in particular, were vastly improved, and that included such weapons as spear and arrow points.

This breakthrough dates back some 5,500 years to the time when humans began to make tools from bronze. The term the "Bronze Age" is used to refer to this prehistoric period falling between the Stone Age (when humans utilized stone tools) and the Iron Age (when humans developed the ability to produce iron tools).

In fact bronze is a rather indefinite term referring to any of several copper alloys. Before 2500 B.C., bronze was generally an alloy of copper and arsenic. After that juncture, bronze was, and still is, an alloy of copper and tin.

Although ferrous metals had long since surpassed bronze (see below) for use in edged weapons, bronze cannon were mentioned in a Florentine ordnance manual dated 1326.

Bronze was the preferred material because the technology of casting bronze church bells and other substantial items was well understood; such technology was easily transferred to casting cannon barrels. By the middle of the 14th century, cannon barrels of wrought iron construction came into use. This allowed a considerable increase in size and power. However, bronze cannon continued to be made and used, and by the early 1400s cast bronze cannon rivaled the largest wrought iron cannon.

Although not as strong as iron, bronze proved more resistant to the corrosive effects of blackpowder. This made it particularly desirable for use aboard ships, as field artillery and in coastal defenses. Bronze cannon of the mid-1500s were also tougher and safer than their inexpensive cast-iron counterparts that had a tendency to burst. Bronze cannon continued to be made well into the 19th century, and were used extensively during the American Civil War.

After the Civil War, advances in materials and metallurgical processes—particularly improvements in producing steel of consistent quality in large quantities—made possible stronger, safer and more accurate barrels, breeches and other firearm parts. Ever since, steel has remained the primary metal used for firearm components, while wood is clearly the preferred material for stocks.

Iron and Steel

At the beginning of the Iron Age about 3,500 years ago, men discovered methods of extracting metallic iron from iron-bearing ores by using heat. This yielded large quantities of iron that could be made into various shapes with reasonably good hardness and toughness.

Steel is iron combined with more than 0.05 percent and less than 2.0 percent carbon. Some amount of manganese is usually also present. Steel was known in the ancient world, having been used in swords by the Spartans, Romans, Persians and others.

Iron and Steel Production

The earliest technique for extracting iron from ores involved heating the ore in a wood or charcoal fire made hotter by a forced-air draft. At a temperature of around 2,000 degrees F, the iron in the ore melted, producing pure iron with very little carbon. This iron could be formed into different shapes by hammering or reheating as required. Called wrought iron, this metal was the primary form of iron in use through much of the 14th century.

Later it was found that when the fire temperature exceeded 2,400 degrees F, the carbon in wood or charcoal would chemically bond with iron to a maximum of 4.5 percent carbon content. The carbon did two things:

- It lowered the melting point of iron allowing it to flow as a molten liquid.
- It caused the resulting product, cast iron, to become very brittle and hard.

As a result, cast iron could not be shaped by hammering and so had limited usefulness to early blacksmiths.

Although wrought iron was of far greater utility than cast iron, it was soft. This led to the development of metal-hardening processes. During the Middle Ages, it was discovered that heating iron in an airtight environment at a temperature below the melting point, then rapidly quenching it in water or other liquid increased its hardness. This is a carburizing process in which some of the carbon in the fire alloyed with the iron's surface to produce case hardening.

When charcoal or other carbonaceous materials are combined with melted iron in an airtight crucible, the carbon becomes evenly distributed throughout the iron, producing crucible steel. When rapidly quenched, the steel becomes hard throughout, not merely on the surface. The process of tempering or reheating the quenched steel to a temperature below the melting point, then cooling slowly reduces brittleness.

Improvements in furnace design led to development of the blast furnace whose high temperatures produced pig iron with a high carbon content and a low proportion of slag or impurities. Similar to cast iron, pig iron was hard and brittle, but could be poured into molds to form useful objects. Subsequent efforts directed at purifying or decarburizing pig iron to produce wrought iron employed various processes such as puddling.

Production of steel from pig iron can be accomplished by a number of methods. The crucible steel process described above was the earliest method used to produce steel of high quality in appreciable quantity. In the middle of the 19th century, the crucible method was supplanted by the Bessemer process. Invented by Henry Bessemer, this process used a high-pressure stream of heated air introduced into the bottom of a crucible of molten pig iron known as a Bessemer Converter. The air burned off the excess silicon, manganese and carbon. Later variations on the Bessemer process such as the open-hearth and basic oxygen processes, differ primarily in the way air and/or pure oxygen is introduced and circulated through the melt. The more recent electric furnace method utilizes electricity to heat the molten pig iron as it offers more precise temperature control and less contamination of the steel.

In modern steelmaking, the furnace is charged with pellets of iron, limestone and coal. Molten iron from the blast furnace, along with recycled scrap steel, goes directly to the steelmaking process, such as a basic oxygen or electric arc furnace. The finished steel is cast in ingots or hot-rolled to various shapes. Additional shaping may be done at room temperature by cold rolling to produce rods, bars, plate, coils, tubes, wire and so forth.

Properties of Steel

Steel is the king of gun making metals. In a part of any particular size, steel offers greater strength and wear resistance than almost any other metal. By selecting the proper alloy and hardening method, it is possible to make steel parts that are extremely tough and wear resistant as well as parts that are as hard and as smooth as glass. Steel is easily fabricated by forging, casting, extrusion, stamping or machining and it can be joined by welding, brazing, silver-soldering and other methods.

The property of a given steel alloy depends upon its carbon content, the type and amount of alloying elements and the microstructure of the steel. Steel microstructure reflects the fact that carbon can associate with iron in different phases which can produce different steel properties. The primary phases are ferrite, cementite and austenite

Other phases such as pearlite, bainite and martensite occur when steel is heated and cooled. Also important is the grain structure of the steel. For firearms applications, fine-grain steel is preferable to coarse-grain steel, as the finer-grain steels offer greater toughness. Transformations among the various phases and grain sizes can be brought about by changes in heat-treatment temperature.

Types of Steel

There are five generally recognized types of steel:

- carbon
- alloy
- high-strength, low-alloy
- stainless
- tool and die.

Carbon, alloy and stainless steels are the types most commonly used in firearms.

Carbon Steels

Carbon steels are those whose composition specifies no particular amount of alloying elements and whose properties are primarily related to the amount of carbon present. Carbon steels can be subdivided into three groups according to carbon content:

- low (0.3 percent or less of carbon)
- medium (0.3 percent to 0.6 percent carbon)
- high (0.6 percent to 2.0 percent carbon).

Generally, the higher the carbon content, the stronger and harder the steel can be made, though brittleness may also increase. All types of carbon steel typically contain small amounts of manganese, phosphorus, sulphur and silicon.

Medium-carbon steel grades termed as 1035, 1040 and 1050 are commonly used for firearms manufacture.

Alloy Steels

Alloy steels are a common choice for firearms manufacture. Each alloying element adds a particular property to the steel. Some of the more common alloy elements are:

boron: increases hardenability

chromium: increases hardness, hardenability and resistance to corrosion, heat and wear.

copper: increases strength and corrosion resistance

manganese: increases strength and hardenability depth

molybdenum: combined with manganese and chromium, increases hardenability and high-temperature strength

nickel: improves ease of heat treatment, improves corrosion resistance and, in large amounts, increases strength and shock resistance

phosphorus: increases strength, corrosion resistance and machinability

silicon: increases resiliency for spring applications

sulphur: improves machinability, but is detrimental to ductility, weldability and impact-resistance

vanadium: increases hardenability.

Often, two or more alloys are combined to confer characteristics of each. AISI/SAE 4140 is the quintessential alloy steel used in gunmaking, representing a nearly ideal combination of properties. Also popular are AISI/SAE 4130, 4150, 4340 and 8620.

Stainless Steels

Stainless steel is produced by alloying steel with large amounts of chromium and nickel. Unlike carbon and alloy steels which are designated by a four-digit numbering system, stainless steels are specified using a three-digit system with numbers in the 300s and 400s.

There are three types of stainless steels, whose names refer to the predominant internal structure of the steel.

Austenitic steels, including all 300-series stainless steels, are the most resistant to corrosion. Because they lack significant amounts of ferrite, they are non-magnetic. They cannot be heat-treated, but they can be work-hardened to high levels of strength.

Ferritic stainless steels such as 405, 430 and 446 are not as corrosion-resistant as austenitic steels, but they are magnetic and cannot be heat-treated.

Martensitic stainless steels, including 405, 410, 414, 416, 420, 431, 440A, 440B and 440C, can be heat-treated to high levels of tensile strength, hardness and resistance to abrasion and erosion. AISI/SAE 416R is widely used for stainless steel barrels. Other grades of martensitic stainless steels used in gunmaking include 15-5 PH and 17-4 PH.

Stainless steel is particularly prone to galling, a phenomenon in which material is transferred between two pieces of metal rubbing together as the result of friction. Galling creates rough areas on both parts and in some cases becomes so pronounced that the parts are welded together by friction. Galling is common when two parts of the same type of stainless steel rub together under pressure and in the absence of lubrication. Thus, many firearms makers specify an alloy steel bolt with a stainless receiver, use two different grades of stainless or the same grade of stainless at two different levels of hardness for the slide and frame of a semi-automatic pistol. Keeping the contact surfaces between the parts well lubricated reduces galling.

Steel Nomenclature—AISI/SAE Numbering System

At one time, specific steel compositions were known by trade names introduced by the steelmaker. Adding to the confusion were thousands of compositions, many of which did not differ materially. The confusion was reduced by introducing a standardized steel numbering system developed by the American Iron & Steel Institute (AISI) and the Society of Automotive Engineers (SAE). This system uses four-digit or five-digit numbers or four-digit numbers with letters to specify carbon or alloy steels and some stainless steels. The numbers specify the composition of the steel so that a steel of a specific AISI/SAE number made by one manufacturer will be identical in composition and properties to that made by another maker.

In this system, the first two digits specify the type of steel; in alloy steels, the numbers represent the major alloying elements. The second number represents the approximate percentage of the primary alloying element. Examples of some of the steel types are as follows:

- **10 - -** plain carbon steel
- **11 - -** free cutting carbon steel
- **13 - -** manganese alloy steel
- **25 - -** nickel percent alloy steel
- **33 - -** nickel 3.5 percent, chromium 1.55 percent alloy steel
- **40 - -** molybdenum 0.25 percent alloy steel
- **41 - -** chromium 0.95 percent, molybdenum 0.20 percent alloy steel
- **43 - -** nickel 1.8 percent, chromium 0.50 or 0.80 percent, molybdenum 0.25 percent alloy steel
- **51 - -** carbon 1.00 percent, chromium 1.00 percent alloy steel
- **61 - -** chromium 0.80 or 0.95 percent, vanadium 0.10 or 0.15 percent minimum alloy steel
- **86 - -** nickel 0.55 percent, chromium 0.50 percent, molybdenum 0.20 percent alloy steel.

The last two digits specify approximate carbon content in tenths of a percent (approximate because each steel designation specifies a range of carbon content). Thus, SAE 4340 steel refers to nickel-chromium-molybdenum steel having between 0.38% and 0.43% of carbon.

Many steelmakers have their own naming and numbering systems which may have nothing to do with the AISI/SAE system. Although the AISI/SAE steel designation system has worked well for decades, the

SAE recently introduced the Unified Numbering System (UNS) which correlates the various numbering and naming systems (including proprietary and trade names) used worldwide by trade associations, metals producers and the like. Each steel alloy is designated by a five-digit UNS number and a single-letter prefix. In most cases, the original AISI/SAE number is incorporated into the new UNS number.

Ordnance Steel

Ordnance steel is a term that refers to a steel specification originated by the U.S. Army Ordnance Department shortly before World War I for the barrels of M1903 Springfield rifles. This steel alloy consisted of 0.5 to 0.6 percent carbon, 1.0 to 1.3 percent manganese and 0.15 to 0.25 percent silicon. Thus "ordnance steel" is not a proprietary or formal name within the steel industry, but instead a coined term used by gunwriters and gun companies.

Aircraft-Quality Steel

Because of the high stresses many gun parts are subjected to, aircraft-quality steels are sometimes specified by gunmakers. These are steels made from carefully selected materials using the most exacting methods of manufacture and forming to prevent internal imperfections that could compromise strength or other properties. Aircraft-quality steels are usually subjected to various tests and analysis to certify chemical composition, grain size, mechanical properties, hardenability and more.

Additionally, the internal structure of steel can be examined by magnetic particle tests. In such tests, a sample of steel is magnetized, then treated with a special magnetic powder. The pattern of adherence of the powder reveals lines of magnetic flux leakage, which reflect discontinuities at or beneath the steel surface. Commercially, this process is known as Magnafluxing.

Stress-Proof Steel

Various steels are described as stress-proof or fatigue-proof. Often, the terms are used generically to refer to steels whose compositions and manufacturing methods confer greater strength, shock resistance and/or resistance to fatigue. Both terms have also been registered as trademarks.

Damascus Steel/Pattern-Welded Steel/Watered Steel

Damascus steel is a term used, sometimes erroneously, to refer to certain types of steel that exhibit intricate surface patterns. True Damascus steel is an alloy that originated in the Middle East around 1000 A.D., persisted for around 300 years, then disappeared. This type of steel originated from metal-working techniques developed by metalsmiths in India in the first few centuries A.D. This resulted in a steel of exceptional purity called "wootz" steel. Subsequent improvements in the Middle East resulted in a technique for producing sword blades having different crystalline structures that made the metal soft in the middle and hard on the edges. Such blades were both sharp and tough—the swordsmith's goal. The differences in structure conferred a visible swirling or wavy pattern on the steel surface.

The name Damascus steel may have arisen from the erroneous belief that the technique for making such blades originated in Damascus, Syria. The superiority of Damascus steel blades was widely recognized by European soldiers who encountered them during the Crusades.

Pattern-welded steel is formed by repeating the mechanical process in which alternating layers, strips or bundles of iron and steel are heated and hammered or forge-welded together to form a bar or block, which is further hammered into shape, sometimes with additional twisting or folding. This was the classical technique for producing Japanese samurai swords, some of which were made with so many repetitions of the hammering/folding process that tens of thousands of layers were produced. Most Damascus steel gun barrels were actually produced by a pattern-welding process, in which steel rods or bars were forge-welded together around a mandrel. Acid etching was used to bring out the pattern on the surface.

Because of the wavy appearance of both Damascus steel and many pattern-welded steels, such steels are also sometimes known as watered steel.

Steel Formation

Regardless of type, steel can be produced in a number of cross-sectional shapes, including round, square and rectangular bar, plate, sheet, wire and so forth. Steel shapes can be formed by being rolled (passed between rollers); drawn (pulled or pushed through a die to reduce its diameter); spun (pressed or formed into a hollow tube); and in other ways. Steels from the mill may come in annealed (soft) or hardened types.

The process of creating steel shapes can be done working with hot metal (hot working) or cold metal (cold working). Cold working increases hardness and tensile strength, but decreases ductility. It may take place at room temperature or any temperature below the recrystallization point.

Other metals used in the fabrication of guns and gun parts are often formed using similar processes and methods.

Heat-Treating Steels and Other Metals

Properties such as strength, hardness, brittleness, machinability and so forth can often be affected by heating and cooling the steel in specific ways. The use of heating and cooling procedures for producing particular metal properties is known collectively as heat treatment.

Hardening

As noted previously, steel can exist in several phases according to the different ways in which the carbon atoms associate with iron atoms. Phase changes may occur when steel is heated to or above a specific temperature called the transformation temperature or critical temperature. Various steels have different transformation temperatures, for example, approximately 1,475-1,550 degrees F for typical medium-carbon steels and 1,550-1,600 F for the alloy steels often used in gun making.

In the hardening process, there is a transformation range of temperatures at which the austenite phase forms upon heating, followed by a second transformation range in which the austenite changes to another phase during cooling. The exact phase depends upon the cooling rate. Slow cooling results in a change to relatively soft pearlite, while rapid cooling produces harder bainite. If the quenching is sufficiently quick, martensite is formed which is the hardest phase of steel that can be made.

Different steel-quenching media including water, oil, brine, sodium hydroxide or molten baths produce different levels of hardness and strength. Heating and rapid quenching often produce distortion and internal cracks in the steel, so selecting the proper quenching medium and temperature is critical. Steels designed for applications in which minimal distortion is desired can be cooled after heat treatment simply by exposure to air.

The full transformation to bainite and martensite can be promoted by the addition of certain alloying elements. Alloys can also promote the retention of hardness at high temperatures. Finally, some alloys themselves form carbide particles that increase the abrasion resistance of the steel.

Tempering

Heating and quenching produces maximum strength and hardness, but is accompanied by an increase in brittleness—an undesirable property for most applications. Brittleness can be regarded as the opposite of toughness. A tough, less brittle steel can be produced by tempering, by which the steel is heated for a prolonged period to a temperature below the transformation temperature, then allowed to cool slowly. Properly done, tempering greatly increases toughness without significantly altering hardness.

Annealing

Annealing is the process of reducing steel hardness by heating. Annealing is often performed to improve machinability or ductility. Additionally, annealing can reduce or eliminate the stresses and undesirable changes in grain structure introduced by forging or other metalworking processes.

In the annealing process, steel is heated above transformation temperature, held there long enough to transform the steel to austenite, then is slowly cooled, producing softer ferrite. Different cooling regimens produce different degrees of softness. A lesser degree of softening can be achieved by prolonged heating of the steel at a temperature somewhat below the transformation temperature followed by slow cooling.

Normalizing

Normalizing is a process of heating a ferrous alloy above the transformation temperature followed by cooling in room-temperature air. Normalizing a piece of steel refines its grain structure, removes internal stresses and increases toughness. It is often used on parts that possess considerable internal stress from welding, forging, cold working and so forth to prepare such parts for final heat treatment.

Stress Relieving

Plastic deformation of steel as by welding, forging, cold working and extrusion can introduce internal stresses that adversely affect mechanical properties, service life, machinability or the ability of the part to undergo additional forming. Such stresses can be relieved by heating the steel for a specific period at a temperature just below the transformation temperature. For example, chromium-molybdenum alloy steel parts are often stress-relieved at 1,350 to 1,400 degrees F for up to three hours per inch of part thickness. The process of stress relief will soften steel, so it is generally avoided with parts that have been heat-treated and tempered to their final hardness.

Carburizing

Carburizing is a process of adding carbon to the surface of steel such that the hardening process yields a hard skin or case over a softer but tougher core. To carburize the surface, the steel is heated to carburizing temperature in the presence of carbon in the form of hydrocarbon gas (gas carburizing), salt baths (salt-bath carburizing, charcoal or coke (pack carburizing).

The steel is then quenched. The depth of the case is controlled by several factors, including the carbon content of the carburizing media and the time of exposure to the media at the carburizing temperature.

Case hardening is a form of pack carburizing in which the surface colors and patterns depend upon both the carbonaceous materials used (charcoal, charred leather, bone, coke, etc.) as well as the quenching medium. In general, the most vivid case-hardened colors are produced by a water quench.

Other Hardening Methods

Other techniques for improving steel hardness include induction hardening and gas nitriding.

In induction hardening, a powerful electrical current quickly raises the steel's surface temperature in a localized area to austenitizing temperature. The time spent at this temperature determines the depth of the hard case produced. Induction hardening is quick, efficient and produces less distortion than heat-treatment of the entire part. Some bolt-action rifle receivers, for example, are induction-hardened only in the receiver ring and extraction cam on the receiver bridge.

Gas nitriding is a process by which a thin case of super-hard nitrides is produced, either by exposure of heated metal to a nitriding gas or by immersion in a hot bath of nitriding salts. The exceptional wear resistance of the nitride skin makes the process desirable for drill bits as well as lathe and milling cutters, whose service life is increased several-fold by the process. Some nitride coatings also increase lubricity. A frequently used process coats metal parts with titanium nitride, which is recognizable by its gold color.

Work Hardening

Work hardening is the hardening of a metal that occurs from deformation such as hammering, bending, drawing and rolling. It is the result of molecular compression of the metal. Annealing is required to restore the machinability, malleability and ductility of a work-hardened part.

Additional Gunmaking Materials

After World War II, rapid growth in materials sciences quickly yielded new alloys of aluminum and steel as well as synthetic materials such as plastics. In recent years, new metal alloys and synthetic materials have found their way into firearm designs, making firearms cheaper, lighter, stronger, more reliable, more durable and more corrosion resistant. Today, synthetic materials and new metal alloys have profoundly influenced the way firearms are designed and manufactured.

Aluminum

Aluminum has become the second most important metal in gunmaking after steel. An ever-increasing number of firearms, especially handguns and shotguns, utilize aluminum alloys for slides, frames, receivers and the like.

Alloys of aluminum have become popular for gunmaking as they offer a high strength-to-weight ratio. A part made of aluminum will be about 35 percent the weight of the same part made of steel. Aluminum alloys can also offer tensile strengths in excess of 80,000 p.s.i. This is nearly the same strength of some common carbon steels such as AISI/SAE 1035 and 1045. However this is only about half the strength of the best steel alloys used in gun production such as AISI/SAE 4340 or 17-4 PH. While aluminum is tough and corrosion-resistant, it is not as hard nor as wear-resistant as steel. As a result, aluminum is unsuitable for barrels and rarely used for bolts, breechblocks, center-fire rifle receivers or pistol slides.

Aluminum is obtained from bauxite ore. The metal is extracted from the ore using an electrically powered smelting process similar to that used to produce iron. Like steel, aluminum is usually alloyed with other elements such as chromium, copper, magnesium, manganese, silicon, zinc, lithium and others.

Most types of aluminum are designated using a four-digit nomenclature system similar to that for steel. For aluminum alloys, the first digit signals the primary alloying element while modifications to the alloy are designated by the second digit. Other alloying elements are denoted by the third and fourth digits:

1 - - - at least 99.0 percent pure

2 - - - aluminum-copper alloy

3 - - - aluminum-manganese alloy

4 - - - aluminum-silicon alloy

5 - - - aluminum-magnesium alloy

6 - - - aluminum-magnesium-silicon alloy

7 - - - aluminum-zinc alloy.

Other numbers refer to aluminum alloys involving other elements. Additionally, as with steel, the properties of aluminum alloys can be enhanced by heat treatment or tempering. Each of the many methods used to heat-treat aluminum alloys is indicated by a suffix appended to the basic alloy number (e.g., 7075-T6).

High-strength applications, such as AR-15 upper and lower receivers as well as handgun and shotgun frames are made of any of several grades of "aircraft quality" aluminum having very high strength such as 6061 and 7075. The latter, an aluminum-zinc alloy, is popular for the manufacture of major gun components as it can be forged and heat-treated to high levels of strength.

Like steel, aluminum comes from the mill in different forms. Depending upon the alloy, aluminum alloy components may be fabricated by casting, machining, forging or welding. However aluminum cannot be brazed or silver-soldered.

Regardless of type or heat treatment method, aluminum alloys cannot be made as hard as heat-treated alloy steel. The surface hardness of aluminum parts can be raised significantly by hard anodizing (*see Chapter 12, Manufacturing*).

Brass

Brass is an alloy of copper containing between 5 and 40 percent zinc. Today, brass is most commonly used in ammunition manufacture for cartridge cases. Cartridge brass has a composition from 70 percent copper and 30 percent zinc (70/30) up to 85/15. Brass for bullet jackets is either a 95/5 or 90/10 alloy.

Historically, brass has been utilized for cannon barrels, gun frames and other major structural components, though many parts so described have been found to be made of bronze. Brass has also been traditionally used for stock furniture. Compared to bronze, brass is more ductile, cheaper and readily melts at lower temperatures. Although softer than bronze, brass is not as resistant to corrosion.

During the 19th century, brass was employed often in the frames of lever-action rifles and in the lower (grip) frames of revolvers. In modern arms, brass is used for the frames and furniture of many replica 18th- and 19th-century arms.

Bronze

In modern terminology, bronze may refer to a number of alloys of copper with various other elements such as tin, phosphorous and silicon.

Tin/copper bronzes are corrosion resistant, strong, hard and durable. As a result, they have long been used in structural gun components. Cast bronze was used for cannon-making as early as the 14th century. Five centuries later, the receivers of Winchester Model 1866 carbines were cast from a bronze alloy known as gunmetal, consisting of 80-88 percent copper, 10-15 percent tin and 2-5 percent zinc. Today, bronze is still used for components on reproductions of 18th- and 19th-century firearms, as well as in the bristles of bore brushes.

Titanium

Titanium is a high-tech metal, the alloys of which are winning growing acceptance in gunmaking. The fourth most abundant metal on earth, titanium offers several advantages over steel in firearm construction. Beneficially, titanium:

- offers the same strength as steel
- has better fatigue properties than steel
- is much lighter than steel
- has a very high melting point and is highly heat- and wear-resistant
- will not corrode on exposure to sweat, water, salts and common solvents.

Some titanium alloys, such as the titanium-vanadium or titanium-cobalt alloys used in firearms, have ultimate tensile strengths in the range of 150,000-170,000 p.s.i. This is comparable to many steel alloys and far stronger than aluminum alloys.

The density of titanium is about 56 percent of steel's density and roughly 1.5 times that of aluminum. Titanium's combination of strength and low density allows the manufacture of firearms considerably lighter than steel arms, but without compromising strength.

Despite its many positive characteristics, titanium has several limitations for firearms manufacture. Namely, titanium:

- is expensive
- requires special machining, welding and forging techniques
- is not as erosion-resistant as many stainless steels
- can not be effectively hardened to the level required for some gun parts
- is not as stiff as steel which is reflected in its resiliency and elasticity.

The elasticity of titanium precludes its use in barrels, as it won't hold rifling. Most commonly, a titanium shroud encompasses a steel barrel or cylinder liner. This limits titanium in guns to revolver frames and cylinders, barrel shrouds, pistol frames, rifle receivers and many smaller parts, such as firing pins. Many of these are produced from forgings, though some parts, such as revolver cylinders, are machined from extrusions.

Abrasive cleaners should not be used on titanium guns, as they can harm the protective surface layer on the metal, decreasing its wear resistance. Also note that the solvent trichloroethylene can cause embrittlement of titanium.

Limited-Use Metals

Chromium

Chromium is very resistant to corrosion, wear and heat. It has three common uses in firearms production:

- as an alloying agent of steel and stainless steel
- as an anti-corrosion plating on firearms
- as a wear-resistant plating in bores.

Chromium is not only very hard with a high melting point, it also increases lubricity.

Copper

Historically, copper has long been an important metal in gun and ammunition manufacture. Its characteristics of ductility and malleability made it a popular choice for use in bullet jackets and cartridge cases. Its resistance to corrosion made it a popular material for blackpowder flasks. It was also used decoratively. Today, it is still used for all these purposes and additionally as an important alloying agent in steel, brass, bronze and silver-solder. Copper can be work-hardened, but lacks strength for structural or high-stress firearm components such as frames, receivers, cylinders or barrels.

Some exotic copper alloys have seen limited use in firearm manufacturing.

- Beryllium-copper is the strongest and most abrasion-resistant of the non-ferrous metals and is easily heat-treated and

corrosion-resistant. It is sometimes used to make extractors.
- Aluminum-bronze combines strength and corrosion resistance. It was used to make barrels in the blackpowder era.

Gold

In gunmaking, gold has been used almost exclusively for decoration as its physical properties are unsuited for any structural purpose. Gold has been utilized in several ways:

gold leaf—an exceptionally thin foil produced by hammering and/or rolling

amalgam—a liquid solution of gold and mercury applied to a metal surface, then heated to vaporize the mercury

gilding—a form of powdered gold applied to a metal surface that has been coated with an adhesive substance called sizing

inlay—a thin piece of gold fitted into a shallow recess in the gun surface with undercut edges, then hammered to lock the gold piece into the undercut

overlay—a thin gold piece soldered onto the gun surface

gold plate—a thin coating of gold laid down by an electro-deposition process.

As with jewelry, the addition of alloy agents such as copper, silver, platinum, nickel and zinc is utilized to produce gold of different colors.

Lead

Lead has been inextricably linked to firearms manufacture from the very beginning. While lead does not have physical characteristic for use in structural applications, it has and continues to play a pivotal role in three areas relevant to firearms:

- as the core for bullets and the main ingredient of shot
- as the base metal in lead styphnate primers
- as a key ingredient in solder and metal alloys.

Today, the toxic aspects of lead have fueled efforts to reduce its use in ammunition.

Columbium

This rare metal has all the characteristics for making the perfect rifle barrel:

- It is easily machined.
- It is substantially more resistant to heat and erosion than any stainless steel.
- It is highly resistant to corrosion.
- It has suitable yield strength, modulus of elasticity, and other characteristics.

The major drawbacks to columbium are scarcity and very high cost.

These limit its application to Gatling-type guns where the high cost can be traded against its superior resistance to heat and erosion.

Nickel

Nickel is commonly used in firearms production for three purposes:

- as an alloy to improve the strength and resistance to erosion and corrosion of steel
- combined with copper and zinc to form the alloy nickel silver (55-75 percent copper, 5-30 percent nickel, 10-15 percent zinc) used for decorative purposes on firearms and accessories
- as a plating applied to the surface of firearms to improve corrosion resistance.

Platinum

As platinum is very expensive, it is used primarily today in the gun industry for decorative inlays and overlays. However, platinum's resistance to corrosion and heat led some gunmakers in the flintlock era to use it in the barrel touch-hole and as an overlay on the flash pan. Additionally, platinum's ability to be drawn into extremely fine wires has led to its use in optical sight reticles.

Scandium

Scandium is a rare earth metal discovered in 1879. In pure form, it is relatively soft with a high melting point. Its main value for firearm manufacture is as an alloying element for aluminum. The benefits of aluminum-scandium alloys were initially investigated by Russian scientists in the 1970s. They found that the addition of small amounts of scandium as an alloying agent made aluminum's grain structure finer as well as:

- considerably stronger than other aluminum alloys
- more fatigue-resistant
- virtually corrosion-proof
- lighter and less expensive than titanium alloys.

These properties led to the use of aluminum-scandium alloys for many aerospace applications. In the firearms industry, aluminum-scandium alloys have been used in lightweight, high-strength revolver frames.

Silver

Like gold and platinum, silver has seen use in gunmaking primarily as:

- decorative metal in overlays, inlays and electroplate
- as a component of silver-solder used to make superior metal-to-metal bonds.

Stellite

Stellite is a proprietary product of the Deloro Stellite Company. It consists of a family of some 20 cobalt-based alloys that also contain chromium and other metals. Stellite is very hard and offers superior resistance to erosion, corrosion and wear at high temperature. These properties have led to the use of Stellite for partially lining machine-gun barrels to prevent excessive wear during sustained fire.

Tin

Tin has always played a significant role in firearms and ammunition manufacture. It has been used as a:

- constituent along with lead for soft solder
- as an alloy of bronze and pewter
- as a protective plating for cartridge cases and gun parts in the 19th century
- as an alloy metal for steel and other metals.

Tungsten

Tungsten is a heavy metal more than three times the density of steel that is exceptionally resistant to heat, wear and corrosion. While it is seldom used in gun parts, tungsten carbide alloys are popular choices for cutters, extrusion dies and other production tooling subject to wear and heat. Used as an alloying element, it increases the wear and heat resistance of steel. Its great weight and hardness in comparison to steel makes it ideal for applications in armor-piercing projectiles. In recent years, tungsten has become a common component in shot pellets used for waterfowl hunting.

Zinc

Zinc is another metal with a long history of use in gun manufacturing. It is a vital alloy in the manufacture of cartridge brass, bullet jackets and as an alloy of other metals. Zinc alloys such as Zamak are a popular choice for casting lightweight, low-to-moderate-strength gun parts such as trigger guards, levers and the frames of .22 LR revolvers and small-caliber, blowback-operated semi-automatics. Zinc has also been used to make lightweight bullets having the same dimensions as lead-core projectiles but with roughly a 50 percent weight reduction, as well as considerably greater hardness than pure lead projectiles.

Wood

Historical records indicate the use of wood for making gunstocks may be traced to the earliest hand-held firearms. As a material, wood is strong, light, plentiful and easy to shape. However, not all woods are suitable for gunstocks. A gunstock requires a strong, dense wood that will stand up to hard use. This limits substantially the number of suitable woods. Over history, nearly every type of wood has been tried for gun stocks. However, few woods have been found to be better than walnut.

Walnut is plentiful, dense, strong and relatively inexpensive. However, beech, maple, laurel, and many other woods are also suitable. *(For further information see Chapter 7, Stocks.)*

Synthetic Materials

Contemporary firearm design is increasingly reaping the benefits of advances in materials science, particularly in the area of synthetics. Man-made materials are now ubiquitous in modern guns, having supplanted metal and wood for components such as stocks, trigger guards, frames, grip panels, magazines, followers, sights and many small parts.

In the past, gun designers focused on designing the firearm, giving only limited consideration to materials and manufacturing methods. It was assumed that a firearm would be made from steel, the exact type of which would be determined by making and testing prototypes. Essentially, this left considerations of materials and manufacturing methods to production personnel. The result was that very often a good gun design proved very difficult and expensive to manufacture.

Today, a gun designer must take an active role in determining the proper materials and the exact manufacturing methods from the very beginning. Modern synthetic materials have dramatically expanded the possible methods used to manufacture firearms and gun designers have had to become much more cognizant of materials, production methods and costs.

Polymers

A polymer is a high-molecular-weight material made up of from 50 to many millions of smaller repeating units, called "monomers," that are chemically linked. While most commercially useful polymers are synthetic, many natural polymers exist such as cellulose, rubber and protein.

Polymers commonly take the form of molecular chains with a carbon backbone. A polymer containing two or more different monomers is called a copolymer. There are two major classes of polymers: plastics and elastomers. Both types of materials are utilized in firearms manufacture.

Plastics

Many synthetic materials used in contemporary firearms manufacturing are known as plastics. These are organic polymers formed from resins using pressure and heat. Organic polymers take the form of a high molecular-weight solid or semi-solid having no fixed melting point. Typically, they are flexible, non-conducting and resistant to water and many common solvents. However, they have low strength. Plastics are made from petrochemicals in contrast to natural polymers.

Plastics have been commercially produced for more than 140 years. The first such material was Parkesine, based on cellulose nitrate and patented in 1861 by English inventor Alexander Parkes. In 1870, American inventor John Wesley Hyatt patented celluloid, also based on cellulose nitrate. Among the first uses of celluloid was in billiard balls, to replace ivory (indeed, this was the original stimulus for his invention), and in dental plates. Probably the first plastic widely used in the firearms industry was Bakelite, a hard material invented in 1907. Often substituting for ebony or ivory, Bakelite found use in handgun grips and the pistol-grip caps of long-gun stocks.

There are two types of plastic materials: thermoplastics and thermosetting resins. Thermoplastics formed into specific parts can be heated and reformed to another shape with no loss of chemical or physical properties. Thermosetting resins, such as epoxies, undergo a chemical reaction when they are formed under heat and pressure that prevents them from returning to the plastic state.

There are an almost infinite number of plastic materials, with more being added constantly. Depending upon the type of monomers used and how they are arranged (i.e. sheet, three-dimensional lattice, etc.), different properties can be produced. Some plastics are tough, hard and can be machined. Others are extremely flexible and elastic. The properties of plastics can be further modified through the addition of plasticizers which are low-molecular-weight chemical agents that make plastic softer and more pliable.

Plastics can be divided into a number of chemical groups, such as:

- acrylonitrile, butadiene and styrene (ABS)
- acetal resins
- epoxy resins
- fluorocarbon resins
- polyamides (better known as nylon)
- polyvinyl chloride (PVC)
- phenolic resins
- polyethylene
- polystyrene
- polycarbonate
- polyester
- polypropylene.

Note that the term following "poly" denotes the monomer used to create the plastic, e.g. polyethylene is made up of long chains of ethylene. These chemical groups are important primarily to chemists, materials scientists and engineers who must choose or design a material having the specific properties needed for each application.

Reinforced plastics are composite materials that combine a strengthening material, such as glass fibers, with a plastic.

Elastomers

Elastomers are flexible, soft materials that will stretch two or more times their initial length when a force is applied, then immediately return to their original shape when the force is removed. Both natural and synthetic rubbers are elastomers.

Polymers Used in Gunmaking

Out of the thousands of polymers available, only a relatively small number have been used in firearms manufacture.

Delrin

Delrin is trademarked name for an extremely hard, strong and stiff acetal resin that is also resistant to fatigue, wear and abrasion. Delrin has high dimensional stability and resistance to solvents as well as a low coefficient of friction. These characteristics make it a popular choice for bearings and bushings. For firearms, Delrin is often chosen for magazine wells and bore guides.

Epoxy

Epoxies are thermosetting resins having wide and varied use in firearms production. They are characterized by strong adhesion, great strength, toughness, and resistance to moisture and chemicals. Epoxy usually requires a curing agent or hardener to turn the resin solid at room temperature.

Epoxy adhesives are widely used in the firearms industry to repair wood and synthetic stocks, for bedding actions to stocks and to attach fore-end tips and pistol grip caps. It is also a major constituent in various metal finishes. When strengthened with materials such as carbon fiber, Kevlar and glass fibers, it is used in the production of synthetic stocks.

Kydex

An inexpensive, proprietary acrylic-polyvinyl chloride polymer, Kydex combines excellent stiffness with formability, strength, toughness and flexibility. This material also offers impact and chemical resistance, thermal stability, excellent memory and a good surface finish. As a result of these properties, Kydex has become popular for use in molding synthetic holsters.

Nylon

A polyamide material, nylon is one of the oldest polymers, being first commercially produced in 1935. Nylons are strong, tough and flexible, stable over a wide range of temperatures and resistant to chemicals and abrasion.

Nylon may be the single most important polymer in firearm production. Its strength has enabled its use in polymer handgun frames such as those from Glock, Smith & Wesson, STI and others, as well as in stocks under the trade name Zytel.

Nylon has been used to make holsters, recoil buffers, bolt handles, magazine bodies, followers and base pads. In some applications, nylon may be reinforced by glass fibers (*see Composites*). Nylon is also used for tools such as punches, hammers and bench blocks where a hard, non-marring material is needed. Finally, nylon bristles are used in brushes and in some epoxy bedding compounds.

Other Plastics

Other plastics used in gun making include:

- polypropylene—rifle stocks
- polyurethane—rifle stocks, non-marring receiver fixtures for gunsmiths
- polyethylene—magazine followers, shotshell tubes, shotshell wads
- polycarbonate—lenses in shooting glasses, .22 rimfire boxes
- ABS—gun cases.

Rubber and Other Elastomers

Rubber is an elastomer that finds use in firearm applications in the form of recoil-absorbing buttpads, recoil buffers, O-rings, gas seals and ear plugs. Synthetic rubbers such as silicone rubber, neoprene (polychloroprene), polyisoprene and polybutadiene are popular choices for such gun parts. Some polyurethane elastomers, such as Sorbathane are used as recoil-absorbing buttpads.

Hard rubber is natural rubber that has been converted to a hard, non-resilient material through prolonged vulcanization that requires the addition of sulfur in the presence of heat. Hard rubber is employed mostly in stocks for handguns, as well as buttplates and pistol-grip caps on long-gun stocks.

Kevlar

Kevlar is a polymer material consisting of aramid fiber that is a highly oriented, long-chain polyamide with aromatic rings. The advantages Kevlar offers to gun designers and manufacturers are strength, toughness, dimensional stability and resistance to cutting and to chemicals. Perhaps best known for its use in bulletproof vests, Kevlar is often used to reinforce fiberglass composite stocks.

Non-Polymer Synthetics

While polymers make up the bulk of synthetic materials used in manufacturing firearms, non-polymer materials have recently found application. The two main materials of this type are carbon or graphite fiber and fiberglass.

Fiberglass

Fiberglass consists of small-diameter glass fibers produced by mechanically drawing molten glass into filaments. The filaments are combined in strands used in continuous, mat or woven forms, or cut into segments to be embedded into a polymer matrix.

Fiberglass is a popular reinforcing material for manufacture of composite stocks and pistol frames. It has also been used to reinforce steel barrels, gun cases and wood stocks.

Carbon Fiber/Graphite

Both carbon fiber and graphite fiber are forms of nearly pure carbon. However, the carbon or graphite used for reinforcing composite stocks and pistol frames has little in common with the soft, brittle substance in lead pencils.

The molecular structure of carbon and graphite takes the form of thin layers or sheets of atoms. While the molecular bonds between the atoms within a sheet are strong, the bonds between the layers of sheets are weak. To make carbon fiber, the sheets of carbon are cut into long, thin ribbons then bundled together to form fibers about one-fifth the thickness of a human hair, but stronger than steel by weight. The properties of carbon fibers depend on the method of fabrication and the internal structure. Typically, carbon or graphite fibers are woven into tubes or sheets, which are then used to reinforce epoxy resins.

Although some references recognize only carbon fibers, others distinguish between fibers containing 93-95 percent carbon (graphite fibers) and those containing 99 percent or more carbon (carbon fibers). All carbon and graphite fibers, however, have high resistance to heat, high strength and extremely high stiffness with natural vibration damping. They are also lightweight and impervious to water and most common solvents and chemicals.

However, carbon and graphite fiber is very expensive and labor intensive as it must be hand laid into molds.

Composites

A composite material is formed from the bonding of two or more dissimilar materials. The properties of the composite material will incorporate those of the individual components. For this reason, the components of a composite are selected so as to create a synergistic blend of attributes.

Composites may take many forms such as laminated and/or orientated layers, fibers embedded randomly in a matrix and particles embedded in a matrix. Some composites may combine two or more of these forms.

Most synthetic materials used in gun manufacture are made from composites. Composites must be strong, stiff, lightweight, stable and resistant to impacts and solvents. This combination of characteristics can only be achieved by carefully combining two or more materials.

The most popular use of composite materials in gunmaking is for synthetic stocks. Many synthetic rifle stocks are molded of an epoxy base material reinforced with hand-laid sheets of woven fiberglass cloth. Fiberglass stocks are often reinforced with the addition of Kevlar cloth in high-stress areas to add strength and carbon or graphite fiber to add stiffness. Fiberglass and Kevlar may also be added to polyurethane, polypropylene and nylon for the production of both handgun and long-gun stocks.

Other fiberglass-reinforced composites of interest in stock production include Rynite (polyethylene terephthalate) and Tenite (a celluose-based plastic).

Fiberglass-filled polymers are commonly used in the manufacture of gun cases and other firearms accessories. Fiberglass-filled polymers typically consist of short, small-diameter fiberglass strands randomly embedded in a molded plastic material such as nylon, polyurethane or polypropylene.

Bedding compounds are composite materials that may contain nylon, fiberglass and/or metal particles embedded in an epoxy matrix.

Some polymer handgun frames and shotgun receivers may contain embedded or molded-in metal parts that act as stiffeners, guides for reciprocating parts or as mating surfaces. A few hybrid designs utilize a composite lower frame with an upper metal frame.

Future Materials

As the science of materials continues to expand rapidly, the demand for firearms that are lighter, stronger, cheaper, more reliable and more resistant to wear and corrosion will assure that new materials are incorporated into firearms manufacturing technology as soon as practicable.

Metals

Improvements in steel alloys, especially stainless steels, will assure this traditional metal a significant place in future gunmaking. New steel alloys will focus on improved machinability, greater resistance to erosion and wear, and lower manufacturing costs. Expect significant advances in treatments for steel barrels such as cryogenic stress relief, gas nitride hardening and electronic polishing and hardening. New surface treatments such as precision chrome-lining and titanium nitride coating will significantly enhance the performance of steel in firearms service.

New alloys of aluminum and other non-ferrous metals may enable these to approach steel's strength, hardness and stiffness, possibly making a rifled aluminum barrel possible. The use of titanium alloys will spread as the cost comes down, machining techniques are perfected and demand for weight reduction and corrosion resistance increases.

Synthetic Materials

Future polymers will be stronger, stiffer, harder, lighter and more heat- and wear-resistant than those currently in use. These will permit the use of synthetic materials for a greater range of stressed firearm components such as bolts, both with and without metal reinforcement. One of the possibilities may be polyimides, a remarkable class of polymers having sufficient strength, heat and chemical resistance to substitute for metals in some applications. When filled with fiberglass, carbon fiber or boron fiber, they can be used in high-stress and structural applications.

Other new firearms applications could include a lightweight, carbon fiber-reinforced polymer receiver, telescopic sight tube, bipod, metal sight or magazine. Undoubtedly, a key area of future polymer research will include development of materials that efficiently absorb recoil.

Composites

The area of greatest potential undoubtedly is that of composites. There are many new areas for potential composite exploration here including polymer/metals, polymer/ceramics and metal/ceramics. A new class of so-called metal/ceramic matrix composites are expected to show special promise.

Ceramics show particularly great promise as they offer high heat tolerance, strength, stiffness, hardness, low density and resistance to wear and chemicals. However, by themselves, ceramics are brittle and lack toughness. When reinforced with fibers of carbide or nitride or with metals, new materials are produced offering many of the benefits of ceramics, but with greater toughness. Such composites could, in the future, be used for gun components.

In the more distant future, we may see engineered, man-made materials using Fullerenes and/or nanotubes. These materials will be designed at the molecular level to offer the characteristics required for each application. They will combine unheard-of levels of strength, light weight, toughness and stiffness, along with heat- and wear-resistance.

Chapter 12
MANUFACTURING

For centuries, gunmaking techniques remained unchanged. Casting, boring, machining, forging and welding all played familiar, well-established roles in firearm manufacture. Firearms were made one-at-a-time by gunsmiths using their own interpretation of designs and concepts of quality. Parts were made to fit and were not interchangeable even in guns made by the same gunsmith. Hand-finishing of individual parts was the order of the day. If a part broke, a gunsmith had to fabricate a replacement part from scratch.

Then along came a clever American inventor named Eli Whitney. In the early 1800s Whitney developed a new way to make firearms. He did not change the traditional methods of firearms manufacture, but he did change the process.

Whitney pioneered the concept of a standardized firearm design with interchangeable parts made in large quantities to an established quality standard. Using Whitney's method of manufacture, large quantities of identical military muskets could be made quickly and at a lower cost. The concept of interchangeable parts spread rapidly to become the foundation for modern mass-production techniques still used today.

In the last half of the 20th century, however, science produced a flood of new materials, new methods for designing guns and new methods for working traditional materials that have virtually revolutionized firearm manufacture.

Despite the increasing use of synthetic materials and composites, metals remain the dominant choice of material for firearms components, such as barrels, frames, receivers, bolts, cylinders and trigger parts. Today, however, firearm manufacturers can select from a bewildering variety of manufacturing techniques and methods, ranging from the traditional to the esoteric, to produce a given metal part.

The choice of manufacturing method and technique is increasingly governed by cost, performance, availability and demand. Nothing may be assumed and tradition is now a minor consideration. The march of development is such that today's high-tech is tomorrow's taken for granted.

Manufacture and Fabrication of Metal Parts

Machining

Machining is a traditional manufacturing process that employs rotating or reciprocating cutter(s) to remove material from castings, forgings, bar stock, tubing, etc., to create a part having the required dimensions. There are three basic machine tools.

Lathe

Lathes rotate the unfinished part while a cutter removes material. A lathe can perform this in four basic ways:

- **Turning**—a cutter removes material from the part's surface
- **Boring**—a cutter creates or enlarges a longitudinal hole in the part
- **Facing**—cutting the end of the work square to the axis of rotation
- **Reaming**—enlarging a bored hole to an exact size.

Lathes have internal gearing that, when engaged, can advance the cutter at a particular rate per turn. This allows threads to be cut.

Mill

A mill holds the part in a vise on a table that can move in three axes in relation to the rotating cutter. By combining the cutter with movement of the table, a mill can produce complex shapes, drill holes and remove material from surfaces.

Drill Press

A drill press also has a table and a vise, but the cutter only moves vertically to produce a hole. Holes made by drills that are not the exact size required can be enlarged to the precise inside diameter using a reamer.

Other Machine Tools

Most firearm manufacturers also make extensive use of several other traditional, basic machine tools including:

- **Surface grinders**—a grinding wheel rotating at high speed removes material from a surface. A surface grinder is capable of making extremely fine cuts, removing less than 0.001" at a time if required.
- **Buffing wheels**—a fabric wheel impregnated with an abrasive buffing compound and turned at high speed is used to smooth or polish the surface of a metal part pressed against it.
- **Belt sanders**—a circular belt running between two rollers or a rapidly rotating sanding disk, is used for shaping and contouring of parts by hand.
- **Bench grinder**—a grinding wheel turned by a small motor is used for shaping and contouring small parts and sharpening cutters and other tools.

- **Sandblasters**—A directed stream of high-velocity compressed air and sand are used to clean metal parts and give them a uniform matte finish.

Traditionally, each machine tool performs a very limited number of operations. Batches of unfinished parts or work in progress are transferred by hand from one machine tool to another. Some parts may be in process for weeks or months before finishing depending on production flow and bottlenecks.

CNC

Most contemporary gunmakers now use computer-numeric-controlled (CNC) machining centers. These computer-controlled machines can perform multiple, sequential machining operations to a very high order of tolerance. They accomplish this by using a magazine of different cutting tools and a cutting head with a quick-change tool holder. In production, the raw metal parts are mounted in a fixture inside the machining center. The cutting head can move through two or three axes depending on the model. The computer selects the proper tool and makes the desired cuts on each part in rapid succession without the operator having to change tools or re-fixture the part. The computer even compensates for wear on individual tools and selects a backup if a tool is broken or worn out.

CNC equipment is fast, precise, efficient and capable of producing parts of superior quality. A single CNC machining center takes up less room than the lathes and mills it replaces, and several CNC centers can be run by a single operator. Now in their fourth generation, CNC machine centers are sophisticated, expensive machines that can quickly make complex parts for many hours without operator intervention.

Specialized Tools

Two special types of machine tools deserve mention for their specialized use in gun making.

- **Broach**—A broach is a specialized type of cutter that is pulled or pushed through a hole in a part. A series of successively higher cutting teeth set one behind the other on the surface of the broach cut slots or recesses in the hole in a single pass. Broaches are used for rifling barrels as well as to cut raceways in receivers of bolt-action rifles.
- **Rifling Machine**—A barrel-rifling machine for cut rifling looks somewhat like a lathe, but has special gearing and a sine bar to both advance and turn the rifling cutting tool in the bore.

Casting

Casting is the process of creating a part by pouring molten metal into a mold with an internal cavity in the shape of the desired part. After the metal in the cavity has cooled, the mold is opened and the part removed.

There are a number of casting methods commonly in use today:

Sand casting—This ancient process is still used for many metal castings. A pattern or replica of the desired part is created, then sandwiched between the halves of a two-piece mold filled with special sand mixed with a binder. The pattern leaves impressions in the sand when it is removed. Molten metal is poured into the mold, allowed to cool and the mold opened to remove the part. The sand can be cleaned and reused. Sand casting is simple and economical but does not produce parts with tight tolerances.

Plaster casting—This technique begins with a two-piece mold body and two separate patterns, each representing half the desired part. Each pattern half is placed in its respective mold body half and coated with liquid plaster. After the plaster hardens, the pattern halves are removed, the mold halves joined together and molten metal poured into the mold. When the metal part has cooled, the mold is opened and the part removed. Plaster casting can be used only with non-ferrous metals, but it is capable of holding much tighter tolerances than sand casting.

Investment or lost-wax casting—This is one of the most commonly used casting methods for manufacturing firearm components and also one of the oldest. This method begins with a replica of the desired part made from wax, then coated with a liquid ceramic material. Next, the ceramic mold is baked to harden it and vaporize or drain the wax from the mold (hence the "lost wax" name). Molten metal is then poured into the mold to create the part. After cooling, the mold is broken open to obtain the part. The part is then placed in a special oven where it is heated and subjected to very high pressure (hipped), which crushes any voids that remain.

Investment casting produces parts with excellent tolerances in complex shapes that would be difficult to machine. It is also an excellent technique for high-temperature metals, such as stainless steel. Both small action parts and large components, such as handgun frames and slides and rifle receivers, are often produced by this method.

Die casting—This term describes two different, but similar, processes. Both processes employ a two-piece mold made of graphite, steel or similar materials.

- **Gravity die casting**—In this technique, molten metal is poured into the mold using only the force of gravity. After the metal hardens, the mold is opened and the part removed. Gravity die casting requires metals that will fill the mold under only the force of gravity. These tend to be metals having low melting points such as iron, aluminum and magnesium alloys. Steel can be cast with this technique using special molds.
- **Pressure die casting**—In this process, molten metal is injected

into an alloy steel mold under pressure to ensure that large or complex mold cavities are fully filled out. This process is capable of turning out parts very quickly to tight tolerances. For technical reasons, however, high-pressure die casting is usually limited to non-ferrous metals such as aluminum, lead, magnesium, zinc and others.

The casting process allows quick production of metal parts with minimal wastage. Complex shapes can be cast, decreasing the machining required to finish the part. However, cast parts have several drawbacks:

- They often shrink from the as-cast size, so molds must be properly proportioned to allow for this shrinkage.
- Internal voids or imperfections may be present that weaken the part.
- Casting leaves a rough surface finish.
- Certain types of metal casting molds are expensive.

These concerns were more of an issue in earlier years and they are rarely encountered in modern guns.

Forging

Forging is the process of shaping metals by means of plastic deformation produced by impact or pressure.

There are many different ways of forging metal:

- **Smith forging**—This process shapes metal by manually impacting the heated part with a hammer as blacksmiths have done for millennia.
- **Hammer forging**—This is basically a mechanized, larger-scale version of smith forging. In firearms manufacture, hammer forging is often used to make barrels and receivers. Hammer forging can be used with hot (hot-hammer forged) metal preforms or with cold (cold-hammer forged) metal preforms. To make a hammer-forged barrel, a cylindrical pre-form both shorter and larger in diameter than the finished barrel, is put into the hammer forging machine. This slug has a lengthwise hole larger than the final bore diameter. A mandrel with a surface having the rifling pattern in reverse relief is inserted into the preform. As the preform is pulled through the forging machine, a series of radial-mounted hammers compress the walls of the preform inward around the mandrel. When the process is complete, the barrel is essentially at its final dimensions and surface finish. If desired, the chamber can also be hammer forged.
- **Drop forging**—Drop forging employs a two-piece die set, each half machined to form a cavity in the shape of half the finished part. The lower die is held on a stationary fixture while the upper die is attached to a hammer that can be dropped on the stationary fixture. A heated piece of metal is placed between the die halves.

The impact of the upper die against the lower forces the hot metal to fill the cavities in the die. Often, several hammer strokes are needed to form the part.

- **Impact forging**—This is a similar process to drop forging except the impact is produced by the collision of two moving hammers, each containing half of the die.
- **Press forging**—Press forging is a non-impact form of forging in which high pressure, not impact, is used to forge a heated piece of metal between the die halves.
- **Roll forging**—In this process, the heated steel is forced between two rollers or wheels that decrease its diameter or thickness and increase its length. This adds strength while also changing its dimensions.

Most forgings require additional machining to finish critical engagement surfaces or to achieve a proper surface finish. Forging also requires costly equipment.

Forged parts are generally considered superior in strength and resistance to fatigue and impact to cast parts. Not only are internal voids and imperfections virtually nonexistent in modern forged parts, but forging also compresses the metal and aligns the grain structure along lines of plastic deformation, which produces directional strength.

Forging can introduce stresses into the metal, but these can be removed using a stress relief process. In gunmaking, many parts are of forged steel or aluminum.

Metal Injection Molding

Metal injection molding (MIM) was developed in the 1980s as an improvement over conventional forms of metal casting. In this process, finely powdered metal particles are combined with a polymer binder, then injected into a heated mold. After cooling, the part is removed from the mold, then heated (sintered) in a vacuum furnace at a temperature over 2,000 degrees F. The heat vaporizes the binding agent and fuses the metal particles together, creating a solid metal part having the same mechanical properties as a part of wrought metal of the same type. Eliminating the binding agent normally causes the part to shrink 20 to 40 percent from its as-cast size. For this reason, MIM molds must be at least 20 percent oversize to allow for part shrinkage during the sintering stage.

MIM offers several advantages to firearm manufacturers:

- MIM can produce a net part with a complex shape to close tolerances.
- In most cases, a MIM part can be put into service without additional machining.

MIM is best suited for small, complex parts that would be difficult to make with other metalworking technologies, or that would require extensive machining. Many small firearm action parts, such as hammers, triggers and levers, are made from carbon and stainless steel using the MIM process.

Sintered Metal and Powdered Metal

Sintered metal manufacturing is a process for producing small metal parts by compacting powdered metal in a die while heating it to a point below the melting point of the metal. The heat and pressure effectively bonds or welds the metal particles together, increasing density and strength, decreasing porosity, and promoting the formation of grain and crystalline patterns.

Powdered-metal manufacturing is a process for producing metal parts by compacting powdered metal in a die, normally in the absence of heat (cold pressing).

Sintering and powder-metal processes offer several advantages:

- The parts formed are net or require very little finish machining.
- Parts made by either method are strong and durable.
- Such parts are cheap and relatively easy to manufacture.

Both processes allow different metals to be easily mixed to yield parts with specific properties.

Stamping

Stamping is a modern metal fabrication technique often used to make small, lightweight parts for firearms, such as magazine followers, fire-control levers, primer anvils and even receivers. Stamping is similar to forging except:

- Stampings are normally made from rolls of sheet metal.
- The part is formed by a punch moving through a die or die stack.
- A stamping press is much smaller than a forging machine.
- Stampings are lighter than forgings and not as strong.
- Most stampings are made by multiple die sets that cut out and form several identical parts at once cookie-cutter fashion with each stroke of the machine.

Stampings can be made from steel, aluminum, copper, magnesium and other malleable and ductile metals.

In gunmaking, stamped-steel components came into widespread use in Germany just prior to World War II. After considerable research, German firearms makers perfected stamping methods for making large firearms parts such as receivers for several military firearms such as the MP38/MP40, G43, Stg 44 and MG42. During the war, Great Britain and the U.S. answered with the STEN and M3.

Today, many military rifles and machine guns utilize stamped-steel components, such as receivers, magazine wells, fire-control assemblies and stock fittings. Often, the only machined parts are the bolt, carrier, barrel and a handful of smaller parts, such as pins and screws.

The stamping process can produce parts to fairly strict tolerances and in quantity with great speed.

Other Methods of Metal Machining and Forming

In addition to the traditional methods of metal machining and forming metals detailed above, modern science has given the firearms industry several new processes.

Electrical Discharge Machining

Electrical discharge machining (EDM) is a relatively new process for removing metal without cutting tools. A pre-form or blank of the part is fastened to a fixture immersed in a dielectric (insulating) liquid. An electrode is then brought into close proximity to the blank part. When current is applied to the electrode, an electrical discharge or spark jumps the gap between the electrode and the part. As it does so, it vaporizes a small amount of metal from the part. A successive series of spark discharges remove the desired amount of metal from the part.

EDM can produce a wide variety of profiles, holes and cavities by varying the:

- electrical current
- the composition and configuration of the electrode
- the movement and position of the electrode.

In many examples, a shape can be created with EDM that would be difficult or impossible to form using conventional machining techniques, e.g., square-sided blind holes. The EDM process is noted for its ability to cut burr-free holes with an even surface finish without inducing stress in the metal part. EDM is also very useful for shaping parts from metals that are difficult or impossible to machine, e.g., tungsten carbide.

The characteristics of the EDM process make it useful in barrel porting, making dies and cutting the raceways in bolt-action rifle receivers.

A variation of this process is known as wire EDM. This uses a thin wire to serve as the electrode for cutting complex shapes such as triggers, hammers and the like.

Laser Machining

This process uses a powerful, focused beam of laser light to cut, melt or vaporize metal. Laser cutters are capable of making a very precise cut without introducing stress in the part. And, there are no tools or cutters to break or sharpen. Laser machining is capable of easily cutting metals that are difficult or impossible to machine using traditional methods.

Arc Cutting

Metals that are difficult to cut by traditional methods can be shaped using an electric arc to melt away unwanted metal. This process is presently used mainly for cutting exotic alloys for aerospace applications.

Electrochemical Machining (ECM)

This relatively new process utilizes an electrolytic process to remove metal. This is accomplished by means of an electrode in an electrolytic (current carrying) liquid.

Chemical Machining

Chemical machining employs acids that will attack metals at known rates. The acids are applied precisely to targeted areas of the metal and allowed to attack its surface for a carefully defined period of time. At the end of the period, the acid is neutralized by various chemical means to end the metal removal process. A good surface finish and a high order of precision are possible in metals difficult or impossible to machine by traditional methods.

Metal Joining

Firearms manufacture often involves techniques for joining metal parts. Examples include brazing bolt handles to the bolt body of rifles, soldering ventilated ribs to shotgun barrels and silver-soldering shotgun barrels into monoblocks. The metal-joining techniques most frequently utilized in firearms production are welding, brazing and soldering.

Welding

Welding is a process of joining two or more metal parts using heat, and sometimes pressure, to melt the parts together at their junction. In most types of welding, a rod of the appropriate material is brought into contact with the molten metal at the junction between two parts to contribute additional material for a stronger joint.

Most metals can be welded and there are several forms of welding.

- **Forge welding**—This traditional process has been used by blacksmiths, swordsmiths and gun makers for over 1,000 years. The pieces of metal are heated on a wood or coke fire until they are red hot, then hammered together on an anvil or around a mandrel to form one piece.

- **Gas welding**—This technique differs from forge welding primarily in the way heat is applied to the parts. In gas welding, compressed gases, such as acetylene and oxygen, are used to heat the parts.

- **Electric welding**—There are two variants of this process. Electrical-resistance welding utilizes the heat created by electrical resistance of current flowing through the work. In electrical arc welding the heat for melting is produced by an electric arc crossing the air gap between the electrode and the parts.

- **Inert gas welding**—Because many metals oxidize readily, for the best possible weld it is desirable to shield the weld from oxygen as it is being made. A popular, modern welding technique directs a stream of inert gas, such as helium or argon, around the arc between the electrode and the part.

- **Spot welding**—This type of welding is often used to join stamped-steel parts such as those on modern military rifles. This is a form of resistance welding in which electrical current passed through both pieces joins at a spot where the parts contact each other. The heat from resistance to the current melts both pieces sufficiently to fuse them together at that spot. Typically, a series of spots is used to join two pieces of metal.
- **Friction welding**—Two metal parts at room temperature are pressed together then rotated or oscillated quickly. The resultant friction between the two parts at the points of contact melt the metal. When the movement is stopped, the two parts are welded together as the hot surfaces cool.

Welding is capable of creating joints as strong as the material being joined. However, the high heat of welding can induce stresses in the metal, changing its dimensions, increasing its hardness and mitigating the effects of careful heat treatment. Welded firearms parts subjected to stress such as frames, receivers and cylinders, must be re-heat-treated. Even unstressed parts that don't require re-heat-treatment after welding must be annealed before further machining.

Brazing

Brazing is a process in which two pieces of metal are joined using a non-ferrous filler alloy. In practice, both pieces are brought to a temperature of approximately 840 degrees F, high enough to melt the filler metal, but below the melting points of the metals to be joined. The filler metal flows by capillary action between the pieces to be joined, bonding to both. Many ferrous and non-ferrous metals can be joined by brazing; the technique even allows pieces of dissimilar metals to be united.

Filler metals used in brazing are usually based on alloys of aluminum, copper, bronze and silver. In gunmaking, brazing involving silver-based alloys (inaccurately called silver-soldering) is often employed to attach sights, ventilated ribs, bolt handles and the like.

The surfaces to be joined by brazing are coated with flux, a paste-like substance that removes surface oxides and prevents them from re-forming. Flux also promotes the flow of molten brazing alloy into the joint and promotes adherence of the brazing metal with the work pieces being joined. There are many different types of fluxes.

Brazed joints are strong, but not as strong as welded joints. Compared to welding, brazing involves less heat and so produces less distortion in the joined parts. Provided the temperature is kept low, brazing may not produce changes in hardness or other properties that welding sometimes causes. However, re-heat-treatment of some components may be necessary.

Soldering

Soldering is a process similar to brazing in that a filler metal (solder) and flux are used with heat to join two pieces of metal.

Normal soldering alloy melts below 800 degrees F and consists of
equal parts tin and lead or silver and antimony. Soldered joints are
not as strong as brazed joints and for this reason soldered joints are
often called soft-solder joints. In gunmaking, a variety of metals,
such as steel, brass, bronze, copper, silver and zinc, may be joined by
soldering.

Sweating is a term for a particular soldering technique in which
the parts to be joined are first tinned, or given a light coating of solder
on the mating surfaces. The parts are then clamped tightly together in
proper alignment and heated until the solder in the joint melts. Heating
opens the pores in the base metal to increase adhesion of the solder and
thus the strength of the joint.

Adhesives

Adhesives serve the gunmaker to reinforce or stabilize wood or metal
parts in a threaded joint or interference fit. Epoxy- or cyanoacrylate-
based, high-strength, high-temperature adhesives are routinely used to
attach compensators and muzzle brakes on barrels. Other adhesives are
used to lock screws and pins in place.

In many competition rifles, epoxy-based adhesives are used to glue
the receiver to the stock. This creates a solid unit in which movement
of the receiver relative to the stock is eliminated, thus contributing to
accuracy.

Joints made using adhesives can be easily disassembled by applying
a low heat that will not affect the heat treatment of the metals. Recently
developed high-strength adhesives are now being used to join metal
parts on a limited scale. However, the major problem with such
adhesives remains their lack of resistance to heat and shock

Metal Surface Treatments

Most metal firearm parts are given some type of surface finish after
shaping and heat-treatment is complete. The exact type of surface treatment
used depends upon the metal and the desired surface properties.

Polishing

Polishing is the smoothing of a metal's surface so that it becomes
more reflective of light. In another sense, polishing is the reduction of
tiny surface irregularities. There is an old saying in gun manufacture
that remains true today: "The surface finish on a metal part is only as
good as the level of polish underneath." Note there are different grades
of polishing ranging from the minimal brushed metal finish made
by applying moderately fine grit abrasive paper on the metal in one
direction to the mirror finish produced by a buffing wheel.

Polishing gun parts remains one of the few manufacturing
procedures that cannot be done by a machine. The human skills of touch
and judgment remain vital aspects of polishing. But, it is not easy. For a

highly accomplished polisher to learn his craft typically takes several years.

Hand polishing of metal surfaces makes use of a fabric buffing wheel turned at high speed by an electric motor and/or fine-grit abrasive papers or paste-polishing products containing fine abrasive particles. In gunmaking, polishing is normally a final preparatory step before bluing, plating or application of some other final surface treatment. In some cases, such as with stainless steel and aluminum components, the metal is left "in the white," with polishing serving to give the metal its finished appearance without an additional coating.

Sandblasting

Like polishing, sandblasting is often used to prepare a metal surface for some successive surface-finishing process but may also be used for the final surface finish in some instances. Sandblasting thoroughly cleans the metal surface, leaving it with a matte finish with reflectivity depending on the size of the sand used. For example, coarse sand will produce an almost completely non-reflective surface while tiny glass particles will create a satin finish known as glass beading.

Sandblasting uses a high-velocity stream of air into which dry sand particles are injected. When the sand particles impact on the surface of the part, they remove metal and create small surface pits. This procedure can be used on nearly all metals, as well as plastics and wood.

Browning and Bluing

Browning and bluing are terms used to describe any of several chemical treatments of metals that are essentially controlled rusting processes. On ferrous metals, bluing appears as a dark-colored, protective oxide layer on the surface.

Probably the earliest surface treatment for metals was browning. The procedure was popular with early gunsmiths and by 1700 the process was understood and used by most. The process begins by dissolving ordinary table salt in distilled water. The parts to be browned are cleaned, polished and thoroughly degreased. If a gun barrel was being browned, the bore was liberally coated with grease and plugged at both ends with tapered wood dowels. Next, the saltwater solution was liberally applied to the surfaces to be browned and the parts left to stand in a humid environment. Within 12 hours or so a thin coat of rust formed. The parts would be lightly rubbed with degreased, fine steel wool to remove the loose rust, leaving a slightly colored surface. The parts were then recoated and returned to the humid environment to allow further rusting. The cycle of rusting/rubbing-rusting/rubbing was repeated until the desired shade of brown was achieved.

Cold rust bluing is a similar process. A solution of hydrochloric and nitric acids diluted in distilled water with a small quantity of iron filings added is prepared. As with browning, the parts to be blued are polished and degreased, the exposed surfaces swabbed with the bluing solution and the part left to stand in a humid location. After 12 hours, the loose rust is rubbed off with degreased steel wool or a stainless steel wire brush, the surface is recoated with bluing solution and the part is returned to its humid environment. The process is repeated until a deep blue finish is achieved—this may take from five to 10 days. Although a very slow process, cold rust bluing produces a deep blue color generally considered to be the most durable type of bluing. Like browning, it can be used on side-by-side or over-under shotguns with barrels joined by soft solder which would be corroded by hot bluing solutions.

- Hot bluing processes can produce a deep blue finish in just a couple of hours rather than several days.

- Hot-water bluing utilizes a bluing solution containing potassium nitrate, sodium nitrate, potassium chlorate and mercury bichloride that is applied by hand to a clean steel surface that has been heated by immersion in boiling water. After applying the bluing solution, the part is immersed in the boiling water for five minutes, then re-coated with bluing solution. This cycle is repeated, with loose rust being rubbed off with degreased 0000 steel wool, until a rich blue-black color is achieved.

- Hot caustic bluing is a fast metal-treatment process suited to high volumes. Consequently, it has become the preferred method for bluing by most gunmakers today. In this process, the clean metal parts are immersed in a solution of sodium hydroxide salts heated to about 300 degrees F. Midway through the immersion period, the parts are removed from the bluing tank, rapidly chilled in cold water, then reimmersed in the salts to promote a deeper final color. Finally, the blued parts are removed from the salt solution, washed in boiling water to remove all traces of salt and coated with water-displacing oil. Hot caustic bluing cannot be used on non-ferrous metals, such as aluminum, magnesium and zinc, as they will dissolve and contaminate the bluing salts.

- Heat bluing is a process often used for finishing small parts, such as pins, screws, triggers and hammers. In this method, the parts are heated to 600-700 degrees F in a propane flame or burning charcoal, then immersed in oil. A variant of this process involves heating the part in a bath of molten potassium nitrate, then dipping the parts in water. Heat bluing produces an attractive deep-blue finish, depending upon the heat and the metallurgy of the part. However, this process is not suitable for large parts due to the difficulty of producing an even shade of blue throughout.

- Cold-bluing solutions usually work through the chemical action of selenium. The finish produced is not as durable as other blued finishes. For this reason, cold blues are not suited for bluing large parts or entire guns. However, cold blues excel for touch-up work to hide nicks, scratches and blemishes in existing blue finishes although they may not match the existing bluing perfectly.

Note that stainless steel is impervious to most bluing solutions, including instant bluing products.

Plating

An electro-deposition process is used for metal plating of most gun parts. In this process, the clean metal parts are immersed in an electrolytic solution of salts of the plating metal. A weak electrical current is then passed from an anode to the part to be plated. The current gives the part a negative charge that attracts the positive metal ions in the plating solution. These ions form a molecular bond to the surface of the metal part.

In contemporary gunmaking, there are three popular types of metal plating: chrome, nickel and gold.

- Chrome-plating produces a durable, very hard, corrosion-resistant and heat-resistant finish that has a satiny silver appearance. While the main purpose of chrome-plating is enhanced resistance to corrosion, the decorative silver finish offered by chrome-plating appeals to many gun owners. Chrome-plating has largely replaced nickel-plating for handguns, but the increasing use of stainless steel for firearms parts has reduced the demand for extra cost, chrome-plated guns. Chrome-plating is also used in lining some rifle bores to improve resistance to erosion. Black chrome-plating is not as hard or durable as chrome-plating, but it is more wear-resistant and corrosion-resistant than bluing. Because of its blue-black color, black chrome is sometimes used on self-defense handguns.

- Nickel-plating has been used as a finish on firearms parts for many years. Normally, nickel-finished guns were offered by factories at additional cost on special order for those customers who needed added protection against corrosion. Nickel-plating produces a hard, durable and corrosion-resistant layer on steel surfaces with approximately the same appearance as stainless steel. Often, steel parts to be electroless nickel-plated are first plated with copper to increase the adhesion of the nickel. This makes electroless nickel finishes somewhat vulnerable to copper-dissolving bore solvents.

- Gold-, silver- or platinum-plating of firearms parts serves an essentially cosmetic function. Because of the expense, gold plating is typically applied only to small gun parts such as triggers, hammers, levers, safety buttons and so forth where they provide a pleasing contrast to blued finishes. Silver may also be used for the same purpose.

Metal Coatings

Nitride Coatings

The application of a nitride coating, typically titanium nitride, on a metal surface will substantially increase lubricity and resistance to wear and corrosion. For this reason, titanium nitride has become a popular coating for drill bits, milling cutters and other tools used in firearms manufacture as it greatly increases tool life. Titanium nitride coatings are applied using a gas-deposition process in which the clean part is placed in a heated vacuum into which nitride-rich gas is introduced. The titanium nitride in the gas then bonds to the part. Plating thickness need be only several ten thousandths of an inch thick to be effective. A titanium nitride-coated part can be readily identified by its bright gold color, however titanium nitride coatings have been developed in other colors are well.

Titanium nitride has been used for decorative purposes on some small gun parts such as triggers, hammers and levers. It has also been used to coat some internal parts subject to wear such as bolts, gas pistons and fire-control parts. Such coatings have not been widely used for large components due to the expense and difficulty of application.

Tenifer is a proprietary finish used on the slides of Glock pistols. It is a hot-bath nitriding process that produces a hard, wear- and corrosion-resistant surface.

Parkerizing

Parkerizing is a metal-finishing process that produces a corrosion-resistant, phosphate coating molecularly bonded to the underlying steel. It can be applied to carbon steel, but not to stainless steel or aluminum. Invented by Clark W. Parker and patented by the Parker Rust Proof Company very early in the 20th century, Parkerizing has been used to finish U.S. military small arms for nearly 100 years.

The Parkerizing process involves immersing clean gun parts in a hot solution of phosphate salts. The original military-specification Parkerizing involved manganese phosphate salts, but most Parkerizing solutions today contain zinc phosphate salts. With either solution, the bare steel is slightly acid etched and a crystalline phosphate precipitate laid down on its surface. A Parkerized finish can be up to 0.0015" thick, is non-reflective, corrosion-resistant and holds lubricant well. The finished color may vary from matte black to matte gray, sometimes with a greenish tinge, depending on the solution used and type of steel.

Parkerizing is a popular finish for military, tactical and self-defense arms, as it is inexpensive, durable, non-reflective and dark-colored.

Anodizing

Because bluing, Parkerizing and most plating finishes cannot be applied on aluminum parts, they may be left in the white or coated using a process called anodizing to increase wear-resistance and to add color. Left in the white, aluminum rapidly reacts with oxygen in the air to form a tough, protective oxide layer that inhibits further corrosion but is not attractive. A scratch in the oxide layer simply exposes the aluminum beneath to the air, resulting in a new oxide layer being formed.

Anodizing is an electro-chemical process conducted in an acid solution. Anodizing produces a dense, hard, crystalline oxide layer. Before the process is complete, a dye can be introduced into the open pores of the oxide layer to achieve nearly any desired color. The pores of the colored oxide are then sealed with water or steam. The process is inexpensive and widely available.

Anodizing is widely used on aluminum handgun frames, shotgun and rifle receivers, magazines and other parts. In addition to providing corrosion-resistance, the hard, durable oxide layer provides good wear-resistance in areas of metal-to-metal friction.

Teflon

Teflon-based finishes such as the NP3 finish offered by the Robar Companies consist of Teflon-coated electroless nickel. Teflon-based coatings are rarely offered by manufacturers due to the cost. As a result, most Teflon coatings are done by aftermarket companies specializing in the process.

Molybdenum Disulphide

Molybdenum disulphide (MoS2) is a solid, dry lubricant with a crystalline lattice structure. The lattice structure has strong molecular bonds within the layers and weak bonds between layers that allow slip. This gives MoS2 its ability to lubricate. It has a strong affinity for ferrous metals, nickel, and chromium, a weak affinity for copper and no affinity for aluminum, titanium, zinc or synthetics. If not passivated, MoS2 will attract water from the air when heated. The water will strip away a sulfur atom to form sulfuric acid that will quickly corrode most metals. Passivated MoS2 does not suffer from this problem.

Often used in aerospace applications, MoS2 has the ability to lubricate over a wide range of temperatures and in high vacuum environments. In recent times the benefits of MoS2 lubrication have been recognized and applied to firearms and ammunition. A firearm lubricated with MoS2 has a dry surface that will not attract or hold dust, dirt or grit.

The most common application of moly is in coating bullets. As moly has only a weak affinity for copper, it must be held on the bullet's surface with a binder, such as epoxy, lacquer or wax.

Moly-based finishes such as that used by H-S Precision, Robar and others is a sub-micron, molybdenum disulfide-loaded polymer that is baked on over bare metal or a phosphate base. Alternately, molybdenum disulphide in a passivated, sub-micron suspension in a supersaturated liquid can be used to impregnate ferrous metals. Once so treated, the moly will remain bonded to the metal unless the metal is physically cut away.

Stainless Blues

Stainless steel is not affected by normal bluing salts used to coat carbon steel. However, it may be blackened using oxidizing solutions of especially compounded alkaline salts, such as Du-Lite 3-0 and Ebonol SS-52. The finish that results is very similar in appearance to normal blue.

Epoxy and Lacquer

Spray-on or paint-on metal finishes based on epoxy or lacquer and fortified with sub-micron molybdenum disulfide or teflon/moly compositions are also used in gunmaking. All offer acceptable resistance to solvents, corrosion and wear.

These inexpensive finishes can be quickly and easily applied to most metals. While some cure at room temperature, the better ones are baked-on at low temperature (300-350 degrees F) to create an extra-durable finish that can only be removed by sandblasting.

Camouflage

Camouflage finishes in a wide variety of patterns have recently become very popular on firearms, especially shotguns and some military rifles. In this process, the gun is disassembled and each part to be coated is cleaned and given an undercoat of paint. Next, a thin sheet of machine-printed, camouflage-pattern polymer film is placed on the surface of the water in a stainless-steel tank. The water dissolves the polymer sheet, leaving the ink, still in the original camouflage pattern, floating on the surface. When the part is slowly dipped into the tank the ink adheres to the part's surface. The part is then dried and clear-coated. Such film finishes have acceptable durability, but they are susceptible to attack by bore solvents, paint thinners and many chemical insect repellents.

Metal Surface Profiling

Metal surfaces on firearms are often checkered, grooved, stippled or engine-turned to increase grip, reduce light reflection or simply for ornamental purposes.

Checkering

Checkering consists of parallel grooves that intersect at an angle, producing small, sharp diamond-shaped projections. Checkering is frequently used on the front strap, back strap, trigger guard, operation levers and safety buttons of semi-auto handguns.

Metal checkering is produced with checkering files having two or more rows of parallel teeth. Checkering files are available with the rows of teeth spaced from 18, 20, 22, 24, 25, 30 and 40 lines-per-inch. Very fine checkering of 40 lines per inch or more is sometimes used on gun surfaces to break up light reflections, such as on the top of a handgun slide.

Grooving

Grooving is the production of a series of parallel cuts in the front strap and back strap, trigger bow or slide of a handgun to increase grip. Very fine grooves cut into the top of a pistol slide or solid rib or ventilated rib serve to reduce light reflection. Grooves are normally cut using checkering files. However, very coarse grooves may be cut on a machine or cast in the part.

Stippling

Stippling is the creation of a rough surface texture formed by a series of shallow, random, overlapping punch marks. A sharp-pointed, hardened stippling punch is held at an angle to the surface and moved slightly as it is tapped repeatedly by a small hammer, creating the indentations. Stippling is normally used to enhance grip, but can also be used to reduce reflections on sighting surfaces.

Engine Turning

Typically used for decoration, engine turning is applied by a small abrasive-loaded rod that is held in a bit and rotated at moderate speed. When the abrasive rod is pressed against the metal surface, it leaves a shallow swirl. By overlapping the swirls, a decorative effect is produced. Typically, engine turning is applied to the magazine followers of bolt-action rifles.

Wood Shaping

Wood stocks for modern firearms are made in commercial quantities using automatic profiling machines. These machines cut up to 10 stocks at once of a specific pattern.

The stock's wrist and fore-end are usually checkered to enhance grip. Checkering may be applied in several ways:

- It can be cut into the stock's surface using tools to remove wood in a predetermined pattern. Cut checkering is produced by skilled stockmakers using hand tools or by machine using a powered quill to cut the wood.
- It can be impressed into the wood's surface by a heated steel plate with the reverse of the desired pattern.
- It can be formed by a combination of first impressing the design, then chasing the lines with a cutter by hand.
- It can be stippled using a punch or sandblaster to make numerous, random indentations in the wood's surface.

Some stocks such as those on heavy-barrel varmint rifles and on many inexpensive firearms have no checkering at all. Checkering on synthetic stocks is molded in place. In general, factory wood stocks that are checkered have a flat diamond-pattern cut of between 16 and 20 lines-per-inch with a single or double border. High-quality (and probably expensive) firearm stocks may have hand-cut checkering as fine as 28 lines-per-inch.

Shooters are nothing if not adaptive. Impromptu additions to stocks and grips are common. The purpose of such adaptions is inevitably to improve the fit and feel of the stock or grip to suit the shooter's preference. Popular materials for this purpose include skateboard tape, wood putty, liquid steel or aluminum, sand in epoxy paint and sprays that increase friction.

Manufacture of Synthetic Gun Components

The method of manufacturing synthetic firearm parts depends upon the shape of the part, its desired characteristics and the type of polymer utilized. Most synthetic gun parts are produced by extrusion or by molding.

Molding

The molding process utilizes heat, pressure and a mold to form material into the desired shape. The mold has a hollow cavity in the shape of the desired part. A simple mold consists of two parts which may not necessarily be halves. However, most molds consist of several components that move separately to produce complex parts with molded-in holes, tunnels, protrusions, undercut areas and other features. The mold's interior is normally textured to impart the desired surface on the part such as shiny, matte, pebbled, ridged or crosshatched. Also, the mold itself must be properly proportioned to allow for the shrinkage of the polymer part as it cools. Most injection molds are multi-cavity, gang molds that will produce many identical parts each time the mold is cycled.

The temperature of the plastic feed stock, the injection rate and pressure, the mold temperature, the cooling rate and dwell time must all be carefully controlled to ensure proper orientation of the polymer chains and consistent quality. In some cases, a release agent may be used to prevent adherence of the molded part to the mold surface.

Metal pieces can be molded or imbedded into a polymer part to reinforce stress-bearing areas, for example metal frame rails in a polymer handgun frame.

There are four types of molding:

- **Injection molding**—Injection molding begins by melting a measured amount of solid polymer pellet feed stock (which may be reinforced with fiberglass) in a heated chamber, then injecting it under pressure into a closed, temperature-controlled mold. As the polymer cools inside the mold, it solidifies, the mold is opened and the finished part ejected. Injection molding is an inexpensive, widely used, high-volume method for producing various types of high-quality parts.

- **Blow molding**—Blow molding also begins with solid pellet polymer feed stock melted in a heated chamber, then forced into the mold under pressure. At this point, high-pressure air is blown into the mold to spread a thin layer of polymer evenly around the inside surface of the mold. Blow molding is commonly used for many kinds of plastic bottles and containers because it is inexpensive and very fast.

- **Compression molding**—In compression molding, a measured amount of polymer in solid or semi-solid form is placed in an open mold. After the mold is closed, heat and pressure are applied to the polymer to form the part. Compression molding is especially suited for producing complex shapes in fiberglass-reinforced and composite materials. It is slower and more expensive than other types of molding and the molds are expensive.

- **Reaction injection molding**—This molding technique begins with two separate liquid monomers that are rapidly pumped into a mold. Short reinforcing fibers, such as fiberglass or carbon fibers, may be contained in one of the monomer liquids. Inside the mold, the two monomers mix, then undergo a chemical reaction to produce polymerization. This process is a form of injection molding, but does not involve heat, melted polymer or pressure.

Extrusion

Extrusion involves forcing heated polymer under pressure through an opening of specific size and shape in a die. This produces a virtually limitless ribbon or stream of polymer having a specific cross-section. The extrusion is then sliced or cut to form the desired parts.

Extrusion can be used to produce various shapes, such as sheets, rods, tubes, I-beams, angles and many other complex shapes.

Machining

Certain types of polymers, such as Delrin, nylon and some polycarbonates, can be machined. Special cutters, tool angles and feed rates must be used, however, the machining process is much the same as for metals.

Machining can be used in combination with other polymer fabrication techniques. For example, drilling may be used to make precisely sized holes in a polymer handgun frame or a polymer rod may be drilled, then sliced into thin segments to produce flexible washers.

Adhesives

Adhesives may be used to assemble a polymer part from two or more separately molded pieces. The most popular adhesives for this purpose are epoxies and cyanoacrylates. Such products are capable of creating a bond as strong as the materials being joined.

Carbon Fiber

Carbon fiber is a form of graphite or carbon in ribbon form. Carbon ribbon is created by subjecting polyacrylonitrile to pyrolysis (heating in the absence of oxygen) to produce thin ribbons that can be bundled together to make strong, stiff fibers. These fibers can be used to make a filament wrap, can be woven into sheets or other forms, or can be cut into short lengths and introduced into a liquid polymer to give a stiffer, stronger molded part.

Quality Control

Quality control plays a pivotal role in firearms manufacture. In fact, manufacture of modern firearms would not be possible without suitable quality-control systems. Quality control begins with a specification and a dimensional tolerance.

A specification determines the physical characteristics of the part for it to perform its function. A specification for a part will describe in detail its material, surface finish, hardness, heat-treatment, toughness, yield strength, tensile strength and coating or plating. Parts made to a specification can be tested to determine if they meet specification or not.

A specification also will establish performance parameters, such as the expected number of rounds in the service life of the gun, the mean time between failure (breakage) and other attributes.

A dimensional tolerance determines the measurement limits of parts. These consist of numbers normally expressed as a range of values with a desired median number and plus or minus figures. These tolerances allow manufacture of parts with minor variations.

Quality control is the production process that governs manufacture of the parts and their performance in a firearm. Basically, there are three general approaches to quality control:

- Full or 100 percent inspection of all parts and assembled firearms. This process is seldom used due to the very high cost involved.
- Statistical analysis that relies on selecting and testing samples of each batch of parts. It is very popular today due to its low cost and proven effectiveness.
- A combination of the two systems above.

Most firearms manufacturers use a mixture of both of the above systems. For example, statistical sampling will be used to accept or reject a batch of parts, but all completed firearms are proof-fired.

Production Flow

Manufacture of firearms consists of various flows of parts that eventually come together to form a gun. Some parts will be made in-house by the manufacturer while others will be purchased from outside suppliers. Most firearm manufacturers will make the following parts in-house:

- receiver or frame
- fire-control assembly
- bolt, slide, cylinder or breech block
- levers, buttons and firing pins.

Most manufacturers will perform the following operations in-house:

- barrel, receiver, frame, bolt, cylinder and slide manufacture
- chambering, threading, headspacing barrels
- machining, milling, drilling parts
- stock shaping and finishing
- polishing
- bluing
- assembly
- function and accuracy testing
- proof testing
- packing, warehousing, shipping.

Firearm parts typically purchased from outside suppliers:

- screws, pins and springs
- magazines
- sights
- wood blanks
- sling swivels and studs
- recoil pads, grip panels
- packaging.

In addition, most manufacturers will send out parts for:

- heat-treatment
- titanium nitride-coating
- chrome-, nickel- or gold-plating
- printing of manuals, catalogs and labels.

Assembly

Most shooters are surprised to learn that firearms assemblers in modern gun companies are not issued or allowed to use files, drills or hammers in their work. If a particular part does not fit correctly, the assembler has been trained to place that part aside and try a second part. If the second part does not fit, that is placed aside and a third part tried. If the third part does not fit, the entire gun is tagged and put aside for remedial inspection and rework at the end of the day. Such is the confidence in the quality control and modern manufacturing methods today. Just a few years ago, this was not possible.

AMMUNITION TECHNICAL

Chapter 13
AMMUNITION

Without ammunition, a firearm is no more than an inefficient club. For this reason, much of the technological development effort in firearms history was devoted to ammunition.

Basically, ammunition consists of four parts: powder, projectile, primer and cartridge case.

Blackpowder Loads

For muzzleloading firearms, a cartridge consisted of a measured quantity of powder and a lubricated projectile held in a paper, wood or vellum tube. In use, the shooter typically tore open the paper or removed the cap on the wood tube and poured the powder down the barrel. He then removed the bullet from the cartridge and pushed it down the barrel onto the powder using a ramrod. The gun was then primed with a small quantity of powder or a percussion cap and fired. Wooden tubes were reusable; paper and vellum cartridge tubes were discarded. Later, paper tubes were treated to enhance combustibility so the whole cartridge could simply be rammed down the barrel without first separating the components.

Modern Cartridges

A modern cartridge is defined as a complete round of loaded ammunition consisting of four parts:

- primer
- propellant powder
- bullet
- cartridge case.

Note that the bullet is only one part of a cartridge. Colloquial references to the "number of bullets in a gun" are technically incorrect. The correct term is the number of cartridges held in the magazine.

Normally, a cartridge for a shotgun is called a shotshell. A modern shotshell consists of five parts:

- primer
- propellant powder
- wad column
- charge of shot pellets
- shell case.

Center-Fire Nomenclature

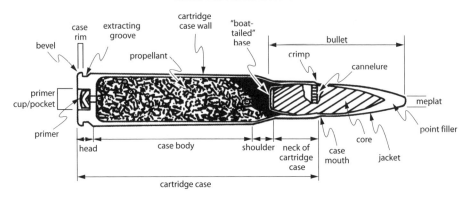

Shotshell Nomenclature

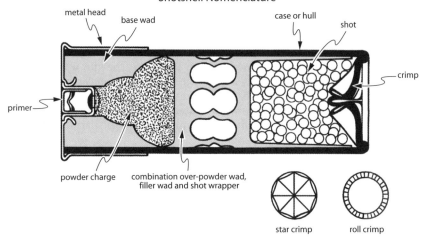

Rimfire Nomenclature

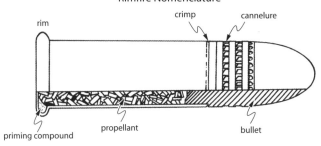

In addition, caseless ammunition has been developed utilizing a solid propellant charge in place of the case, but has not caught on with shooters.

Primers

The purpose of a primer is to ignite the propellant powder. To do this, the primer contains a very small amount of explosive held inside a metal primer cap. In technical terms, when the firing pin strikes the primer cap, the priming mixture is crushed between the cap and the anvil. This causes the priming mixture to explode, sending a stream of hot gases through the flash hole and into the cartridge case. The stream of hot gas rapidly increases the temperature and pressure inside the cartridge case, igniting the propellant powder.

There are two basic types of center-fire rifle and handgun primers. The Boxer primer consists of a three-part assembly containing a U-shaped metal cap, a metal anvil and the priming mixture. The Berdan primer consists of only two parts, a U-shaped metal cap and the priming mixture.

Primer Caps

Primer caps are stampings made from rolled copper-alloy sheet. The sheet is fed into a small stamping press where a multiple die set produces more than a dozen caps on each stroke. The caps are often nickel-plated.

Primer caps are made in different diameters for different

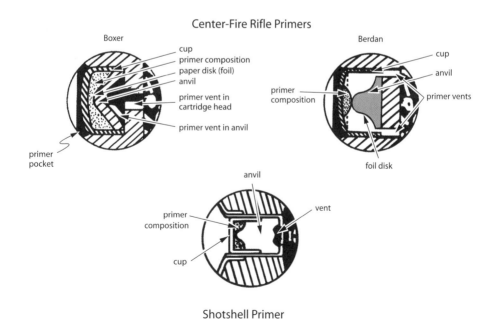

Center-Fire Rifle Primers

Boxer

cup
primer composition
paper disk (foil)
anvil

primer vent in
cartridge head

primer vent in anvil

primer
pocket

Berdan

cup
anvil

primer
composition

primer vents

foil disk

anvil

primer
composition

vent

cup

Shotshell Primer

applications. The descriptions of the finished primers indicate their intended use:

- large rifle magnum
- large rifle
- large rifle match
- large pistol magnum
- large pistol
- small rifle
- small rifle match
- small pistol

Basically, there are two diameters in use as noted above. Within each diameter, the cup height varies to suit the application. For example, cups intended for use as large rifle magnum primers are higher than those intended for use in large pistol applications although both are the same diameter.

Boxer Primer Dimensions

Small Pistol
Diameter 0.175"   Height 0.122"

CCI 500	Winchester WSP
CCI 550 Magnum	Winchester WSPM Magnum
Fiocchi SP	Remington 1½
Federal 100	Remington 5½ Magnum
Federal 200 Magnum	RWS 4031
Norma SP	RWS 4047 Magnum
Vihtavuori 22	Hirtenberger 1206

Small Rifle
Diameter 0.175"   Height 0.123"

CCI 400	Norma SR
CCI BR4 Match	Vihtavuori 82
CCI 450 Magnum	Winchester WSR
Fiocchi SR	Remington 6 ½
Federal 200	Remington 7½
Federal 205M-Match	RWS 4033
Federal 205 Magnum	Hirtenberger 1205

Large Pistol
Diameter 0.210"   Height 0.123"

CCI 300	Vihtavuori 48
CCI 300 Magnum	Winchester WLP
Fiocchi LP	Remington 2½
Federal 150	RWS 5337
Federal 155 Magnum	Hirtenberger 1207
Norma LP	

Large Rifle
Diameter 0.210"   Height 0.130"

CCI 200	Vihtavuori 68
CCI BR2 Match	Winchester WLR
CCI 250 Magnum	Winchester WLRM Magnum
Fiocchi LR	Remington 9½
Federal 210	Remington 9½ Magnum
Federal 210 Match	RWS 5341
Federal 215 Magnum	RWS 5333 Magnum
Norma LR	Hirtenberger 1204

Berdan Primer Dimensions

Pistol	Diameter (in.)	Height (in.)
RWS 4506	0.18	0.0866
RWS 4521 (for 9x19mm)	0.18	0.0866
RWS 5005	0.20	0.0866
Hirtenberger 1105	0.18	0.0906
Hirtenberger 1103	0.18	0.0906
Vihtavuori 6	0.18	0.0866

Rifle	Diameter (in.)	Height (in.)
RWS 4520	0.18	0.0827
RWS 5608	0.22	0.1102
RWS 5620	0.22	0.1043
RWS 6000	0.25	0.1161
RWS 6001 Magnum	0.24	0.1339
RWS 6504	0.25	0.0925
Hirtenberger 1101	0.22	0.1102
Hirtenberger 1106	0.18	0.1024
Vihtavuori 3	0.22	0.1102

Priming Mix
The primer caps are filled with primer mix using a method called "rubbing." This process begins with a thin steel plate containing several hundred (normally about 330) holes. The plates are placed on shaker tables and primer caps broadcast over their surface. The shaking motion causes a cap to fall into each hole. Next, the plate is sent into the primer "rubbing room." This is a heavily built and spotlessly clean room where plates sit on a metal table and wet priming compound is hand-rubbed over the surface to fill each cap. A second plate containing anvils is then placed over the plate containing the primer caps and a multi-punch press seats the anvils in the caps.

Priming compound is a true high explosive. Typical ingredients include:
- high explosives such as TNT, PETN or similar
- lead styphnate (normal or basic)
- binder (gum Arabic)
- stabilizers (to prevent decomposition)
- solvents (to form chemical mix)
- distilled water (to desensitize for handling)
- dye (for identification)
- frictioning agent (ground glass—rimfire only)
- metallic solids (powdered aluminum or magnesium).

When wet, priming mix remains insensitive and is safe to handle. However, when it dries, it becomes very sensitive and is not safe to handle in bulk. For this reason, primers are made using a wet mixture. Primers for handloading are sent to a drying house for several days before shipment. Primers for use in factory ammunition are sent to the primer insert machines where they are inserted into cartridge case while still wet and inert as a safety measure.

A primer inserted into a cartridge case while still wet is more consistent than a primer inserted into a cartridge case when dry. A wet priming mixture will dry around the anvil tip while a dry primer will not.

Prior to 1955, many primers, especially those used in military ammunition, were corrosive. This was because the chlorate priming mixtures contained salts that remained in the barrel after the gun was fired. Moisture in the air combined with the salts to cause corrosion in the bore. This made it necessary to clean the gun after firing with hot soapy water or a suitable bore cleaner to dissolve the salts. Corrosive primers worked very well and were used in many countries, such as Russia and China, up to recent times. U.S. military ammunition has been loaded exclusively with non-corrosive primers since 1955. Watch this carefully! Always note whether surplus ammunition is corrosive or not. Non-corrosive surplus ammunition commands a higher price. Beware of claims that surplus ammunition is "mildly corrosive." Primers are either corrosive or not. There is no such thing as "mildly corrosive!"

In general, military ammunition made before or during World War II should be considered corrosive. All NATO-specification 5.56x45 mm ammunition is non-corrosive, as is all military .30 Carbine ammunition. Other calibers such as 7.62x51 mm are generally non-corrosive, but there are exceptions.

Non-corrosive, lead styphnate-based priming mixtures began to replace corrosive primers in sporting ammunition before World War II. After World War II, virtually all sporting ammunition made in the United States has used non-corrosive primers.

There are two types of lead styphnate:

Normal—Normal lead styphnate may be characterized by its large, irregular crystal structure, and it is acidic (will attack copper) when wet. This type of priming is widely used by military arsenals and manufacturers of sporting ammunition. Ignition characteristics are generally good, especially at low temperatures below -10 degrees F. Normal lead styphnate is also good for rimfire priming. However, normal lead styphnate does not ignite large charges of slow-burning propellants well, such as those used in magnum rifle cartridges and shotshells loaded with steel shot. In such applications, normal lead styphnate is often boosted with the addition of powdered aluminum or magnesium.

Basic—Basic lead styphnate crystals have a small, very regular structure, and it is basic (will not attack copper) when wet. Basic lead styphnate primers have ignition characteristics that have proven especially suitable for magnum rifle cartridges and shotshells loaded with steel shot. These primers have also proven especially good for match ammunition. Drawbacks include weak ignition characteristics at temperatures below -10 degrees F. and weak performance in rimfire applications.

While primers are filled with an explosive mix, each primer has only a very small amount in the cap. For example, a large rifle magnum primer or a 209 shotshell primer may contain only 36 milligrams of priming compound. Many small rifle and small pistol primers contain only about 20 milligrams of priming mix.

Anvils

Every percussion primer has an anvil. The purpose of the anvil is to provide a surface against which the priming mix in the primer cap can be crushed.

In Boxer primers, the metal anvil is a part of the primer assembly. Anvils may have either two or three legs. There seems to be no important ballistic drawback to either type. Anvils are made of either steel or copper alloy that is stamped out on small stamping machines.

When the primer is assembled at the factory, the anvil is seated in the lip of the primer cap. In this position, the anvil is not fully in position and not in contact with the priming mixture in the cap. When a wet primer is inserted in a cartridge case, the anvil is fully seated against the priming mixture that then dries around it.

Berdan primers do not incorporate the anvil in the primer assembly. This makes manufacture of Berdan primers much easier and cheaper than Boxer primers. For this reason, the Berdan primer has been the preferred type for military ammunition in most countries except the United States and Canada.

On the other hand, Berdan primers require a special cartridge case that incorporates the anvil inside the primer pocket in the case head. This increases the complexity and cost of making the cartridge case.

Primers for handloading are packaged and shipped with the anvils out where they do not contact the priming mixture as a safety precaution during shipment. When you seat a primer during handloading, the anvil is pressed home into contact with the dry priming mix. This activates the primer.

Most handloading machinery and procedures have been designed around the Boxer primer. Berdan-primed cartridge cases can be reloaded; however, the process is much more complicated. Furthermore, Berdan primers are not made in the United States, thus making them very scarce and expensive. Fortunately for reloaders, most ammunition manufacturers have or are switching to Boxer primers.

Shotshell Primers

Modern No. 209 shotshell primers are a "battery cup"design featuring a three-piece assembly consisting of a primer cap, primer body and a flat steel anvil. The steel anvil has two legs that hold it up inside the hollow primer body so that the anvil on the upper tip is in contact with the priming mix in the cap. A 209 shotshell primer somewhat resembles a .22 Short blank cartridge in appearance. The flash hole in the front end of the 209 primer is usually closed with paper or a drop of lacquer.

Rimfire Priming

The rimfire cartridge case has no separate primer assembly and no anvil or cap. Instead, the primer mix is contained inside the case in a hollow rim. As there is no anvil, merely crushing the rim (and the priming mix inside) would not cause ignition. For this reason, rimfire priming mixture must contain a frictioning agent such as ground glass.

Cartridge Cases

Center-fire rifle and handgun cartridge cases are normally made of metal. Over the years many types of metal alloy have been tried such as:
- brass (83 percent copper and 17 percent zinc)
- steel
- aluminum
- plastic
- hybrids combining two of the above.

Brass has proven to be the best choice for center-fire cartridge cases for the following reasons:
- It is readily available in large quantities.
- It is inexpensive.
- It is easy to draw and form.
- It can be hardened to make it springy.
- It can be annealed to make it soft.
- It requires no anti-corrosive coatings.

Experience and customer preference have made brass the metal of choice for sporting and competitive use. Brass is also the best metal for rimfire cartridge cases and for the metal head on shotshells.

Steel has proven popular for military use, particularly in Russia, China, Germany and France. While steel is cheap and widely available, manufacture of steel cartridge cases is more complex and expensive than brass. The main reason steel is popular for military ammunition is that it is readily available in wartime while brass (a "strategic" metal) is often not.

Technology for making steel cartridge cases was developed in Germany during World War I and was well-developed by the time World War II began in 1939. It is important to note here that Germany and Russia fought World War II almost exclusively using steel cartridge cases. The U.S. military lagged behind in steel cartridge case manufacturing but launched a crash program to develop them during World War II. This program was successful and steel-case small-caliber military ammunition was made in large quantities in the United States during the war. However, it was used mainly for training, qualification and practice and was never used overseas. After World War II, the U.S. military standardized brass cartridge cases, and the use of steel-cased ammunition was limited to large calibers.

Until recently, **aluminum** was not considered suitable for small-caliber center-fire cartridge cases due to a characteristic called "burnout" that completely destroyed the gun if the case head failed. This phenomenon was caused by high-temperature propellant gas igniting the aluminum metal as it escaped through the failure point. Modern alloys have eliminated this problem in handgun calibers and metal heads for shotshells. However, aluminum alloys remain unsuited to high-pressure rifle cartridge cases unless complex and expensive measures are taken to protect the metal from burnout.

Plastic has been the holy grail of center-fire cartridge case materials. On initial consideration, plastic seems the perfect material for a cartridge case in that it is:

- inexpensive
- widely available in many different formulations
- moldable using well-known technology
- lightweight
- non-toxic
- waterproof
- non-corrosive.

Plastic has several major drawbacks for use in a center-fire cartridge case:

- It will not hold a primer securely.
- It will not meet bullet push or pull requirements.
- It does not spring back like metals.
- It lacks resistance to heat from hot barrels.
- It lacks strength to resist rough handling during feeding and extraction.

Never ones to give up on a good idea, ammunition manufacturers have invested considerable money and effort in developing plastics for ammo

263

applications since the early 1950s. Their efforts have not been in vain. Packaging is a successful application of plastics that immediately comes to mind in the form of boxes, trays and belt carriers. Successful ballistic applications include shotshell hulls, shotshell wads, sabots, bullet tips and bullet coatings. Plastic center-fire cartridge cases have been tried, but thus far none has proven satisfactory. That may change, spurred by the promising development of hybrid cases in the late 1990s.

A **hybrid cartridge case** utilizes two or more different materials in its construction. The key is using materials in the application to which they are best suited. While this seems basic and simple, in practice it was not. Only recently have such efforts been successful. A modern, hybrid, center-fire cartridge case is made of a molded plastic front end and a metal (brass or steel) head. The metal head provides strength for extraction and holds the primer securely in position. A blow-through panel under the plastic case neck provides the requisite levels of bullet push and pull. The hybrid cartridge was a long time in coming, and only time will tell if it will be a commercial or military success.

Cartridge Case Manufacture

Brass cartridge cases are made in a series of steps.

Draw—The cup is drawn, washed, annealed and trimmed. This step may be repeated up to four times to obtain the necessary length.

Head form—The head is formed on the drawn tube by upsetting it with a punch and die set. This step also forms the headstamp and primer pocket.

Head turn—The head is turned on an automatic lathe to form the rim.

Taper and plug—The case neck, shoulder and body taper are formed and the case trimmed to length.

Neck anneal—The neck is flame- or induction-annealed to soften it and relieve stress.

Primer insert—The primer-insert machine punches the flash hole in the primer pocket, inserts a primer into the pocket and places lacquer sealer around the primer annulus. It also crimps the primer in place if required.

Case Types

There are several types of cartridge case head and rim configurations:

rimmed   semi-rimmed   rimless   rebated-rim   belted

In addition, there are various cartridge case body configurations:
- straight
- tapered
- necked.

These configurations are combined to describe a cartridge case. For example, rimless tapered (.30 Carbine), rimless necked (.270 Win.), belted necked (.300 Win. Mag.), rimmed necked (.30 30 Win.) and rimmed straight (.44 Mag.).

Shotshell Cases

A modern shotshell is a type of hybrid cartridge case. It consists of an extruded hull of high-density, polyethylene plastic, a base wad and a metal head with a pocket for a 209 battery cup primer. All shotshells are rimmed with a straight-sided case. Shotshells are offered in several gauges such as 10 , 12 , 16, 20, and 28 ga. as well as .410 bore. Case lengths vary from a maximum of 3½" to 2". Many gauges are offered in several shell lengths. A short shotshell may be fired safely in a longer chamber, but a long shotshell must never be fired in a shorter chamber.

The extruded plastic tubes are often color-coded by gauge. For example, brown is utilized for 10 ga., red is used for 12 ga., purple for 16 ga. and yellow for 20 ga. At the mouth, the hull may be chamfered to provide a better crimp. Both six-fold and eight-fold crimps are in common use. The six-fold crimp is normally used on hunting shells and the eight-fold crimp is used on target loads for trap, skeet and sporting clays competition. Rifled slug shells are roll crimped.

For nearly 100 years, shotshell hulls were made of paper. The paper hulls were made by rolling a number of layers of glue and paper over a short steel mandrel, then cutting the long tube into short lengths. However, paper had little resistance to moisture. Contact with water caused it to swell to the point of being useless. When reliability was paramount in those days, all-brass shotshells were used, although they were much more expensive. Paper shells today are used almost exclusively for target shooting, although they are favored in some hunting areas for their environmentally friendly characteristics.

Inside every plastic or paper shotshell is a base wad. The base wad serves to control internal volume, reinforce the base area and help hold the primer in position. As a direct function of controlling volume, base wads are of different heights and configurations. There are two types of base wad:

Separate—This type of base wad is made separately and inserted into the tube prior to crimping the metal head in position. The metal head holds the base wad in place. A separate base wad may be made of rolled paper, molded composite or molded polyethylene plastic.

Integral—An integral base wad is part of the tube itself and formed when the tube is manufactured. It is not a separate piece and can never become loose or be pulled into the bore.

Most shotshells have a metal head made of brass, brass-plated steel or brass-plated aluminum. Shotshells that do not have a metal head generally are molded types that have a metal reinforcing disk embedded in the rim. The primary function of the metal head is to reinforce the rim for positive extraction and ejection. Metal shotshell heads are available in different heights, with target loads generally having the lowest and magnum hunting shells the highest (thus the popular terms "low brass" and "high brass"). The height of the metal head serves chiefly to distinguish hunting loads from target loads as shotshells with high metal heads are not stronger than those with lower metal heads.

Rimfire Cases

Rimfire cartridge cases have been in continuous production since the mid-1850s, making this type of self-contained cartridge the oldest in production. In the 1800s, there were many calibers of rimfire ammunition ranging from the humble .22 Short to massive .50-caliber examples. Presently, new .17-caliber rounds have joined traditional .22 cartridges as commercially loaded rimfire offerings.

In concept, the rimfire cartridge is elegantly simple. A one-piece cartridge case is drawn from thin brass and formed with a hollow rim. Priming compound is forced into the rim by centrifugal force from spinning. The primed case is then charged with powder and a bullet seated in the case mouth. To provide sufficient bullet push and pull, the bullet is crimped securely into the case mouth. When the firing pin of the rifle strikes the thin brass rim, it crushes the hollow rim and ignites the priming mixture within. There is no anvil or separate primer cap.

However, the thin brass rimfire case is weak and will not withstand high breech pressures. Ignition is also weak resulting in a very inefficient powder burn. However, the rimfire case is cheap and easy to manufacture. When loaded to moderate breech pressures within its strength limitations, the rimfire cartridge has and continues to provide generations of shooters with low-cost practice, training and small-game hunting capability.

Bullets

Perhaps no part of a cartridge receives more scrutiny than the bullet. This is because it is right up front where it can be seen and its performance estimated. After all, the propellant and primer are wholly or partially hidden and thus taken for granted.

Historically, bullets have been made of lead for several reasons:
- Lead is cheap and abundant.
- Lead is soft and easy to work.
- Lead has a low melting point.
- Lead is dense.

For these reasons, lead has historically been the material of choice for making simple bullets and round balls. It is important to note here that while lead was a popular choice, it was by no means the only available material. Bullets have been and continue to be made from other materials:

- bismuth
- brass and copper
- steel and iron
- zinc
- aluminum
- uranium
- tungsten
- composite materials
- wood and paper
- plastic
- porcelain
- hybrids of two or more of the above.

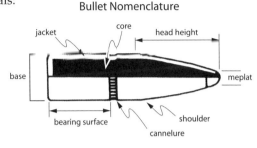

Bullet Nomenclature

It must also be noted that lead is seldom used by itself. Lead is commonly coated with lubricant, patched with cloth or paper, held in a plastic or metal sabot, jacketed with copper, brass or steel, or coated with a polymer. These measures are necessary to protect the soft lead from stripping or being deposited in the bore.

The first bullets were simple cast-lead balls. With the advent of rifling in barrels, spin stabilization made elongated bullets possible. The field of bullet shapes then expanded enormously. Today, we recognize the following shapes of elongated bullets:

- round nose
- semi-round nose
- flat nose
- wadcutter
- semiwadcutter
- pointed or spitzer-tangent ogive

Examples of Rifle Bullet Types

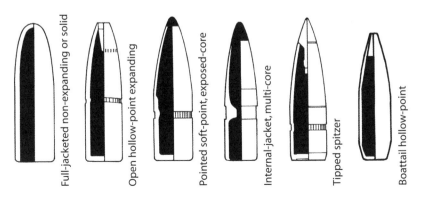

In addition, modern bullets are offered with several base configurations.

Flat—Flat-base bullets are the most common type and the easiest to manufacture. This base is found on many hunting rifle bullets and most handgun bullets.

Hemispherical—This type of base is rarely seen in the United States; occasionally used on some hunting bullets in Europe.

Boattail rebated—Boattail bullets are a popular choice for target shooting and hunting at long ranges by virtue of their streamlined, low-drag design. The rebated design is not as efficient as the standard boattail, but is easier to make.

Boattail-standard—This type of boattail bullet is by far the most popular low-drag design. For maximum efficiency, the angle and length of the boattail vary with the bullet diameter, length and weight.

Hollow or recessed—This type of base is often found on handgun bullets where an effort has been made to maximize bearing surface and/or gas sealing. This type of base is seldom used in modern rifle bullets.

To this mix must be added the distinct types of bullets such as:

Full-metal-jacket—This is a common type of military design that can also be used for practice, training, qualification and some types of competition and hunting.

Hollow-point—This very popular expanding design is common on many handgun bullets and lightweight, small-caliber rifle bullets for varmint hunting. It is also a dominant design for rifle competition. Hollow-point hunting bullets in calibers over 6 mm are somewhat rare.

Soft-point—The expanding soft-point bullet remains the popular jack-of-all-trades for nearly all types of hunting. It is not nearly as popular as the hollow-point in handgun calibers.

Hollow soft-point—This combines the best of hollow- and soft-point designs in a revolver bullet. The design is seldom used outside of revolver bullets.

Capped—This is a rifle bullet design with a soft metal cap over the soft point that collapses on impact, aiding expansion. A fairly rare design, the chief example in contemporary bullets remains the Winchester Silvertip.

Tipped—This type of expanding hunting bullet features a metal or plastic tip on the ogive that is designed to prevent tip deformation in the magazine, enhance the ballistic coefficient and assist expansion on impact. Older examples include the Remington Bronze Point while newer examples include the Nosler Ballistic Tip.

Frangible—Frangible bullets are usually lead-free bullets made of composite materials designed to break up into small particles on impact with a hard surface. This eliminates lead in the environment while reducing back splatter and range costs.

Bonded—Reliability in the field has made bonded bullets, like the Swift A-Frame and Scirocco, Trophy Bonded Bear Claw and Hornady InterBond, a favorite of savvy big-game hunters. Bonding the core to the jacket ensures the controlled-expansion performance so desirable on heavy game animals like elk, moose and bears.

Solid—Solid bullets may be either monolithic (made of one piece of homogenous metal) or heavily jacketed with a lead core. In addition, some hybrid types combine a monolithic body with a heavy metal insert. The purpose of a solid is to reliably penetrate heavy or dangerous game. Examples include the Barnes Solid and the Woodleigh Weldcore.

Hybrids—These bullets combine two or more of the above characteristics above, often with a unique twist of their own. Examples include the Nosler Partition, Winchester FailSafe, Hirtenberger ABC and Brenneke TUG.

Bullet Jackets

Modern bullet jackets are made from materials such as:

Clad steel—This is a popular selection for making tough jackets for non-expanding "solid" bullets for large or dangerous game. Good clad steel strip is hard to get.

Copper alloy—Copper alloy is by far the most popular choice for bullet jackets based on performance, availability, cost and ease of manufacture. Preferred jacket alloys are 95 percent copper/5 percent zinc or 90 percent copper/10 percent zinc.

Aluminum alloy—Pioneered by Winchester for Silvertip expanding handgun bullets, aluminum alloy has not been taken up as a jacket material by other manufacturers.

Polymers—Polymer jackets are formed in situ on the bullet by first tumbling the bullet in powdered polymer then using infrared heat to fuse it to the bullet surface. The bullet is then sized to the correct diameter. Pioneered by Federal Cartridge for use in handgun bullets.

Metal bullet jackets are drawn from metal cups in similar manner to cartridge cases, except on a smaller size scale. After the jackets have been drawn, washed, annealed and trimmed, they take the form of metal tubes closed at one end. These jackets are then fed into multi-stage bullet-assembly machines that begin by inserting a lead core in the jacket using many tons of pressure. The remainder of the bullet, including the point and base, is then formed in stages by the press. If necessary, the finished bullet is cannelured. Finished bullets are tumbled in barrels to knock off sprues and sharp lead edges, and then washed, dried and packed or used in loading machines.

Shotshell Pellets and Wads

Pellet Production

Shotguns and some specialized types of handgun cartridges are loaded with small round pellets called shot. These pellets are made in different diameters with the smaller sizes below .200" in diameter being called shot or pellets and larger sizes being called buckshot. Shot and buckshot can be made from different materials. The most common include:

Lead and lead alloys

Lead has historically been the material of choice for making shot as it is cheap, abundant, easy to work and has a low melting point. Lead is commonly alloyed with 0.5 to 6 percent antimony as a hardening agent.

Bismuth

Similar in many ways to lead but lighter, bismuth has recently come into use for shot making because of its non-toxic characteristics and acceptable ballistic qualities. In addition, bismuth shot can be loaded with lead-shot wad columns and will not damage older shotgun barrels.

Tungsten composites

Tungsten matrix—Tungsten-matrix shot is a compressed mixture of powdered tungsten and powdered copper in a binding agent. It offers similar ballistic qualities to lead shot and it is non-toxic and will not damage shotgun barrels. However, it is more expensive than lead shot.

Tungsten polymer—This is a molded mixture of powdered tungsten and powdered copper in a polymer binder. It is expensive, but it offers acceptable ballistic performance, is non-toxic and will not damage shotgun barrels. Its chief drawback is that it is more expensive than lead shot.

Tungsten iron—Tungsten-iron shot is made by sintering a mixture of powdered tungsten and powdered iron. This yields an expensive, very hard, non-toxic pellet of equal or greater density than lead. Exterior ballistic properties of tungsten iron are very good. However, special wads are required to prevent barrel damage and tungsten-iron shot cannot be used through some barrels and choke tubes.

Tin

Primarily used as an alloy in making lead shot, tin also can be used to make shot pellets. However, high cost and poor ballistic performance due to its light weight make tin a poor choice for this purpose.

Zinc
Cheap, abundant and easy to manufacture, zinc shot suffers from poor ballistic performance due to its light weight and softness. It is also toxic, making it unsuitable for modern shotshells.

Steel
Relatively soft steel shot is now common for hunting migratory waterfowl. Steel shot is cheap, abundant and non-toxic, but it is also very hard, so special wads and barrels are needed to prevent barrel damage. The light weight of steel shot offers poor ballistic performance that is partially offset by increasing its muzzle velocity and switching to larger pellet sizes.

Small lead and bismuth shot sizes are made by a process called dropping. The metal is melted and then dropped through a pan with holes in the bottom into a water bath. Larger sizes of lead and bismuth shot are swaged in dies or cast in molds.

Composite shot is molded or sintered. Steel shot is made in a manner similar to ball bearings by rolling a pre-form cut from wire between counter-rotating steel plates, then annealing.

Shot pellets may be plated with copper, nickel or zinc. Such plating on lead pellets serves to harden the surface for improved patterns and reduce feather draw on impact. Plating on steel shot serves to reduce corrosion.

Wad Columns
A wad column for a shotshell serves a number of important functions. It must:
- seal the hot propellant gas from the shot charge
- cushion the shot charge from the forces of acceleration
- be as tough and light as possible
- be cheap and easy to manufacture
- protect the shot charge from abrasion on the bore surface
- take up the appropriate amount of space inside the shell
- not travel long distances after exiting the muzzle
- not degrade in long-term storage or react with the chemicals in powders
- be biodegradable.

Wad columns were originally made of waxed felt and paper card disks. When felt became too expensive in the 1950s, molded wads of low-density plastic were developed. Plastic wads were cheap, tough, light and easier to load than felt wads. They were also designed with pouches on the front end to protect the shot charge from abrading on the bore surface.

In practice, plastic wads also sealed propellant powder gases much more effectively than felt or card wads. The lighter weight of plastic wads also reduced recoil.

Plastic wad columns and plastic-hulled shotshells quickly replaced paper-hulled shells and felt or card wads in the mid-1960s. When steel shot became mandatory for hunting migratory waterfowl in the late 1980s, wad columns of high density polyethylene plastic were developed to positively prevent the steel pellets from contacting the bore surface. Unlike lead shot wads, steel shot wads have no cushion section.

Plastic wads are normally designed for a specific weight of shot charge with a broad selection of powders. As many plastic wads look alike, it is a common practice to color-code them. Recent technology has developed wad columns made of a more biodegradable plastic, thus eliminating a major complaint about plastic wads being left in the environment.

Card wads were originally used with a roll crimp to seal the front end of shotshells. However, tests indicated that such wads had an adverse effect of pattern quality which led to the development of the folded crimp closure on modern shotshells.

Propellant Powder

Gunpowder is a flammable solid that stores chemical energy. When ignited, it releases the stored chemical energy in the form of hot, rapidly expanding gas. In a firearm, propellants do not explode, rather they deflagrate or burn rapidly. The rate of deflagration is what separates smokeless propellants from true explosives. An explosive may be defined as an energetic substance that deflagrates at velocities greater than 4000 f.p.s. Smokeless propellants deflagrate at much slower velocities.

There are three principal types of propellant powders.

Blackpowder—Blackpowder is a physical mix of three ingredients in the following proportions: charcoal—15½ percent; sulphur—10½ percent; and potassium nitrate—74 percent.

Semi-smokeless—This type of propellant is a mixture of smokeless and blackpowder. It was used in early .22 rimfire ammunition but has been obsolete since the late 1930s.

Smokeless powder—This is a chemical mix of various ingredients that locks chemical energy into the molecular structure of the material. The main feed stock of smokeless powder is nitrocellulose obtained from either wood (good) or cotton (best).

There are three types of smokeless powder:

Single-base—Main ingredient is nitrocellulose. Examples include most IMR stick powders. Single-base propellants are a popular choice for many non-magnum rifle and handgun loads.

Double-base—The nitrocellulose base is enhanced by the addition of 2 to 39 percent nitroglycerin. Examples include ball powders and Bullseye flake powder. Double-base propellants are a popular choice for many handgun and shotgun loads as well as most rimfire ammunition.

Triple-base—Nitroguanidine is added to double-base powder to increase the energy content even more. Examples include propellants for tank guns and artillery. This type of propellant is not often used in small-arms ammunition.

In addition to nitrocellulose and nitroglycerin, smokeless powder has several other ingredients including:

- solvents
- stabilizers
- flash inhibitors
- deterrent surface coatings
- anti-static surface coatings
- identity markers (inert).

Perhaps the most important of the above are the deterrent coatings that serve to help control the burning rate along with the shape and size of the powder granules.

Emissions from Burning Propellants

Typical products emitted by burning smokeless and blackpowder propellants (in average lbs. of gas per ton of powder burned).

Propellant Type

Product	Blackpowder	Single-Base Smokeless	Double-Base Smokeless	Triple-Base Smokeless
carbon monoxide	0	798.2	327.4	794.4
carbon dioxide	844	757.6	1,137	142.6
nitrogen	204.8	239.6	297	0
water	0	146.6	163.4	480.7
hydrogen	0	46	26.4	43
carbon	18.8	0	0	0
methane	0	10.4	14.4	13.8
ammonia	0	0.03	0	2.72
hydrogen cyanide	0	0	0	2.21
potassium	273.8	0	0	0
carbon oxisulfide	330.2	0	0	0
sulphur	0.6	0	0	0
carbon disulphide	26.3	0	0	0
total average pounds emitted	1,698.5	1,998.4	1,965.6	1,479.4
calorific value		3,600-5,600 kJ/kg	3,000-3,700kJ/kg	

Gunpowder Characteristics

Propellant powder granules come in various shapes including:

- sticks or extruded (with one or more holes through them)
- flakes (round, square, trapezoidal or irregular; with or without holes)
- balls (of various diameters)
- flattened spheres (of various diameters).

Smokeless powder burns in one of three ways. It is either:

Degressive—The burning rate and breech pressure steadily decrease, leaving very little area under the pressure/time curve, which is not efficient and wastes much of the energy contained in the propellant powder.

Neutral—The burning rate is steady. More efficient than degressive propellants, neutral burning can provide a larger area under the pressure/time curve. However, this type of burning still wastes much of the energy in the powder.

Progressive—The burning rate increases as it progresses. This provides a steady and prolonged "push" on the bullet for maximum efficiency by keeping the area under the pressure curve as high as possible.

Cartridge Efficiency

A firearm is a heat engine that converts stored chemical energy to kinetic energy. As a heat engine, a firearm is very inefficient, avgeraging less than 40 percent efficiency.

Average energy loss breakdown:

unburned propellant	2%
friction	3%
heat to barrel	25%
unused energy in hot gas	30%
	60% propellant energy wasted
efficiency	**40%**

Heat loss breakdown:

transferred to barrel/action	30%
recoil, noise, escaping gas	40%
	70% propellant gas heat lost
heat converted to kinetic energy (efficiency)	**30%**

When one considers that even the best balanced loads are only about 30 percent efficient, it becomes clear that there is no excess energy to waste in smokeless powders. For this reason, nearly all modern smokeless propellants are progressive burning.

Relative Burn Rates for Smokeless Propellants
(From fastest to slowest for canister powders)

Position	Manufacturer	Propellant
1.	RWS	P805
	Norma	R1
2.	Vihtavuori	N310
3.	Hodgdon	Titewad
4.	Alliant	Red Dot
5.	Hodgdon	Clays
6.	IMR	700X
7.	Alliant	Bullseye
8.	Hodgdon	International
9 .	Alliant	American Select
10 .	Accurate Arms	Solo 1000
11 .	Alliant	Green Dot
12.	Hodgdon	Titegroup
	Winchester	452AA
13.	IMR	PB
14.	Vihtavuori	N320
15.	Winchester	WST
16.	Accurate Arms	No. 2
17.	IMR	SR7625
	RWS	P804
18.	Hodgdon	HP-38
	RWS	P801
	SNPE	BA10
19.	Winchester	231
	Winchester	473AA
20.	Alliant	Unique
21.	Hodgdon	Universal
22.	Alliant	Power Pistol
	RWS	P803
	SNPE	BA9
23.	Vihtavuori	N330
24.	Alliant	Herco
25.	Winchester	WSF
26.	Vihtavuori	N340
27.	IMR	800X
	Winchester	540
28	IMR	SR4756
29.	Accurate Arms	No. 5
30.	Hodgdon	HS-6
	Winchester	571
31.	Vihtavuori	3N37
32.	Vihtavuori	N350

Position	Manufacturer	Propellant
33.	Alliant	Blue Dot
34.	Accurate Arms	No. 7
35.	Alliant	2400
36.	Accurate Arms	No. 9
37.	Norma	R123
38.	Vihtavuori	N110
	RWS	P806
39.	Hodgdon	H110
40.	Winchester	296
	Winchester	680
41.	IMR	4227
42.	Hodgdon	H4227
	RWS	Nobel 3
43.	IMR	SR4759
44.	Accurate Arms	1680
45.	Norma	200
	RWS	R901
46.	Alliant	Reloder 7
47.	IMR	4198
48.	Hodgdon	H4198
	SNPE	Tubal 1
49.	Vihtavouri	N120
50.	Hodgdon	H322
51.	Accurate Arms	2015 BR
52.	Vihtavuori	N130
53.	IMR	3031
	RWS	R902
	RWS	Nobel 2
	Norma	201
54.	Vihtavuori	N133
55.	Hodgdon	H335
	SNPE	SP10
	RWS	R903
56.	Vihtavuori	N135
	SNPE	Tubal 4
57.	Accurate Arms	2230
58.	Accurate Arms	2460
59.	Hodgdon	H4895
60.	IMR	4895
61.	Alliant	Reloder 12
62.	IMR	4320
63.	Accurate Arms	2495 BR
64.	IMR	4064
	RWS	Nobel 1
65.	Norma	202

Position	Manufacturer	Propellant
66.	Accurate Arms	2520
67.	Alliant	Reloder 15
	SNPE	Tubal 5
68.	Vihtavuori	N140
69.	Hodgdon	Varget
70.	Winchester	748
71.	Hodgdon	BL-C (2)
	SNPE	Tubal 2
72.	Hodgdon	H380
	RWS	R907
73.	Winchester	760
74.	Hodgdon	H414
	SNPE	Tubal 6
	RWS	R904
75.	Vihtavuori	N150
	RWS	Nobel 0
76.	Accurate Arms	2700
77.	IMR	4350
78.	Hodgdon	H4350
79.	Accurate Arms	4350
	SNPE	Tubal 7
	Hodgdon	H450
80.	Norma	204
81.	Vihtavuori	N550
82.	Alliant	Reloder 19
	Winchester	785
83.	IMR	4831
	SNPE	Tubal 8
84.	Accurate Arms	3100
85.	Vihtavuori	N160
86.	Hodgdon	H4831/H4831SC
	RWS	R905
87.	Norma	MRP
88.	Alliant	Reloder 22
89.	Vihtavuori	N165
90.	IMR	7828
91.	Vihtavuori	N170
92.	Hodgdon	H1000
93.	Accurate Arms	8700
94.	Hodgdon	H870
95.	Vihtavuori	24N41
96.	Hodgdon	H50BMG
97.	Vihtavuori	20N29

Relative Burning Rate of Powders by Brand
(From fastest to slowest)

Accurate Arms	Alliant	Hodgdon	IMR	Norma
Solo 1000	Bullseye	Titewad	700X	R1
Nitro 100	Red Dot	Clays	PB	R123
No. 2	Green Dot	International	SR7625	200
No. 5	Unique	Titegroup	800X	201
No. 7	Herco	HP-38	SR4756	202
No. 9	Blue Dot	Trap 100	SR4759	203
1680	2400	HS-5	4227	204
2015BR	Reloder 7	HS-6	4198	MRP
2230	Reloder 12	HS-7	3031	
2460	Reloder 15	H110	4064	
2495BR	Reloder 19	H4227	4895	
2520	Reloder 22	H4198	4320	
2700		H322	4350	
4350		BLC2	4831	
3100		H335	7828	
8700		H4895	5010	
		H380		
		H414		
		H450		
		H4831		
		H1000		
		H870		

RWS	Vectan	Vihtavuori	Winchester
P805	Ba10	N310	231
P801	As	N320	WST
P804	A1	N330	WSL
P803	Ba9	N340	WAP
P806	Ao	3N37	WSF
30 Carb	Sp8	N350	540
R901	Sp2	N105SM	571
R902	Sp3	N110	630
R903	Ba6	N120	296
R904	Tu2000	N130	680
R905	Tu3000	N133	748
	Sp10	N135	760
	Sp9	N140	WMR
	Sp7	N150	
	Tu5000	N160	
	Tu7000	N165	
	Tu8000		

Types of Military Small Arms Ammunition

Modern Types

Ball—Ammunition loaded with a non-expanding bullet of full-metal-jacket construction designed for general combat issue. Ball ammunition normally has no identification painted on the bullet ogive.

- Short Range Training (SRT)—a lightweight bullet with limited range for training only. Bullet of molded plastic or jacketed with core of aluminum, plastic or other light material. Lethal at close range, but not intended for combat issue.

- Normal—A full-metal-jacket bullet of specified weight for general combat issue. Bullet core generally of lead, lead/soft steel or other combination with copper alloy or clad steel jacket. Pointed ogive with boattail or flat base.

  5.56x45 mm NATO—M193
  .30 Carbine—M1
  .30-'06 Sprg.—M2
  7.62x51 mm NATO—M59, M80
  9x19 mm NATO—M882
  .45 ACP—M1911
  .50 BMG—M33

- Long Range—A full-metal-jacket bullet of heavier than normal weight with a boattail base for increased range. Issue generally limited to snipers or machine gunners. Often identified with a yellow tip.
  5.56x45 mm NATO—M855A1
  .30-'06 Sprg.—M1
  7.62x51 mm NATO—M118
  .50 BMG—M1

- Duplex—A ball cartridge loaded with two clad-steel, flat-base, solid bullets of approximately half the weight of a normal ball bullet. On firing, the two bullets separate and impact within several inches of each other at 100 yds. Designed for machine gun use at night for firing high-volume, final defensive lines of fire. Not common. Identified normally with a green tip.
  7.62x51 mm NATO—M198

- Subsonic—A round of ball ammunition usually loaded with a heavier-than-normal full-metal-jacket bullet to subsonic muzzle velocities (less than 1150 f.p.s.). Designed for combat use at close ranges with a suppressor or silencer to substantially reduce the muzzle signature. Low muzzle velocity eliminates the supersonic report of the bullet as it travels through the air. Limited issue and use. May have a silver or yellow tip.

Tracer (T)—Ammunition loaded with a bullet having a pyrotechnic compound in the base that emits a visible flame as the bullet travels through the air. Common trace colors are red, orange, green and white, but other colors may be used. Tracers enable machine gunners to adjust fire, and for this reason, they are commonly inserted in belts or magazines in a ratio of one tracer to five ball or whatever ratio the gunner prefers. Accordingly, tracer bullets are designed so that their trajectory matches the ball bullet. Tracer bullets have substantial incendiary effect on impact and frequently start fires. Tracer bullets are normally identified with a red, orange or green tip.

- Short-Range Tracer—A tracer version of the SRT ball ammunition as above. For training use only.
- Normal Tracer—For combat issue. Tracer element usually functions between specified distances—i.e., 100 yds. to 800 yds.—then burns out.
  5.56x45 mm NATO—M196, M856A1
  .30 Carbine—M16, M27
  .30-'06 Sprg.—M1, M25
  7.62x51 mm NATO—M62
  .50 BMG—M1, M10, M17, M21
  .45 ACP—M26

- Dim Ignition Tracer—A tracer bullet with substantially reduced light output for use at night where a normal tracer would blind the machine gunner. Also used with night-vision equipment to prevent blooming. Not common.

- Infrared Tracer—A tracer bullet that emits light in the infrared spectrum. Visible when using infrared night-vision equipment, but invisible to the naked eye. Not common.

- Signal Tracer—An especially bright tracer for handgun ammunition designed for downed aircrews to fire into the air to attract search and rescue teams. Not common, now obsolete.

Incendiary (I)—Ammunition loaded with a bullet containing an incendiary mixture designed to start fires after impact. Early incendiary bullets were filled with metallic potassium that burned on contact with air. This type is long obsolete. Modern incendiary bullets depend on zirconium for their incendiary effect. Incendiary bullets do not trace and are often identified by a silver tip.
  .50 BMG— M1, M23

Armor Piercing (AP)—Ammunition loaded with a full-metal-jacket bullet having a hardened metal core designed to penetrate resistant targets. Common materials for armor-piercing bullet cores are hardened steel and tungsten alloys, often with a lead sleeve. Armor-piercing bullets are normally identified by a black tip.

- Armor Piercing (AP)—Ammunition with a full-bore-caliber, full-metal-jacket bullet having a hardened core to penetrate resistant targets.
  5.56x45 mm NATO—M855
  .30-'06 Sprg.—M2
  7.62x51 mm NATO—M61
  .50 BMG—M2

- Armor Piercing Discarding Sabot (APDS)—Armor-piercing ammunition loaded with a hard metal, spin-stabilized, sub-caliber penetrator held in a sabot that is discarded at the muzzle. The penetrator, being much lighter than a normal AP bullet, can be launched at substantially higher muzzle velocities to enhance armor penetration and reduced time of flight. Not common. Sometimes called HVAP or Hyper Velocity Armor Piercing

- Armor Piercing Fin Stabilized Discarding Sabot (APFSDS)— Ammunition loaded with a fin-stabilized, sub-caliber dart or flechette of hard metal held in a sabot that is discarded at the muzzle. Very high muzzle velocities are possible due to the light projectile weight, and excellent armor-piercing capabilities and short flight times result from the high length-to-diameter ratio

Armor Piercing Incendiary (API)—Ammunition loaded with a bullet combining armor-piercing capability with an incendiary element in the nose cavity. Identified by a black bullet ogive with a silver tip. Not common.
  .30-'06 Sprg.—M14
  .50 BMG—M8

Armor Piercing Tracer (APT)—Ammunition loaded with a bullet combining an armor-piercing hard core with a tracer element in the base. Armor-piercing capability reduced because of tracer, but tracer adds incendiary capability. Identified by a black bullet ogive with a red tip. Not common.

Armor Piercing Incendiary Tracer (APIT)—Ammunition loaded with a bullet attempting to combine armor-piercing, incendiary and tracer functions. A compromise design with reduced armor-piercing and incendiary capability. Identified by a black bullet ogive with a silver band and a red tip. Not common.
  .50 BMG—M20

Frangible—Ammunition loaded with a bullet designed to disintegrate into small, non-lethal particles on impact with a hard surface. Frangible bullets may be jacketed or monolithic with lead-free cores that are lighter in weight than ball bullets with reduced range. Designed for training use only, frangible ammunition will not cycle modern military arms without modification. In the past, frangible rifle ammunition has been identified by a bullet having a green ogive with a white tip. May be found in rifle and pistol calibers.

.30-'06 Sprg.—M22
7.62x51 mm NATO—M160

Blank—Ammunition loaded without a bullet, but designed to either propel a device or to simulate the sound and flash of ball ammunition.

- Maneuver—Ammunition loaded without a bullet to simulate the sound and flash of ball ammunition for training and saluting purposes. When loaded in a standard-length case, mouth closure may be with a red lacquer-coated fiber wad or a plain or colored wooden bullet. Modern blanks are loaded using a case having an extended-length neck closed with a star crimp and sealed with white lacquer. Loaded with very fast-burning powder.

  5.56x45 mm NATO—M200
  .30-'06 Sprg.—M1909
  7.62x51 mm NATO—M8
  .50 BMG—M1
  .45 ACP—M9

- Grenade Launching—Blank ammunition designed for combat use as the propelling or launching charge for a rifle grenade. Normally found with crimped case mouth on a standard-length case with black lacquer sealer. Loaded with very slow-burning propellant to push heavy weight. Normally packed with a rifle grenade.

  5.56x45 mm NATO—M195
  .30 Carbine—M6
  .30-'06 Sprg.—M3
  7.62x51 mm NATO—M64

- Line Throwing—Blank ammunition designed for use in special guns for throwing a weight with a line attached. Normally used on ships for throwing lines and for rescue purposes.
  .45-70 Gov't—M32

- Ignition Blank—Blank ammunition designed especially for igniting flame throwers.

Multipurpose—Combat ammunition loaded with a bullet having a chemical fuze, an explosive filler and a steel internal body. Designed for penetration of light-armor arrays with explosive effects after penetration. Not common in small calibers.

Match—Ammunition loaded using special manufacturing procedures and components to enhance accuracy, consistency and reliability. May be used for competition or for combat issue to snipers. Often found with full-metal-jacket or hollow-point, boattail bullet of heavier-than-normal weight.

.30-'06 Sprg.—M72
7.62x51 mm NATO—M118, M852
.45 ACP—M1911

Proof/High Pressure Test—Ball ammunition loaded to substantially higher-than-normal breech pressures and designed only for proofing firearms. Limited distribution and not for combat issue. Proof cartridges normally have distinctive markings such as a tinned case, red painted base, knurled rim or other similar markings.

5.56x45 mm NATO—M197
.30 Carbine—M18
.30-'06 Sprg.—M1
7.62x51 mm NATO—M60
9x19 mm NATO—M905
.45 M1911—M1
.50 BMG—M1

Dummy

- Dummy Cartridge—A dummy cartridge for use as a training aid. A dummy cartridge is loaded with a standard full-metal-jacket ball bullet heavily crimped in place so as not to come loose. A dummy primer is used for safety and there is no filling inside the case. Normally, a training dummy cartridge is distinguished by indents or flutes in the case body.
5.56x45 mm NATO—M199
7.62x51 mm NATO—M63
.30 Carbine—M13
.30-'06 Sprg.—M40
9x19 mm NATO—M917
.45 ACP—M1921

- Inert-Loaded Dummy—An inert-loaded dummy cartridge has a standard ball bullet heavily crimped into the case mouth, a dummy primer and an inert filler in the case to provide weight and balance similar to ball ammunition. Normally, the case is tinned, nickel-plated or blackened for identification. Inert-loaded dummy cartridges are used by armorers to safely check firearms feeding, chambering, extraction and ejection.
5.56x45 mm NATO—M232, M857
7.62x51 mm NATO—M172
.50 BMG—M176

Reference—Ammunition loaded to a high level of quality, tested and meeting specifications established. Used to calibrate range equipment in arsenals and other manufacturing facilities.

Gauge—A precision-made, inert, dummy cartridge normally made of machined steel. Gauge cartridges are used by designers, production engineers and armorers to check chamber, headspace and other dimensions of military firearms.

Low Lethality—Ammunition designed specifically for control of mobs, riots and belligerent individuals. At close ranges (approximately 50'), low-lethality bullets may be lethal. However, at ranges beyond 50' they are normally less than lethal. Low-lethality bullets function by striking the subjects with enough force to make them cease and desist their actions without permanently injuring them. Low-lethality bullets may be made of rubber, wood, plastic or other soft substances and are launched at low velocities.

Underwater—A new type of ammunition pioneered by the Russian military for use in special handguns and rifles designed to be fired under water. A conventional steel cartridge case and primer are loaded with a finned, steel dart with a very high length-to-diameter ratio. The darts are designed to be stable in water, but effective range is limited. Underwater ammunition can also be fired through the air at short ranges.

Obsolete Types

Guard—A round of rifle ammunition having a reduced powder change and a lightweight bullet for use on guard duty. Low velocity and reduced penetration were safety measures.

Gallery—A round of ammunition having a round lead ball at reduced velocity for use in training on indoor ranges.

Antenna Erecting—This was a variation of a grenade-launching blank loaded in a standard rifle-caliber cartridge case and designed to project a weight trailing an antenna wire over trees, buildings, etc.
.30-'06 Sprg.—T61

Spotting—Ammunition used to estimate range for direct fire purposes such as antitank guns. Spotting bullets have a tracer in the base, an impact-detonating nose fuze and a small bursting charge in the nose cavity. On impact, the bullet explodes with a bright flash and a puff of smoke to indicate the gunner is on target so the main gun can be fired.
.50 Spotter-Tracer—M48

Shot—Rifle or pistol ammunition loaded with a charge of lead shot held in a paper, wooden or metal container. Used for foraging for edible game or survival purposes.
.45 ACP—M12, M15

High Explosive—Ammunition loaded with a charge of high explosive. May be mechanically fuzed or chemically fuzed. Designed for air combat/antiaircraft use in machine guns.

Lachrymatory—Military ammunition designed to disperse powdered tear gas on impact. Intended for use against armored vehicles, buildings and bunkers. Found ineffective and discontinued. .50 BMG—T86

Poisonous—Military full-metal-jacket bullet having a frangible capsule of poison under the tip. On impact, the poison capsule is ruptured and the poison dispersed assuring the death of the target. Outlawed for military use by various Geneva Conventions.

Salvo Squeezebore—A variation of the duplex bullet principle using from three to five hollow-base, cone-shaped, copper-jacketed bullets held in a plastic sleeve loaded in a standard cartridge case. The assembly travels down the bore intact until it reaches a tapered section that squeezes the cone diameter down substantially and at the same time ruptures the plastic retaining sleeve. At the muzzle, the multiple projectiles disperse in a shotgun pattern. Used only in machine guns.

Tropical—Military ammunition loaded for use in high heat or tropical climates. This involved changes to the propellant charge and increased attention to case mouth and primer sealing. Tropical ammunition was often indicated by a narrow green band on the bullet ogive. It has been made obsolete by improved propellants and sealing methods.

High Velocity—Military ball, armor-piercing and tracer ammunition loaded to higher pressure and velocity for rifle-caliber machine guns used in air combat.

Silenced—A modern military cartridge designed for use in tunnels and confined spaces where a reduced signature is required. Silenced or QSPR ammunition was loaded in cases of standard exterior dimensions with a threaded section inside the case mouth just under the bullet's base. Beneath the bullet was a U-shaped, flexible internal element of aluminum alloy that held the propellant charge against the primer. On firing, the expanding propellant gases unfolded the flexible internal element. The unfolding internal element slapped the bullet out of the barrel. The flexible internal element is prevented from leaving the cartridge case by the threaded section inside the case mouth. The flexible element then balloons out of the case mouth, but does not rupture, thus containing the propellant gases. In this manner, the gun firing such ammunition is silent but requires no silencer. Mainly made in pistol calibers, such ammunition was nicknamed "hushpuppy" by the soldiers.

Sub-Caliber—Ball ammunition used for training in sub-caliber devices in artillery barrels.

A Hunting Bullet Is a Compromise

As the physical link between hunter and game, the bullet plays a vital role in any hunt. For this reason, a heavy reliance and high expectations ride on a hunting rifle bullet's performance. While a hunting bullet may appear a simple assembly of two or more unsophisticated parts, every bullet combines a complex series of engineering compromises and tradeoffs. Because a well-designed bullet requires a unique combination of engineering and experience, the design process comprises equal parts art and science.

From the standpoint of interior ballistics, the ideal hunting rifle bullet would be a bore-diameter, homogenous cylinder. Such a bullet would be cheap, easy to manufacture and have maximum bearing surface for superior accuracy.

From the standpoint of exterior ballistics, an efficient hunting rifle bullet would have a high length-to-diameter ratio, a sharp, drag-reducing point and a tapered base (boattail). Such a bullet would offer high retained velocity and energy, flat trajectory and minimum wind drift.

From the standpoint of terminal ballistics, the ideal hunting rifle bullet would combine sub-m.o.a. accuracy with reliable penetration, consistent double-diameter expansion and 100 percent weight retention.

The above requirements pull rifle bullet designers in different, often mutually exclusive, directions. As a result, all rifle bullets are a compromise; none is perfect. All bullet designers begin with a set of performance criteria that determines the engineering compromises they will use in designing a specific bullet. Their criteria may meet your requirements or prove totally unsatisfactory. For this reason, manufacturers offer hunting rifle bullets in a bewildering variety of calibers, weights, profiles and constructions.

Ogive Profiles

Because a flat cylinder is undesirable for exterior ballistic reasons, rifle bullets have one of three ogives or point profiles: flat nose (FN), round nose (RN) or pointed (spitzer). Of these, the spitzer is the most popular. Flat-nose bullets and round-nose bullets are typically used for hunting at ranges under 150 yds. where poor exterior ballistics caused by their blunt point are not a significant drawback. Pointed bullets are the best choice for hunting at medium and long ranges.

Flat-nose bullets are preferred for rifles with tubular magazines where a round-nose or pointed bullet might accidentally strike the primer of the cartridge in front of it and cause that cartridge to fire with catastrophic results. FN bullets are easy to make and common in medium and heavy weights. Popular rifle calibers using FN bullets include the .30-30 Win. and .45-70 Gov't.

Round-nose bullets are optimized for heavyweight bullets as the point shape maximizes internal volume. RN bullets are easy to make and offer plenty of bearing surface. In large calibers for dangerous game such as the .416 Rigby, .458 Win. Mag., and .470 Nitro Express, RN bullets are standard fare. In lighter calibers such as .270 Win., 7 mm Rem. Mag., and .30-'06 Sprg., RN bullets are offered only in the heaviest weights. Popular RN bullets include the Remington Core-Lokt SP, Winchester Super-X PowerPoint and PowerPoint Plus and the Federal Power-Shok, as well as the Barnes Original.

Spitzer or pointed bullets may have a tangent-ogive profile (sharp) or a secant-ogive profile (sharper). Of these, the tangent-ogive profile remains the most popular as it allows more bearing surface with a suitably sharp point. Many general-purpose, medium-weight hunting bullets therefore are tangent-ogive spitzers. Popular examples include: Federal Power-Shok SP, Winchester Super-X SP and Super-X PSP, Remington Core-Lokt PSP, Sierra Pro-Hunter and Speer HotCor. Secant-ogive spitzer bullets are a specialty of Hornady with their SP Interlock and A-Max bullets. Popular calibers that use spitzer bullets nearly exclusively are the .223 Rem., .243 Win., .270 Win. and 7 mm Rem. Mag.

Bullet Tip Designs

Bullet tip designs for hunting may be divided into the following four types: soft-point (SP), hollow-point (HP), full-metal-jacket (FMJ) and capped or tipped. Any of the four designs may be applied to an ogive profile such as a round-nose/full-metal-jacket (RN-FMJ) or a flat-nose/hollow-point (FN-HP).

By far the most popular bullet tip design for hunting is the soft-point. When the point is formed, the jacket is not fully closed, leaving lead exposed at the tip. Examples of this type of bullet include the Sierra Pro-Hunter, Hornady SP InterLock, Speer HotCor, Barnes Original, Winchester Super-X Power Point, Remington Core-Lokt and Dynamit Nobel DK. On impact, the jacket peels back and the lead core mushrooms as the bullet continues to penetrate. Penetration and energy transfer can be controlled by varying the size of the jacket opening, by tapering, notching or cutting the jacket and by varying the hardness of the lead core. Soft-point bullets are cost effective and commonly available in great variety to suit nearly any hunting application.

Hollow-point rifle bullets are popular for varmint hunting where explosive expansion is desired and retained weight is unimportant. Popular choices for this type of hunting include the Speer TNT, Winchester Super-X HP, Remington Power-Lokt HP and Sierra Varminter. However, there are successful hollow-point designs with controlled expansion for hunting big game such as the Sierra GameKing, PMC Starfire, Winchester FailSafe and Barnes X-Bullet.

Full-metal-jacket bullets are designed for penetration, not expansion. For this reason, FMJ bullets are heavily constructed with hard lead cores and thick copper-alloy or clad-steel jackets covering the entire bullet to prevent deformation and enhance penetration. Hunters choose FMJ bullets for deep penetratiom on large, dangerous game or for hunting furbearing game where expanding bullets might ruin the pelt. Popular examples of such bullets are the Woodleigh Weldcore, Trophy Bonded Sledgehammer, Hornady FMJ and Speer AGS Solid.

Capped bullets are three-piece designs with a separate metal nose cap on the ogive. During handling and feeding, the cap protects the lead core; on impact, the cap collapses, allowing the core to expand. The major example of this type of bullet available to U.S. hunters is the aluminum-capped Winchester Silvertip.

A tipped bullet is normally of three-piece construction with a sharp, pointed, metal or polymer tip crimped in a hole in the jacket nose. The tip may be of bronze (Remington's seminal Bronze Point) or polymer (Nosler's Ballistic Tip and Hornady's SST). The sharp point minimizes tip drag, then serves to facilitate mushrooming on impact as it is driven into the core. Some recent designs have a cavity beneath the tip while others do not.

Bullet Base Basics

Hunting rifle bullets may have a flat base or a boattail (tapered base). Flat-base bullets are the most common and easiest to manufacture. For hunting North American game at average ranges, flat-base bullets are hard to beat. They combine accuracy with low cost and wide variety. For these reasons, they are the choice of most hunters.

Boattail bullets are more difficult to manufacture and therefore more expensive. The streamlined, tapered base of the boattail bullet significantly reduces base drag which results in higher striking velocity and energy, flatter trajectories and reduced wind drift. Although the advantages of boattail bullets accrue at all ranges, the effect builds, and the advantages become more apparent at long ranges. At ranges under 200 yds., boattail bullets offer the hunter only minimal gains. Due to both the increased cost of manufacture and superior long-range ballistics, boattail bullets are normally considered a premium product for long-range hunting under difficult conditions and are priced accordingly. As a result, boattail bullets such as the Sierra GameKing, Hornady SST, Speer SPBT, Winchester Supreme Ballistic Silvertip, Remington Premier Scirocco Bonded, Barnes X and Nosler Ballistic Tip are excellent choices for high-velocity cartridges, long-range magnums and many standard calibers where added effective range may be needed. Boattail bullets offer no advantage in low-velocity calibers such as .30-30 Win. or .45-70 Gov't.

Jackets

A well-dressed hunting rifle bullet wears a jacket of copper alloy or clad steel. Typical copper-alloy jackets are made of 95 percent copper and 5 percent zinc (95/5) or 90/10 copper/zinc. Both are popular because of low price, ease of drawing and excellent ballistic performance.

Typical steel jackets are clad with one or two layers of copper and often one layer of nickel. In the past, clad-steel jackets were used for soft-point bullets such as the Norma Alaska when copper became scarce or expensive. Today, clad steel finds its major use in heavily constructed, full-metal-jacket bullets intended for dangerous game such as the Hornady FMJ or Woodleigh Weldcore Solid.

Typically, a soft-point bullet jacket is thinly tapered at the nose to promote expansion. In addition, there are often notches, seams or cuts made in the jacket nose to canalize jacket rupture and to control jacket upset. Most hunting bullets also have a circumferential cannelure or belt rolled or cut into the bearing surface. Although primarily applied to help control seating depth and bullet push/pull, the cannelure can also significantly aid controlling jacket upset and core retention.

Some premium bullets offer more sophisticated bullet jacket and core designs. For example, the famous Nosler Partition and Partition Gold bullets feature an H-shaped jacket with two separate lead cores. The Speer Grand Slam and Dynamit Nobel DK use two lead cores of differing hardness and the Winchester FailSafe bullet uses a rear lead core reinforced by a steel liner and copper base plug inside the jacket.

The Core of The Matter

Cores for hunting bullets are typically of lead—often alloyed with antimony as a hardening agent. In most instances, the lead is extruded into wire, then cut and swaged into core pre-forms. The pre-form is then fed into a bullet-assembly machine that inserts the core in the jacket and forms the bullet. This is the method Hornady, Sierra, Winchester, Federal, Remington and Nosler use. Some Speer hunting bullets are made by a method called the HotCor system wherein the lead is melted, then poured into the jacket prior to forming. Of course Nosler is famous for its Partition bullet with two cores separated by an H-shaped jacket and Remington is well-known for its electrolytically applied jacket in its Power-Lokt bullets.

Depending on the performance desired, the core may be hard or soft. Soft cores (0 percent or trace amounts of antimony) open quickly and easily, but may disintegrate or lose excessive weight. Hard cores (up to 5 percent antimony) resist weight loss and disintegration, but may not mushroom evenly or at all. The best hunting bullets are a compromise with 1- to 1½-percent antimony cores.

Ideally, a double-diameter expanded bullet retains 100 percent of its weight. This is rarely the case, however, with average retained weights from 50 percent up. Greater retained weight doesn't necessarily indicate a better bullet. The highly regarded Nosler Partition reliably retains about 65 percent, while a conventional soft-point of identical weight and caliber may retain 80 to 90 percent original weight. Which is better? It depends entirely on what the hunter is looking for.

Many premium hunting bullets like the Swift A-Frame and Scirocco, Nosler AccuBond, Hornady InterBond, Trophy Bonded Bear Claw, and Norma Oryx feature a core bonded to the jacket. Typically, this is accomplished by coating the core with low-temperature solder before inserting it in the jacket, then heating the bullet after forming to solder the core to the jacket. Bonded-core bullets effectively resist core/jacket separation on impact, but the process adds considerably to cost. A cheaper alternative is an inner belt that physically locks the core to the jacket such as Hornady's or Remington's designs.

And then there is the homogenous bullet. Some homogenous bullets are swaged while others are turned, but all have no jacket and are monolithic in that their core and body are made of one metal—usually a copper alloy. Examples of this type of bullet are the Barnes X-Bullet, XLC and Triple Shock, and Speer African Grand Slam Solid designs. Although each of these bullets is of slightly different construction and purpose, the basic monolithic body and jacket construction are similar. The Barnes X is an expanding, spitzer, hollow-point design of copper alloy with a boattail, while the Speer African Grand Slam is of solid copper with a tungsten core inserted in the rear for added mass.

Selecting a Hunting Bullet

In the end, the sportsman must first determine the performance parameters needed from his rifle bullet, and then select the bullet profile, weight and construction that will provide the performance sought. Begin this process by reviewing all the bullets offered in your particular caliber in manufacturers' literature. Then select an appropriate ogive and tail profile based on the ranges expected to be encountered. Next, select a bullet weight appropriate for the intended game. Lastly, select a bullet construction appropriate to the hunting conditions and size of the game.

In this connection, there may be no simple answer in that several very different rifle bullet types may work for an intended purpose.

Judging Bullet Performance

Most hunters judge rifle bullet performance on four criteria: accuracy, retained weight, penetration and reliability.

Accuracy determines the basic ability to hit the target at the aiming point. The recommended method of determining bullet accuracy is to fire five groups of five shots each at 100 yds., then average the extreme spread. How much accuracy required depends on the type of hunting. For hunting medium North American game in brush or at ranges of less than 100 yds., an average extreme spread of up to 4" can be acceptable. For hunting most game at ranges out to 200 yds. an average extreme spread of 2-3" is acceptable. For varmint hunting and hunting at long ranges, an average extreme spread of 1" is desirable.

Retained weight of the expanded bullet should be 60 to 100 percent of the original weight. For heavy game requiring deep penetration, 60 to 80 percent bullet weight retention is common, as the requirement for penetration with expansion will cause additional weight loss from wiping. For thin-skinned game at ranges to 400 yds., retained weights of 75 to 90 percent are common. Heavy bullets fired at close ranges should retain about 80 percent of original weight. Lightly constructed varmint bullets should disintegrate on impact, while full-metal-jacket bullets should retain virtually all of their original weight at all ranges.

Ideally, after striking the target, a bullet should penetrate deeply to transfer as much energy as possible to vital internal organs. A bullet that has done its job may be resting against the hide on the opposite side from the impact. On most North American game, reliable penetration of 18-24" will suffice. The entrance wound should be about 2" or large enough to leave a blood trail in case the hunter must track a wounded animal that has run off. If the aiming point was a shoulder or clavicle, the bullet should ideally break that structure, then penetrate.

Determine reliability by reading manufacturers' literature, then by asking for recommendations from experienced hunters. Next, conduct your own tests by taking the selected bullet into the field to build your fund of experience and confidence.

Remember, as the user, you are the ultimate arbiter of bullet success or failure. If a particular rifle bullet gives you consistent, reliable performance, then stick with it. Never bet the success or failure of a hunting trip on an unproven bullet.

Hunting Bullet Selector

	Bullet Tip				Bullet Core				Bullet Base	
	SP	HP	CT	FMJ	Con	LR	B/D	HM	Flat	BT
1.	X	X	X		X			X	X	X
2.	X	X	X	X	X			X	X	X
3.	X	X	X		X	X	X	X	X	X
4.	X		X		X	X	X	X	X	X
5.	X			X	X	X	X	X	X	

1. Varmints, Small Game
   ground squirrels, prairie dogs, squirrels, crows, badgers, groundhogs, nutria, rabbit, raccoon, opossum

2. Furbearers
   fox, coyote, mink, bobcat, beaver

3. Medium North American Game
   deer, antelope, bighorn sheep, mountain goat, black bear

4. Large North American Game
   moose, elk, bear, bison, nilgai

5. Dangerous Game
   brown bear, polar bear, lion, elephant, hippopotamus, Cape buffalo

Abbreviations: SP—soft-point; HP—hollow-point; CT—capped/tipped; FMJ—full-metal-jacket; Con—conventional; LR—locking ring; B/D—bonded/dual; HM—homogenous; BT—boattail

Chapter 14
BALLISTICS

What is Ballistics?

Ballistics may be defined as the science of the motion of projectiles in flight, as well as the analysis of the flight characteristics of a projectile. Additionally, ballisticians study the processes within a firearm as it is fired, along with the end result of a projectile (or multiple projectiles) striking a target. As a result of centuries of cumulative ballistic investigation shooters and hunters are now able to obtain a working knowledge of both the expected and actual performances of firearms and ammunition.

The word ballistics is derived from the Greek word *ballista,* which was an ancient military siege engine resembling a large bow stretched with cords and thongs and employed to hurl stones.

Types of Ballistics

The science of ballistics is usually divided into three sequential parts, interior, exterior and terminal.

Interior ballistics may be defined as:
- the study of the processes within a firearm as it is fired
- the firing characteristics of a firearm or cartridge.

Exterior ballistics may be defined as:
- the science of the motion of projectiles in flight
- the flight characteristics of a projectile.

Terminal ballistics may be defined as:
- the study of projectiles as they strike, penetrate and—in the case of military, security or hunting use—incapacitate or kill the target.

In plain terms:
- Interior ballistics studies phenomena that occur inside the firearm.
- Exterior ballistics studies the bullet as it flies through the air.
- Terminal ballistics studies the bullet as it strikes and penetrates the target.

Standard Conditions

The standard atmospheric conditions at which sporting ammunition ballistic figures are reported:

- altitude: sea level (0 ft.)
- temperature: 59 degrees F.
- relative humidity: 78 percent
- barometric pressure: 29.58" Hg.

Interior Ballistics

Of the three types of ballistic studies, interior ballistics probably remains the most mysterious for the average shooter. This is because what goes on inside the chamber and bore of a firearm is usually accessible only with specialized equipment.

While a knowledge of interior ballistics will enhance any shooter's ability to get the most out of his or her guns and loads, it must be remembered that it's still largely an empirical science. In the end, optimizing the performance of the gun and load usually comes down to careful experimentation. And for many shooters, that's where the fun is.

Typical Firing Sequence

When the trigger is pulled, the sear releases the hammer or the striker (firing pin), thereby initiating a complex but predictable chain of events.

- The hammer rotates forward until it hits the firing pin, driving it forward; or the striker (firing pin) moves forward if there is no hammer.
- The tip of the firing pin strikes the primer cup, deforming it and crushing the priming compound inside against the anvil underneath.
- The priming compound explodes, sending hot, rapidly expanding gas through the flash hole and into the case. This gas rapidly raises the temperature and pressure inside the cartridge case, thus igniting the propellant.
- As the propellant burns, it generates hot, expanding gas at a temperature of about 5,600 degrees F. that quickly raises the pressure inside the cartridge case to peak levels up to 62,000 p.s.i. The increasing pressure irons the cartridge case sidewalls outward against the chamber walls, creating a seal that prevents hot gas from escaping to the rear.
- At shot-start pressure (normally 2,000-10,000 p.s.i.), the bullet overcomes case neck tension, allowing the expanding propellant gases to accelerate it down the bore.
- After traveling a short distance in the chamber throat, the bullet contacts the rifling and engraves. As the bullet accelerates down

the bore, the rifling lands grip the bullet's surface, imparting spin. About one-third of the way down the barrel, the bullet breaks the sound barrier.

- As the bullet accelerates farther down the barrel, internal volume increases, which, in turn, causes chamber pressure to begin to drop. Progressive burning of the propellant offsets the pressure drop to some extent, but does not prevent it.
- As the bullet clears the muzzle, a jet of hot, high-velocity propellant gas, still at 10 to 30 percent of peak chamber pressure, is released. As the gas jet escapes, it compresses the air surrounding the muzzle, thus creating a loud "report."
- The pressure inside the barrel and chamber quickly drops to ambient levels, allowing the cartridge case sidewalls to spring back from the chamber walls for extraction.

While the process may sound complex, the entire sequence is completed very quickly. Typically, the time from firing pin release to the bullet exiting the barrel is measured in milliseconds.

Breech Pressure

Pressure is the force or thrust exerted over a surface divided by its area. Modern breech pressures are measured in:

- pounds per square inch (p.s.i.) in the United States
- kilograms per square centimeter (k/cm^2) in Europe.

In the past, breech pressures were sometimes expressed in other units such as:

- lead units of pressure (L.U.P.) for shotguns (U.S.)
- copper units of pressure (C.U.P.) for rifles and handguns (U.S.)
- short tons per square inch (Britain)
- atmospheres (Europe)
- pascals (Europe).

Modern breech pressure measurement systems employ piezoelectric transducers that produce a pressure vs. time curve. This curve can be recorded by a plotter on paper or saved on a computer to create a permanent record. The pressure/time curve is an important tool in interior ballistics. Chamber pressure is plotted on the Y or vertical axis against elapsed time on the X or horizontal axis. The curve typically rises to a peak (representing maximum pressure) in the first fractions of a second after ignition, then drops as the bullet travels down the bore. Both the rise to peak pressure and the subsequent drop in pressure can be rapid or gradual, depending on the burning characteristics of the propellant powder. The area under the curve is proportional to the work done by the propellant gases in accelerating the bullet, and thus to bullet velocity.

Relative Quickness and Burning Rate

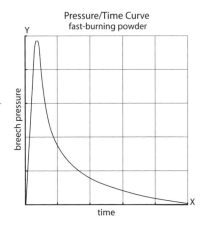

Pressure/Time Curve
fast-burning powder

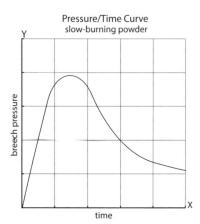

Pressure/Time Curve
slow-burning powder

Relative quickness is the speed at which the burning front moves through a propellant. This is a relative or comparative measurement determined under standard conditions by laboratory tests which are compared to samples of previously known control propellants. Relative quickness is normally expressed as a number that is relative to the speed of a standard control propellant. This enables a given propellant's burning speed to be compared to other propellants.

Burning rate is proportional to the amount of propellant that is free to burn. Burning rate is measured in two ways:

- Linear burning rate: the rate of regression of a burning propellant surface or the speed at which the flame front advances. This depends upon the rate at which the surface of the powder grains receive heat from the surrounding combustion.
- Mass burning rate: the time required for a given mass of propellant to burn completely.

Relative quickness and both types of burning rate are measured in a sealed vessel called a ballistic or closed bomb.

There are three ways that a propellant can burn:

Degressive—As the propellant granule burns, the surface area continuously decreases. Gas production rate is initially high, then decreases. Fast-burning flake powders or small spheres with this burning characteristic are commonly used in shotgun, pistol and revolver cartridges.

Neutral—A powder grain with a single hole down the middle that burns from the outside in and from the inside out, counterbalancing each other. The rate of gas production remains constant. This type of stick propellant is often used in rifle ammunition.

Progressive—A multi-perforated or mixed-sphere-diameter powder grain whose burning area increases as the grain is consumed. The rate of gas production is initially low, then increases. Powders with this characteristic are a popular choice for modern center-fire rifle cartridges.

Several factors affect burning rate:
- pressure
- gas velocity of the burning surface
- initial propellant temperature
- composition of the propellant
- shape and perforation of the propellant grains
- amount of propellant
- primer ignition characteristics
- bullet weight
- case shape.

Smokeless powder is an energetic, flammable solid that burns very quickly when ignited in a closed volume. Smokeless propellants vary in their:
- chemical composition
- energy content
- grain size and configuration
- deterrent coatings.

All these factors combine in different ways to yield powders with specific burning characteristics. Relative quickness and burning rate are two ways of measuring these characteristics.

The pressure curve explains why two powders of different burning rates may generate the same peak pressure, but produce different velocities. A fast-burning powder may reach peak pressure quickly, then drop to a low pressure level just as quickly, giving little area under the curve. A slower-burning powder may reach the same peak pressure more gradually, maintain that pressure longer and drop less abruptly, thus giving more area under the curve. This produces more propellant energy to transmit to the bullet.

Efficiency

When a cartridge is fired, the burning propellant is converted to hot, rapidly expanding gas that releases energy. Firearms are not efficient heat engines. Only about 35 percent of the energy stored in the propellant is converted to bullet kinetic energy in a typical firearm. Where does the lost energy go?

- **Heat transferred to barrel.**
  about 20 to 30 percent
- **Friction against bore by both bullet and powder gas.**
  about 2 to 4 percent

- **Pressure gradient or change rate, powder gas not exerting a full push on the bullet.**
  about 15 to 20 percent
- **Expansion ratio, the amount of volume into which the gas can expand before bullet leaves muzzle.**
  about 20 to 25 percent

There are two measures of interior ballistic efficiency:

- Thermodynamic efficiency is the percentage of the propellant's total available chemical energy used to accelerate the bullet.

- Piezometric efficiency is the ratio of the mean effective pressure to the peak pressure. In simpler terms, it is a measure of the constant pressure on the base of the bullet. The higher this pressure, the greater the velocity. With a given cartridge and bullet, a powder that produces higher velocity at peak pressure than another powder (at the same peak pressure) has greater piezometric efficiency.

Primer Performance

When ignited, primers produce hot, high-velocity gas. This gas ignites propellant powder by raising the pressure and temperature inside the cartridge case above the ignition temperature of the propellant. The ignition potential of a primer comes from the volume, temperature and velocity of this gas. Some primers are fortified with metallic solids such as powdered magnesium or aluminum metal that produce a shower of white-hot particles to aid propellant ignition.

Primers consist of a high-explosive base material mixed with stabilizers, solvents, frictioning materials, binding agents and other chemical compounds. Most modern, non-corrosive primers are based on compounds containing either normal or basic lead styphnate. Basic lead styphnate is utilized only on a limited basis, because most ammunition manufacturers, including military arsenals, use normal lead styphnate. Lead-free primers are based on diazol compounds and contain no heavy metals.

The exact chemistry and amount of priming composition in primers varies according to the manufacturer and the specific application. Because of these variations, different brands of primers may produce different levels of velocity and/or accuracy with a given powder charge, bullet and firearm. For example, magnum primers may have more priming composition than standard primers to ignite large charges of slow-burning propellants. For this reason, always use the exact primer specified in the reloading data.

Brisance is a term often mistakenly used as a synonym for primer potency. Brisance refers to the shattering effect of the sudden release of energy in an explosion. However, propellant powders are designed to burn with their powder granules intact, not shattered by the ignition of the primer. For igniting propellants, high brisance is an undesirable primer property. For this reason, very small quantities (a maximum of 45 milligrams) of priming compound normally are used for ignition purposes.

Case Shape

Cartridge case shape can effect peak pressure, propellant burning rates, efficiency and muzzle velocity. However, there is no general agreement on how cartridge case shape affects these factors as there is no easy way to look into a gun's chamber when a cartridge is fired.

- Given two cartridges that use the same bullet diameter and weight, but with different powder capacities, the cartridge with the smaller case will be more responsive to pressure and will require less powder to achieve the same velocity. For example, the *Sierra Rifle Reloading Manual* says that a .30-06 Sprg. loaded with a 150-gr. bullet can achieve 3000 fps with just 52.8 grs. of IMR 4064. The same source says that .300 Win. Mag. needs 63 grs. of the same powder to achieve the same velocity with the same bullet.
- A larger-than-necessary primer can raise peak pressures. Normally this is no problem as each caliber uses a commonly agreed upon primer size appropriate to its capacity. However, manufacturers disagree on the appropriate primer size in some calibers.
- A shoulder on the case helps prevent unburned powder from being blown down the barrel, thus promoting efficiency by improving the pressure gradient.

Short, fat-cased designs now popular for benchrest shooting and hunting are notably efficient. The short, wide powder columns appear to burn particularly uniformly with consistent velocities and pressures.

Throat Length

Long throats or freebore (the unrifled portion of the bore just forward of the chamber) tend to lower breech pressures as the bullet builds up velocity before engaging the rifling. Some rifle manufacturers take advantage of this by reaming their chambers with a long throat. This makes it possible for handloaders to safely increase their powder charge slightly for a modest increase in velocity. However, freebore is normally not conducive to accuracy, especially with boattail bullets. When a bullet engraves at high velocity, slipping and jacket damage can more easily occur. For this reason, large amounts of freebore are not common.

Seating bullets so that they touch the rifling is a well-known accuracy technique, but it may increase peak pressure, and should be avoided with maximum or near-maximum loads. The safest method of seating the bullet is to leave it a small amount of travel before it engraves.

Expansion Ratio

Related to cartridge efficiency is expansion ratio. This is the ratio of the volume of the case and bore together to the volume of the case alone with the bullet seated. A high ratio of bore volume to chamber volume is better and more efficient. For this reason, a longer barrel normally increases the expansion ratio while a short barrel or a large-volume cartridge case will lower it.

As a general rule, the greater the expansion ratio, the more energy contained in the powder goes to accelerating the bullet.

For example, a single-shot handgun with a 12-inch barrel chambered for the 7 mm Rem. Mag. has an expansion ratio of 2.8. Lengthen the barrel to 26 inches, and the expansion ratio grows to 5.5. From this it can be seen that the longer barrel will be more efficient.

Cartridges such as magnums with a large case volume in relation to the bore are called "overbore" cartridges.

Shotshell Interior Ballistics

Shot

For maximum effectiveness, the ideal pellet swarm from a shotshell should strike the target in a pattern having uniform pellet distribution and a short, compact shot-string length. To achieve such performance, engineers manipulate some or all of the following factors:

Pellet uniformity

Pellets of the same diameter and roundness will have the same time of flight, ballistic coefficient and striking energy. However, pellets of different diameters or irregular shape will have a variety of ballistic coefficients, different flight trajectories and varying times of flight. If pellet diameter and roundness is not uniform, the results can be longer shot strings and uneven pellet dispersion leaving holes in the pattern.

Pellet hardness

Lead shot can be alloyed with up to 6 percent antimony to increase pellet hardness. Other metal alloys, such as tin, can be used as well. Hard shot pellets effectively resist deformation on acceleration and retain their sphericity and ballistic coefficient for uniform patterns and trajectories.

Pellet diameter

Smaller-diameter shot pellets benefit more from antimonial hardening than larger pellets. This is due to the greater surface area and mass of larger pellets. An imperfection on the surface of a large pellet effects the exterior ballistic performance much less than it would on a smaller pellet. For this reason, lower percentages of hardening alloys are needed on large shot.

Shot charge weight

Heavy shot charges increase payload inertia as well as the number of intra-pellet collisions. These factors can cause significant damage to the shot pellets as they accelerate. For this reason, hard pellets, wad columns with cushion bases and granulated buffering material should be used with heavy or magnum lead-shot charges.

Cushioning

As soft lead pellets are accelerated down the bore, inertial and intra-pellet collisions can deform the shot, causing poor patterns. A properly designed wad column cushions the force of acceleration and helps preserve pellet roundness. In some shotshells, a granulated plastic buffer material may be added to the shot charge to further cushion the pellets. Heavy shot charges take up more volume inside the shell body, thus reducing the amount of space left for the wad cushion.

Protection

As the pellets accelerate past the forcing cone and down the bore, they must be protected from abrasion on the bore surfaces. Modern plastic wads with pellet protector shot pouches and fingers prevent abrasion. However, some shot pouches are too short for the shot charge and allow the front pellets to contact the bore. Wads designed for steel shot are thick and molded of high-density polyethylene plastic to positively prevent pellet scrub-through.

Stacking

The inside contours of a plastic wad's shot cup or pouch can significantly affect the quality of shot patterns by the manner in which pellet stacking is controlled or reduced. When the wad and shot charge enter the forcing cone, the diameter of the shot column is abruptly and significantly reduced. As the shot charge is squeezed, elongated bridging can occur wherein the pellets jam together forming a bridge. With soft-lead pellets, the bridging effect simply deforms the pellets. Steel or tungsten-iron shot bridging can cause pressure excursions and scrub through the protective fingers of the wad to cause bore damage. Wads having tapered pouch bases, posts and recesses can reduce or prevent these problems.

Chamber pressure

High chamber pressures with a short, fast initial pressure rise can increase the acceleration forces on the shot charge significantly, thus aggravating pellet deformation. For this reason, manufacturers often reduce peak chamber levels to reduce pellet damage and improve pattern quality.

Muzzle velocity

High muzzle velocities can substantially increase the forces of acceleration that increase pellet damage. However, high velocity by itself will not damage patterns. Most shotguns pattern best with moderate-velocity shells having low chamber pressures, well-designed plastic wad columns and hard, high-quality lead shot.

Wad Columns

The wad column serves several functions:

- It seals the powder gases.
- It cushions the shot charge.
- It reduces the energy of intra-pellet collisions.
- It reduces slumping from high acceleration forces.
- It protects the shot pellets from abrasion on the bore surfaces.

Wads for steel and tungsten-based shot must protect the bore from the shot.

- Wads prevent shot pellet bridging and stacking. Bridging can cause pressure excursions and bore scratching. Stacking can degrade pattern quality by deforming pellets.

- Wads must separate from the shot column cleanly and reliably after exiting from the muzzle. To accomplish this, most wad columns have from two to eight petals cut into the shot pouch that open upon exit. The aerodynamic drag caused by these petals causes the wad to drop away from the shot column.

- Wads must be lightweight to minimize total ejected mass, increase efficiency and reduce recoil.

- Wads must be tough to resist acceleration, scrub-through, high propellant temperatures and deterioration in long-term storage.

- Wads must be affordable. Yearly wad column consumption easily reaches into the billions, so costs can add up quickly.

- Wads must be easily manufactured in large quantities.

- Wads' soft-plastic, lightweight construction ensures the wad will not become a dangerous secondary projectile at separation from the shot swarm.

- They must degrade quickly once exposed to sun, moisture and earth. Additives such as corn starch may be necessary to accelerate degradation.

While most modern shotshell wad columns are molded of plastic, this was not always the case. Early shotshells used a stiff, thick card wad over the powder charge for sealing, followed by a series of felt cushion wads (often impregnated with wax). Sometimes another stiff card wad was added beneath the shot charge. The pellets in the shot charge were allowed full contact with the bore surface on firing. Finally, another thin card wad was used to close the shotshell at the mouth with a roll crimp. After felt became too expensive to use for shotshells, wads of compressed paper, molded composites and similar materials were tried. They did not work nearly as well, as they proved expensive, heavy and sealed poorly. Plastic had none of these problems, but added a few of its own.

Upon powder ignition, the wad collapses slightly to absorb some of the impact of acceleration, minimizing the distortion of the relatively soft shot. The crimp at the front of the hull unfolds to allow the wad and the contained shot charge to travel forward. The base of the wad upsets slightly to fit the bore with sufficient snugness to prevent hot propellant gas from blowing forward past it. During its travel, the wad often leaves streaks of plastic material in the bore. The flexibility of the wad allows it to squeeze down at the choke constriction at the muzzle.

Different plastic wads vary their internal and external dimensions; this means that each load with a particular hull, powder charge and shot charge usually requires a specific wad. What's important in terms of shotshell load performance is that the wad has the dimensions, design and composition to properly fit in the hull when inserted with the correct pressure, compresses to the desired level upon firing, and properly matches the size of the bore to prevent yaw, gas blow-by or direct contact of the shot charge and barrel.

Interior Ballistics and Accuracy

Accuracy requires optimizing the gun and cartridge for optimum precision by:

Case shape—Using a short, fat case shape with a small length-to-diameter ratio reduces the amount of powder blown down the bore and thereby produces very consistent velocities. This helps each successive bullet to leave the barrel at exactly the same point in the barrel vibration pattern, yielding small groups.

Load density and air space—Loading density is defined as the weight of the powder charge in grains divided by the weight of water, in grains, required to completely fill the empty cartridge case. High-density loads uniformly fill the case, reducing air space inside the cartridge case for more uniform muzzle velocities.

In-Bore Yaw

Bullets can yaw inside the bore which, in turn, causes yaw in flight proportional to the amount of in-bore yaw. In-bore bullet yaw is caused by the bullet starting at an angle to the bore axis instead of concentrically. This can be caused by:

- a chamber that is not concentric with the bore
- an oversized chamber
- a case neck thicker on one side than the other

- a bullet that is not seated straight in the case neck
- throats with overly long freebore
- a reverse-taper bore (one that expands in diameter toward the muzzle)
- an undersized bullet
- bullet imperfections, such as inconsistencies in jacket-wall thickness
- static and dynamic bullet imbalance
- damaged muzzle crown.

In flight, yaw causes the bullet's nose to pivot right, left, up or down so that the bullet's longitudinal axis forms an angle with the line of flight.

Interior Ballistic Safety

Safety concerns in relation to interior ballistics center around two areas.

Pressure

Each caliber or cartridge has a specific maximum average chamber pressure that must not be exceeded. For American-made ammunition, such pressure levels are established by the Sporting Arms and Ammunition Manufacturers' Institute (SAAMI). In Europe, such pressure levels are established by the Commission Internationale Permenente (CIP).

As a general rule, muzzle velocity increases as average chamber pressures rise. However, it is important to note that breech pressure figures quoted in most reloading manuals and computer ballistics programs are maximum allowable peak pressures. Maximum average pressure levels to which ammunition must be loaded are substantially lower.

While factory ammunition average pressures are normally under these limits, reloaders sometimes assemble loads that exceed it. By adhering rigidly to the tested load specifications published in reloading manuals, and never exceeding maximum loads, reloading normally is quite safe.

From this, it can be seen that the shape (height and duration) or area under the pressure curve is the determining factor in muzzle velocity. Be aware that variations in component specifications, gun condition, bore and chamber dimensions and high ambient temperatures can boost pressures of both factory ammunition and reloads beyond safe levels.

All shooters should learn to recognize the signs of excessive breech pressure. These include:

- hard bolt lift
- flattened, leaking or loose primers
- imprinted case heads
- case head expansion or separation.

Headspace

Headspace is the distance from the face of the closed breech of a firearm to the forward surface in the chamber on which the cartridge case seats. Headspace measurements are taken from one of four places depending on the type of cartridge case:

- the rim of a rimmed case
- the shoulder of a necked case
- the case mouth of a straight or tapered case
- the belt of a belted case.

Types of Headspace

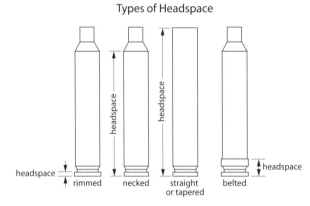

In addition, the term "headspace" also informally denotes the fore-and-aft clearance of the cartridge case in the chamber.

Excess headspace can lead to case head separations, high-pressure gas leakage and gun damage. Too little headspace should also be avoided, as it can lead to chambering and locking problems.

Exterior Ballistics

Exterior ballistics deals with the flight of the bullet from the muzzle to the target. This is the branch that most people are referring to when they use the general term "ballistics."

Exterior ballistics is the oldest of the three branches of ballistic study. Gun makers, target shooters, hunters and military ordnance officers have long understood the value of being able to accurately predict the path and impact point of firearm projectiles. The earliest works on the subject, dating from the Renaissance, were essentially practical manuals for cannoneers.

When rifled bores made accurate long-range shooting a practical reality more precise methods for calculating bullet trajectories were needed. Some of the first mechanical computers, for example, were designed to make the arduous calculations required to direct the big main-battery guns on large naval ships. Today, even the most basic home computer can run readily available exterior ballistics programs capable of calculating the path of nearly any bullet to 1,000 yds. or more. The experienced shooter uses his knowledge of exterior ballistics to make the most of his shooting experience.

Exterior ballistics concerns a number of different factors. Among them are:

Velocity

- the rapidity of movement or the quickness of motion
- the rate of change of position along a straight line with respect to time.

For firearms, velocity is normally expressed either in feet per second (f.p.s.) or meters per second (m.p.s.).

Note that with a given cartridge and bullet, increasing muzzle velocity can be achieved by increasing the maximum allowable peak pressure (which raises the pressure curve peak), increasing the area under the curve by using a slower-burning powder or by a combination of the two.

Bullet Drop

Bullet Drop

Gravity begins to act on the bullet the instant it leaves the muzzle. Regardless of the angle of the bullet's trajectory, the force of gravity always acts to accelerate the projectile toward the center of the earth at a rate of 32.17 f.p.s. per second.

Trajectory (Bullet Path)

The bullet's flight path from muzzle to target is called its trajectory. Because a bullet begins to drop from the pull of gravity as soon as it leaves the muzzle (see illustration), it is necessary to elevate the muzzle, launching the bullet in a slightly upward direction, to hit a distant target. For this reason, the bullet begins its flight at a point below the

Basic Exterior Ballistics

line of sight (LOS), rises above the LOS to its maximum height, then descends back to and below that line as it travels toward the target.

Mid-Range Trajectory

The maximum height above the line of sight of the bullet's path at one-half the distance for which the gun is zeroed is called the mid-range trajectory (i.e., the height at 100 yards for a gun zeroed at 200 yards), typically measured in inches or millimeters.

Maximum Ordinate (Maximum Height)

Maximum height (ordinate) occurs at a point roughly 55 percent of the way to the zero range or the range at which the bullet path and line of sight intersect. Normally expressed in inches or millimeters, this figure is important to determine the maximum point-blank range of a cartridge.

Line of Departure

The line of departure is a straight-line extension of the axis of the bore and is the path taken by the bullet immediately upon exiting the muzzle. However, after exiting the muzzle, the bullet begins to drop immediately and does not rise above the line of departure. A flat trajectory is one in which the curvature of the bullet path is less pronounced; increasing bullet velocity and/or ballistic coefficient (see illustration) can produce a flatter trajectory. Finally, a bullet's trajectory reflects not only drop, but also deflection due to crosswinds and other aerodynamic influences.

Wind Deflection

Wind deflection is the lateral deviation of the bullet's trajectory from its original line of departure, caused by crosswind. A popular term for wind deflection is wind drift.

Wind drift is not the simple result of crosswinds blowing the bullet sideways. For example, a typical .30-cal. 150-gr. spitzer flat-base bullet launched at 2900 fps in a 10-mph crosswind will suffer about 14½" of lateral deflection at 400 yards. If you drop that same bullet sideways into the airstream of a fan blowing at 10 mph, the bullet will hardly move laterally at all as it falls.

Crosswinds affect bullet trajectory by slightly changing the direction of the drag forces which produce an angular change in the bullet's path from its original line of departure. As the bullet follows its new

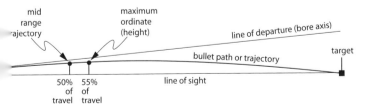

trajectory, it deviates farther and farther from the line of departure. A small angular change in the bullet's path at the beginning of its flight will produce a large deviation downrange. This is why a crosswind at the muzzle has more effect than the same crosswind at the target.

Crosswinds perpendicular (90 degrees) to the bullet's trajectory will have the greatest effect on wind deflection. Crosswinds running at any other angle to the bullet's path, will have less effect. To find the equivalent 90-degree value of an angled crosswind, multiply its velocity by the sine of its angle to the bullet trajectory. Alternatively, a crosswind deflection diagram can be used.

Winds blowing parallel to the bullet's path (in either direction) have only a limited effect, and for most real-world purposes can be ignored.

slant distance = 400 yds.

Steep-Angle Trajectory

Although the straight-line distance from a hunter to a ram on a steep slope is 400 yds., the effect of gravity on his bullet is equal to the horizontal-distance trajectory at 328 yds.

horizontal distance = 328 yds.

Shooting Uphill or Downhill

Shooting uphill or downhill can be a problem because the eye and brain perceive the range to be the longer slant distance to the target while the actual bullet drop more closely approximates that of the shorter horizontal distance.

Whether the angle is uphill or downhill makes no difference. The strike of the bullet will be above the point of aim. For shots within 10 degrees of horizontal, the correction is so small that it can be ignored.

For example, a hunter using a 7 mm 150-gr. bullet at a muzzle velocity of 3110 f.p.s. takes aim at a bighorn sheep on a 35-degree

Point Blank Range
bullet never travels more than 5"
above or below line of sight

scope

barrel

hillside at a slant distance of 400 yds. (as determined by using a laser rangefinder). However, if a perpendicular line could be extended downhill from the ram it would intersect the level on which the hunter is standing at a horizontal distance of 328 yds.

With his rifle zeroed at 200 yds., the bullet will strike 19.9" below point of aim at 400 yds. on level ground. But in firing at the steep angle, the bullet drop equates to the 328 yds. of horizontal distance. At that shorter yardage the bullet's strike below point of aim is 9.5". If the hunter adjusts his point of aim to allow for a 400-yd. trajectory, the bullet will arrive 10.4" above his hold (19.9 -9.5 = 10.4) and quite possibly miss his quarry altogether.

In most cases, all that it is necessary to do when shooting uphill or downhill is to aim a few inches lower on a long shot on a steep grade.

Maximum Point-Blank Range

Maximum point-blank range is the farthest distance at which a given bullet at a given muzzle velocity will hit a target of a specified size without adjusting the sights or the aiming point. Though of no consequence in competitive shooting, maximum point-blank range can be of critical importance in hunting.

To determine maximum point-blank range, you must know:
- the trajectory of the bullet used
- the range at which the rifle is zeroed
- the size of the vital area of the game.

For example, the vital area of a mature whitetail deer is usually estimated at 10" in diameter. Thus, the maximum point-blank range would be that at which the bullet neither rises nor drops more than 5" from the point of aim.

There is a point-blank range for any zero. Given this, the maximum point-blank range for a specific load is achieved at a unique zero distance. This specific distance can be determined by experimentation, using ballistic tables or by using a computer program.

Factors Affecting The Bullet
Coefficient of Form

Coefficient of form is a number that reflects the drag characteristics of different bullet shapes. At supersonic velocities (above 1120 f.p.s.),

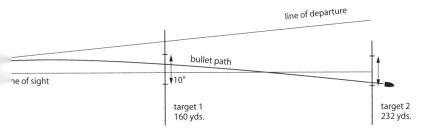

nose profile is the most significant aspect of bullet shape. Base shape is especially important at velocities below the speed of sound.

Bullets have a curved nose profile called the ogive. The ogive can be sharply pointed or bluntly round-nosed. Most spitzer (pointed) hunting and target bullets have either a tangent or secant ogive point. Secant-ogive bullets are sharply pointed and aerodynamic with a high ballistic coefficient. Tangent-ogive bullets have less sharply pointed noses than secant-ogive bullets, but are only slightly less aerodynamically efficient.

The radius of the ogival curve is usually expressed in bullet calibers (diameters). Thus, a .30-cal. bullet with a four-caliber ogive will have an ogive radius that is 4 x .308" or 1.23" long.

Boattail bullets have a streamlined, tapered base that reduces base drag by reducing the size of the partial vacuum formed at the base during flight. The beneficial effects of the boattail are evident at all ranges, but more so at ranges beyond 300 yds. where the effect has time to build. The length, shape and angle of the boattail base depends on the muzzle velocity, weight, diameter and ogive shape of each bullet. Thus, there is no single size, shape or angle that fits all. In general, the angle on a boattail bullet's base can vary from 7 degrees to 13 degrees and the length from about one-half caliber to one caliber.

Bullet tip configuration may seem significant, but it is actually of less importance than the shape of the ogive or base. Although it would seem that a dead sharp tip would be the most aerodynamically efficient, in reality the lower drag is achieved with a small flat called a meplat about 0.03 to 0.045" across on the tip. Most spitzer (pointed) bullets have a meplat.

Note that all bullets having the same ballistic coefficient and fired at the same muzzle velocity, will have the same wind deflection at any range. For example, an 80-gr. .224"-diameter bullet with a ballistic coefficient of .500 will have exactly the same trajectory as a 165-gr. .308"-diameter spitzer boattail bullet with a ballistic coefficient of .500. This is difficult for many shooters to accept, as it seems counterintuitive to the traditional notion that "heavy bullets buck the wind and brush better."

Sectional Density

Sectional density (Sd) is the bullet weight in pounds divided by its diameter in inches squared. Sd is normally expressed as a three-digit number calculated as follows:

$$Sd = \frac{wb}{db^2}$$

wb = weight of the bullet in pounds; db = diameter of bullet in inches

Ballistic Coefficient

For any projectile at a specific velocity, there is a number called the ballistic coefficient that reflects the total drag on that projectile. The ballistic coefficient is therefore a quantification of the efficiency with which the bullet slices through the air. For a given bullet at a known muzzle velocity, the ballistic coefficient determines the bullet's trajectory.

Ballistic coefficient (BC) is simply the bullet's weight divided by its form factor times bullet diameter squared:

$$BC = \frac{bw}{ixd^2}$$

bw = bullet weight; i − form factor; d = bullet diameter

In general, the higher the ballistic coefficient of a bullet:

- the higher the retained velocity
- the greater the striking energy
- the flatter the trajectory
- the less the wind deflection.

Tests have shown that the ballistic coefficient is not a fixed number, rather it varies slightly at different velocities. In particular, the ballistic coefficient changes markedly through the transonic velocity range of 900 to 1200 f.p.s.

Shooters seek four ballistic parameters from their bullets related to ballistic coefficient:

- maximum retained velocity
- maximum striking energy
- flat trajectory
- minimal wind drift.

How important is ballistic coefficient? Consider this example comparing two .308 bullets zeroed to point of aim at 100 yds., fired at a muzzle velocity of 2900 f.p.s at a range of 500 yds. from the muzzle.

Bullet Weight	Bullet Style	Ballistic Coefficient	Remaining Velocity (f.p.s.)	Retained Energy (ft.-lbs.)	Maximum Ordinate (inches)	90° Crosswind Deflection (inches)
150	RN-FB	.233	1,273	540	-83.46	50.11
150	FMJ-BT	.416	1,847	1,136	-53.32	23.11
Variation			+574	+596	-30.14	-27.00
Variation %			+45%	+110%	-64%	-46%

RN = round nose
FB = flat base
FMJ = full metal jacket (pointed)
BT = boattail

Ballistic coefficient can be determined in two ways:
- empirically by conducting firing tests that measure velocity at the muzzle and at a distance downrange
- mathematically by using the formula above.

Drag

Drag may be defined as:

- the resistance of the air to the passage of an object through it
- an aerodynamic force that acts in the direction opposite to that of the bullet's flight
- the net aerodynamic force parallel to the relative trajectory of the bullet.

There are three types of drag affecting a bullet in flight:

Bow-Wave Drag

As the bullet flies through the air, an area of compressed high-pressure air is created in front of the nose called a compression wave. The compression wave creates bow-wave drag. At velocities below the speed of sound (1120 f.p.s. at standard conditions), air piling up in front of the bullet creates the compression wave that travels ahead of the projectile.

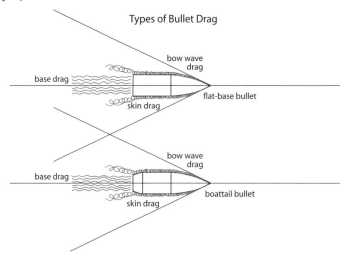

At supersonic velocities, the pressure wave is not able to travel ahead or get out of the way fast enough. This causes a substantial increase in air density and air pressure on the bullet nose resulting in a major increase in bow-wave drag. Bow-wave drag is the single largest contributor to total drag.

Parasitic Drag or Skin Drag

This is the friction of the air molecules as they slide along the outer surface of the bullet. Air is retarded along the surface in layers with the air velocity of the innermost layer at nearly zero and the outermost layer at full airstream velocity.

At the intersection between the full-velocity airstream and the stagnant airstream, the boundary layer of air breaks. The rough air at the broken-down boundary layer causes parasitic drag. Parasitic drag is a small percentage of total drag.

Base Drag

As a bullet flies through the air, it leaves a void in its wake. The high-speed air stream cannot close in behind the bullet's base quickly enough to fill the void until after the bullet has passed forward a short distance (about half a bullet's length). This creates a partial vacuum at the base, further increasing the pressure on the bullet's nose which in turn increases the drag. Base drag is the second largest contributor to total drag.

All three of the above types of drag added together comprise the total drag on the bullet.

Air density and pressure also affect drag. Essentially, the denser the air and the greater the air pressure, the greater the drag on the bullet. Thus, for a given projectile, at sea level where air pressure is 14.7 lbs./sq.-in., total drag is greater than at 10,000' altitude, where pressure and density are less.

Bullet yaw also increases drag. The rate of drag increase varies quadratically with the increase in yaw angle.

For any projectile, the higher the drag, the more inefficient the bullet. Inefficient bullets lose velocity and energy faster, suffer from higher trajectories and are deflected more by crosswinds over a given distance.

At subsonic velocities the amount of drag on a bullet increases as the square of its velocity. For example doubling the bullet's velocity increases drag four times.

At supersonic velocities (above 1120 f.p.s.), the increase in the amount of total drag is much more rapid and pronounced.

It is not practical to have a separate drag function for every type of bullet. Consequently the drag function of bullets is usually divided into four broad families that are adequate to cover the broad range of sporting bullets in most ballistic tables.

G1: for all bullets except those noted below.

G5: for bullets with low base drag such as boattails and tracers.

G6: for flat-base, full-metal-jacket bullets with sharp points.

GL: for hollow-point or soft-point flat-base bullets.

Each G function has a standard bullet model with the general characteristics noted above. By conducting firing tests, the drag model of a given bullet can be categorized into one of these four models which cover the broad range of sporting bullets. Short of computing actual trajectories, there is no way to compare the ballistic properties of two bullets if their ballistic coefficients are referenced in different drag models.

Bullet Stability

Bullet stability broadly refers to the ability of an elongated projectile to reliably and accurately fly point forward as a result of rotation imparted by the rifling in the barrel. To do this, the bullet must dampen or overcome yaw resulting from the disturbances of launch.

Bullet stability depends upon a number of factors, including air density and the bullet's:

- diameter
- length
- shape
- rate of spin
- sectional density
- balance
- velocity
- construction.

The stability of a given bullet may be expressed as a "stability factor" which is a quantitative measure of the bullet's stability. This is normally expressed as a number.

Bullet stability varies directly as the square of the axial moment of inertia and inversely as the first power of the transverse moment. The implications of this are:

- If two bullets of identical diameter and shape are fired from the same barrel at the same muzzle velocities, the bullet made of a dense material such as lead will have a higher stability factor than one constructed of a lighter material such as copper or aluminum.
- Bullets having long ogives and boattails have a lower ratio of axial-to-transverse moment of inertia, and thus a lower stability factor than shorter bullets fired under the same conditions.
- Bullets with features that increase the ratio of axial-to-transverse moments of inertia, such as hollow-points, flat-points and flat-bases, have higher stability factors under the same firing conditions.
- The location of a bullet's center of mass is also a factor in stability. Bullets in flight are subjected to an overturning moment—an aerodynamic force that continually attempts to turn the bullet nose away from the actual trajectory. The farther rearward the center of mass in relation to the line of the overturning moment, the less stability.

When a bullet's center of mass is located on its axis of form, it exhibits static balance. A bullet having its center of mass off the axis of form exhibits static imbalance.

When a bullet's axis of form is coincident with its axis of rotation, it exhibits dynamic balance. A bullet having its axis of form off its axis of rotation exhibits dynamic imbalance.

Dynamic imbalance can be caused by mass asymmetries fore and aft of the center of mass.

While static and dynamic balance have nothing to do with bullet stability, they can and do affect dispersion.

The most significant factor in bullet stability is spin, which produces gyroscopic stability. Without spin, the bullet would not be able to resist the overturning moment and would tumble in flight.

For each bullet, a rifling twist rate is desirable that will produce adequate, but not excessive, spin for stability. An appropriate rate of twist for cylindrical projectiles can be estimated using Greenhill's Formula.

Greenhill's Formula is old but simple and provides a useful approximation of the correct rifling twist for most contemporary bullets.

Bullet length is more important than weight in determining the proper rate of twist. In general, long bullets with high ballistic coefficients require a fast twist rate for proper stability.

Both underspin and overspin can have detrimental effects on accuracy. Underspin can lead to tumbling when temperatures or air density increase. Excessive spin may amplify static and dynamic imbalance also causing tumbling. In most instances, the effects of either condition are small. Modern practice acknowledges it is better to use too fast a twist than one that is too slow.

Gyroscopic Drift

Gyroscopic drift is the lateral deviation of the bullet path as a result of bullet rotation. The direction of gyroscopic drift will always be in the same direction as the rifling twist. In normal circumstances, the effects of gyroscopic drift are small and can be ignored at most hunting ranges. For example, the M2 152-gr. spitzer bullet used in .30-'06 military ammunition has a gyroscopic drift of about 1½" at 500 yds.

Other Factors

Other factors that influence bullet trajectory include:

- the Coriolis effect
- Magnus force
- Magnus moment
- vertical drift
- aerodynamic jump.

While of interest to professional ballisticians, these phenomena generally do not affect the trajectory enough to be of practical significance to most shooters.

Exterior Ballistics of Shotshells

The projectiles in most shotshell loads take the form of round pellets. From the earliest years, these pellets were exclusively of lead, but current regulations may require non-lead pellets, which in turn spurred the development of pellets made of steel, bismuth and tungsten.

In flight, shotgun pellets conform to the same ballistic laws as other projectiles. Their trajectory is curved so they lose velocity and energy as they fly and they are deflected by crosswinds. Most shooters do not think of shotgun pellets in this way as the average range at which shotguns are used is very close, so these factors are not significant and relatively unknown.

The sectional density of round shot projectiles is very poor due to their light weight. Round projectiles also have a poor ballistic coefficient, so they lose striking velocity and energy very quickly. This limits the effective range of shotshell pellets to 50 yds. or so. Beyond that distance, individual pellets may not have sufficient striking energy to penetrate into the vital organs of live game. Also, the target may not receive a sufficient number of pellet hits due to low pattern density at long ranges.

Steel shot is much less dense than lead. Thus, steel shot pellets of a particular size weigh less than lead pellets of the same size. When fired at the same muzzle velocity, steel pellets have a lower ballistic coefficient resulting in lower striking velocity and less striking energy than a lead pellet of the same diameter. To offset these limitations, ammunition makers recommend that shotgunners select steel shot two sizes larger than the lead shot they would normally use. For example, replace No. 6 lead shot with No. 4 steel shot.

Other lead substitutes such as bismuth and tungsten-based alloys, are often sufficiently similar in density to lead that no such change in shot size is required.

Note that striking energy and the number of hits on the target are the key factors in breaking targets or killing game. Serious shotgunners will carefully pattern their guns and loads to establish both the maximum range at which the minimum number of hits may be obtained, as well as to select the load that provides the most uniform pattern density at the desired range(s).

Pellet Patterns

A major factor in pattern density and quality is choke constriction. For each choke constriction there is a standardized range of pattern performance, represented by a range of expected hit percentages within a 30" circle at 40 yds. (25 yds. for skeet chokes and .410-bore shotguns).

As a rule of thumb, shotshell patterns can be expected to increase about 1" for every yard of travel beyond the muzzle. This dispersion may be reduced 50 percent or more with the proper combination of bore size, shotshell load and choke constriction.

Shotgun Choke Performance

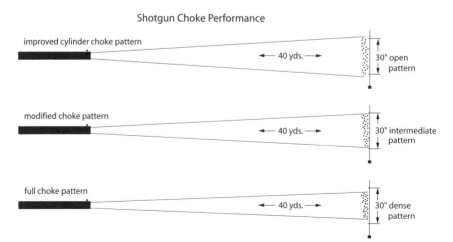

Unlike the rifled bores of rifles and handguns, which are made with exact tolerances, shotgun bores are much more variable. Though the nominal diameter of a 12-gauge bore is 0.729", it is not hard to find bores measuring 0.725" to more than 0.740". Such variations in bore dimensions can contribute significantly to the performance of a given load.

Reading Exterior Ballistics Tables

Do not be intimidated by the ballistics tables published by bullet and ammunition manufacturers. Ballistics tables are the result of sophisticated measurements and calculations specifically designed to help you get the maximum performance from your firearms. On a practical level, ballistics tables provide information that enable you to:

- select the most efficient bullet and cartridge combination by comparing trajectories and downrange remaining velocity and energy levels
- zero your rifle for short or long range
- determine precisely how much to hold off for shots at long or short ranges and/or uphill or downhill
- predict the effect crosswinds will have on bullet impact
- determine the striking energy your bullet will have at normal ranges.

A typical ballistics chart will include the following information for a given caliber and bullet combination:

Caliber, bullet weight and style—This information identifies the actual bullet weight in grains or grams, the bullet style (ie. spitzer, soft-point, boattail) and specific cartridge.

Barrel length from which test data was calculated—Normally, test barrels are 24" in length. However, your rifle may have a longer or shorter barrel. This can be important as barrel length affects muzzle velocity.

Remaining velocity of the bullet at selected ranges in feet per second (f.p.s.)—Remaining velocity numbers indicate the aerodynamic efficiency of a bullet. Higher retained velocity means a bullet is more efficient at slicing through the air.

Remaining (striking) energy of the bullet at the same selected ranges, expressed in foot-pounds (ft.-lbs.) of energy—Higher remaining velocity translates in turn into greater retained striking energy. This is an important number to use in matching the efficiency of your bullet to the game hunted. Selecting the most efficient bullet of suitable weight in a specific caliber will result in maximum striking energy.

Expected bullet drift (displacement) in a 10-mph crosswind at selected ranges, expressed in inches—Experienced hunters know that the wind must always be taken into consideration before firing a shot. At long ranges, crosswinds will dramatically affect a bullet's impact point. At shorter ranges, wind drift may not be a significant factor. Ballistic charts tell you exactly how much wind will affect your shot at various ranges. Deflection values for 10-mph crosswinds are normally listed as other crosswind velocities are proportional. In other words, if a 10-m.p.h. crosswind deflects a bullet 1.0" at 100 yds., a 20-m.p.h. crosswind will deflect it about 2.0" at that distance, and a 5-m.p.h. wind about 0.5".

Bullet path or trajectory when zeroed at 100 yds. and 200 yds.— This useful information should be memorized or written on a piece of tape attached to your rifle stock. Basically, the figures tell you how much above or below the line of sight the bullet will strike at a given range based on the rifle's zero. This is very useful in determining where to hold at a given distance for long-range shots.

Shooters often want to know the exact trajectory of a particular bullet, fired at a specific muzzle velocity they have determined using a chronograph. These figures can be calculated using a modern ballistic computer program or interpolated from published ballistic chart.

Maximum Point Blank Range (MPBR)

Many ballistic computer programs can be used to calculate maximum point blank range for a given rifle and cartridge combination. This is a very useful method of zeroing your rifle to take maximum advantage of the bullet's trajectory. Basically it tells you at what range to zero your rifle so the bullet covers the maximum possible distance and yet will strike within the kill zone of the target. For example, if you zero a given rifle load at 311 yds., the bullet's flight path will be no more than 4" above or below the line of sight to nearly 400 yds. This gives you the advantage of aiming at the center of the kill zone on deer-sized game and hitting the vital areas reliably to long distances without holding under or over your target.

Approximations and Variations

It is important to note that ballistic charts published by the ammunition makers are approximations calculated at standard conditions. By agreement, most manufacturers publish identical, industry-standard ballistics for similar loads. Your actual results may vary due to variations in individual guns. Also, manufacturers frequently make changes to bullet configurations, change muzzle velocity levels or switch propellants. Normally, the changes are minor and do not greatly affect ballistic performance. In some cases, however, the changes can affect ballistic performance to a noticeable extent and, for those instances, a ballistic computer program can be used to determine specific results.

Other Data

Ballistic charts may include some or all of the following data:
- bullet drop
- time of flight to a given distance
- maximum range to point of first impact at optimum elevation

- maximum height (if fired vertically)
- the effects of temperature, humidity and altitude
- the effect of longer or shorter barrels on muzzle velocity
- ballistic coefficient of the bullet, expressed as a number
- sectional density of the bullet
- momentum
- mid-trajectory (normally used for rimfire calibers)
- power factor.

While technically interesting, the above data is not normally useful for most sporting applications. For this reason, it is seldom shown on published charts in catalogs.

Example of a Comprehensive Ballistic Chart

Caliber: .308 Win.
Test barrel length: 24"
Bullet weight: 165-gr. Sierra
Bullet style: jacketed, tangent-ogive, spitzer soft-point boattail
Sectional density: .247
Ballistic coefficient: .404
Maximum range to point of first impact: 4,655 yds.
Maximum vertical height: 10,473 ft.
Maximum point blank range: 0 to 330 yds.
Maximum point blank range zero: 236 yds.

	Range in Yards					
	muzzle	100	200	300	400	500
Striking velocity (f.p.s.)	2700	2480	2273	2077	1891	1716
Striking energy (ft.-lbs.)	2670	2254	1892	1580	1310	1079
Momentum (lb.-secs.)	1.978	1.817	1.665	1.521	1.385	1.257
Time of flight (sec.)	0	.1159	.2423	.3803	.5317	.6981
Drop (inches)	0	-2.5	-10.7	-25.5	-48.5	-81.2
Trajectory, inches:						
100-yd. zero	-1.5	0	-4.1	-15.0	-34.6	-62.8
200-yd. zero	-1.5	+2.0	0	-8.8	-25.7	-52.3
Wind deflection, inches:						
10 m.p.h.	0	0.8	3.5	8.3	15.3	25.1
20 m.p.h.	0	1.6	7.0	16.6	30.6	50.2
30 m.p.h.	0	2.4	10.5	24.9	45.9	75.3
Trajectory, 100-yd. zero						
Uphill, 30 degrees	-1.5	+0.3	-2.7	-11.6	-27.7	-52.2
Downhill, 30 degrees	-1.5	+0.3	-2.7	-11.6	-27.4	-51.6

Special Types of Projectiles

Sabots

A sabot is a full-bore-diameter carrier made of lightweight material that is used to launch a projectile of less than full bore diameter. A sabot may be discarding or non-discarding. The advantage of sabots include:

- higher muzzle velocity by virtue of the substantially larger area for the propellant gases to push on
- the lower mass of the bullet/sabot together as compared to a full-bore-diameter bullet
- protection of the bore from hard metal projectiles.

Sabots for firearms are not new, in fact they date from early guns. However, the sophisticated technology to make them work effectively was not available until the mid-20th century. Early sabots were crudely made of wood, paper, leather and other materials. More modern sabots are precision-made of reinforced polymers and aluminum alloys.

Examples of modern small arms sabots include:

- plastic blackpowder sabots as offered by numerous sources
- plastic smokeless-powder rifle sabots such as the Remington Accelerator series
- sabot shotgun slugs.

Shotgun Slugs

Shotgun slugs are essentially large, heavy bullets that obey the same ballistic laws that govern other single projectiles.

Slugs generally come in two varieties: those designed to be fired through smoothbore (unrifled) barrels and those designed for rifled barrels. Many of the former type are, ironically, called "rifled slugs," and may even have a pattern on their circumference that suggests the marks made in a rifled bore. These do not spin fast enough for stabilization and they depend upon having their center of mass in front of their center of aerodynamic pressure much like a badminton shuttlecock.

The rifled slug was invented by a German named Brenneke who founded a company that continues to this day. In the 1930s, an American designed the Foster rifled slug so commonly in use by contemporary hunters.

The last decades of the 20th century saw the increasing popularity of rifled slug barrels, as well as the development of many new sabot slugs designed to take advantage of their accuracy and trajectory benefits. Some of these slugs are full-diameter projectiles, while others are saboted designs (*see above*). The latter slugs in particular are approaching the performance levels of some hunting rifle cartridges, with muzzle velocities approaching or exceeding 2000 f.p.s., muzzle energies of 3000 ft.-lbs., and effective ranges exceeding 100 yds.

The maximum range of slugs depends largely upon the type of slug used. Foster and Brenneke slugs have poor aerodynamic properties and may lose 40 percent of their energy in the first 50 yards, and 60 percent in 100 yards. Their accuracy also usually limits effective range to 75 yards or less. The slugs utilized in high-velocity sabot loads, however, retain a greater proportion of their velocity and energy, enabling humane kills at ranges of 100 yds. and beyond.

As the construction of shotgun slugs varies considerably, so does their terminal performance. Traditional Foster and Brenneke lead slugs depended on their large diameter to transfer energy and their heavy weight for penetration. Modern examples of some Foster and Brenneke slugs are redesigned to expand on impact for significantly improved performance on thin-skinned game.

Modern saboted shotgun slugs are designed to expand and penetrate much as modern hunting bullets do. This allows the taking of a greater variety of game and doing so at longer ranges than was possible with older slug designs.

Buckshot

Buckshot are simply large round balls of lead, bismuth, or a tungsten-based composite. Buckshot sizes range from .27 caliber (No. 4) to .33 caliber (000). Buckshot pellets in flight are governed by the same laws as smaller and larger round balls in that they have poor sectional density and a poor ballistic coefficient. Because of this, they lose velocity and energy very quickly, limiting their effective range. Buckshot loads are a popular choice for law enforcement and for hunting large varmints and sometimes deer at close range.

Blanks

Contrary to common misconception, blanks may have a projectile. However, the projectile is usually made of a lightweight frangible material that reduces lethality, range and penetration. In many cases the projectiles in blanks are paper wads, plastic wads, paper bullets, wood bullets and even empty bullet jackets.

Although blanks have a very limited danger zone, they can inflict serious injury or even death at close range.

Round Balls

The same laws of exterior ballistics that apply to cylindrical projectiles also apply to round balls, with the exception of projectile stability and yaw factors related to differences in the location of the center of gravity and the center of form do not apply. In a homogeneous, spherical projectile, the centers of gravity and form coincide, leaving the ballistic coefficient as the main factor influencing round ball exterior ballistics.

Since the form factor is the same for all spherical projectiles, the ballistic coefficient for a round ball depends on its sectional density. The sectional density of a round ball increases with the diameter. Thus, a round ball with a larger diameter will have a higher ballistic coefficient, resulting in higher retained velocity, more striking energy, flatter trajectory and less wind deflection.

Terminal Ballistics

Terminal ballistics is the study of projectiles as they strike and penetrate the target. This includes changes to the bullet itself and its effect on the target.

Terminal ballistics are of interest to:
- hunters, to match the terminal ballistic performance of projectiles to their game
- law enforcement agencies seeking incapacitation without overpenetration
- military forces seeking incapacitation while conforming to international law
- civilian gun owners seeking suitable loads for self-defense
- silhouette shooters seeking bullets that knock down steel targets
- action shooters who need to knock down reactive targets
- range designers and builders who need to ensure containment of projectiles.

Bullet Performance

Striking Energy

As a bullet strikes then penetrates the target, it transfers some or all of its kinetic energy to the target. As the bullet penetrates, the kinetic energy performs work by deforming the target and the bullet. Since energy is defined as the capacity to do work, bullet kinetic energy at impact is widely used as a measure of cartridge power. The striking energy of a bullet is normally expressed in the number of foot-pounds (ft.-lbs.) or Joules.

While a bullet's muzzle energy is often used for ballistic comparisons, the striking energy of a bullet is a more realistic measure of ballistic potential. However, the striking energy a bullet retains downrange is not necessarily proportional to its muzzle energy. The striking energy of a bullet in foot-pounds (ft.-lbs.) is given by the formula:

$$E = \frac{W \times V^2}{450,400}$$

E = striking energy of the bullet in ft.-lbs.
W = weight of the bullet in grs.
V = striking velocity of bullet in f.p.s.

Striking Velocity

As a bullet travels downrange, it continuously sheds velocity. Striking velocity is the velocity of a bullet on impact with the target, and it will always be less than the muzzle velocity. In general, the higher the striking velocity the better.

Striking velocity affects terminal performance of the bullet in several ways:
- striking velocity determines bullet energy on impact
- striking energy varies directly with bullet weight
- striking energy varies as the square of velocity.

In other words, a change in bullet striking velocity will have a much greater effect on bullet striking energy than a proportional change in bullet weight. Doubling bullet weight doubles bullet striking energy, whereas doubling bullet striking velocity quadruples striking energy.

At initial impact and penetration, a bullet creates a localized area of high pressure that rapidly displaces target material outward from the impact point. As the bullet penetrates, it creates a permanent wound path. As it does so, it may expand or tumble, considerably increasing the size of the permanent wound path. Bullet fragments, bits of bone and pieces of clothing can become secondary projectiles that can damage tissue at a distance from the point of impact.

In addition, the shock wave from bullet impacts greater than 2000 f.p.s. may create a temporary wound cavity in the tissue of a live target. Since liquids are incompressible, the hydrostatic shock wave created at bullet impact is rapidly transmitted to other areas of the target. The higher the bullet's striking velocity, the larger the temporary wound cavity which can stretch or tear blood vessels, nerves and other tissues outside the bullet track.

Penetration

To fulfill its function, a bullet must penetrate the target after impact. The amount of bullet penetration required depends upon the nature of the target.

Target penetration depends on an intricate interplay of the following features:

- bullet construction
- bullet diameter, weight and sectional density
- striking velocity
- striking energy
- target structure
- obstacles in front of the target
- angle of entry
- bullet stability.

In general, the greater a bullet's sectional density, the farther it will penetrate. Sectional density is a measure that relates bullet mass to its cross-sectional area. It is normally expressed as a three-digit number. The heavier a bullet is for its diameter, the higher its sectional density.

Despite many efforts to develop an experimental method to predict bullet penetration for hunting and self-defense, in real-life situations penetration is only approximately predictable.

Bullet Expansion

Bullet expansion is normally desired for optimal terminal performance in hunting and defensive situations.

Most modern bullet jackets are pre-scored and tapered to guide and control expansion.

Because a bullet that expands inside the target has more frontal area to better transmit its energy to the target while creating a larger permanent wound cavity. Expansion decreases the projectile's sectional density to control penetration; enhance energy transfer; increase the size of the permanent wound cavity; and minimize the likelihood of bullet pass-through.

Different levels and rates of expansion are required in different situations. These rates and levels of expansion are accomplished through bullet design and construction features such as:

Core hardness and shape—core/jacket bonding.

Point configuration—soft point (spitzer, round-nose, flat-nose), hollow-point, polymer tip, metal tip, capped.

Jacket—material, hardness, thickness, taper, length, shape, pre-scored jackets

Base shape—flat, boattail, hollow or cupped.

Designing a soft-point bullet to expand is fairly easy, and such bullets will reliably expand over a wide range of impact velocities. On the other hand, expanding hollow-point bullets are more difficult to design for reliable expansion. The range of impact velocities over which a hollow-point bullet will expand is considerably narrower than soft-point bullets. Hollow-point bullets striking at velocities below their expansion threshold behave like full-metal-jacket bullets, i.e., they do not expand at all.

Weight Retention

Ideally, a properly designed expanding, jacketed bullet should retain 100 percent of its original weight after expansion. However, in the real world this is difficult to achieve. The amount of retained weight depends on:

• bullet design
• construction materials and methods
• intended use of the bullet.

Because of their construction, premium-quality bullets can be designed to perform well over a wider range of striking velocities than standard bullets. For this reason, they are a popular choice for high-intensity magnum calibers. Many hunters select premium-quality bullets for hunting under difficult conditions, at very long ranges or for hunting large, heavy game.

For hunting dangerous game, non-expanding "solid" bullets are often used because they penetrate deeply and reliably. Such bullets are made with steel-reinforced jackets and hard-lead or solid-copper cores to prevent deformation even if they hit heavy bone.

Standard-quality bullets are designed to perform best in non-magnum calibers on medium game at lower muzzle velocities. For this reason, they do not offer the flexibility of premium bullets, but they are substantially less expensive and may be perfectly suitable to the task at hand. Most hunters find this perfectly adequate for hunting thin-skinned, medium game such as deer and antelope at normal ranges and conditions.

Varmint bullets are designed to disintegrate shortly after penetration in order to transfer all kinetic energy to the target as quickly as possible. This explosive expansion normally results in a clean, instantaneous kill leaving only small fragments of the bullet.

Bullet Tumbling

Some bullet designs are less stable than others. A bullet that is stable in air, may be extremely unstable inside the target   tumbling rather than simply boring straight through. This is a particular characteristic of bullets such as match-type hollow-points in which the center of gravity has been displaced rearward.

The tendency to tumble can reduce penetration and produce an unpredictable bullet path. This makes such bullets unsuited to hunting or defensive applications, but acceptable for some military or target-shooting applications.

Bullet Rotational Velocity

A bullet exiting a rifled barrel spins on its axis at a rate determined by the muzzle velocity and the rifling twist rate. The bullet will rotate either to the left or to the right depending on the direction of the rifling twist. The rotation stabilizes the bullet, causing it to travel point first.

The speed of bullet rotation is normally expressed in revolutions per minute (r.p.m.). Rotational speeds range from a low of 50,000 r.p.m. for a heavy, slow-moving projectile to more than 500,000 r.p.m. for a light, high-velocity bullet.

Lightweight bullets with thin jackets launched at high muzzle velocities can come apart in mid-air from the tremendous centrifugal force imposed by high rotation rates. However, bullet rotational speeds play only a minor part in bullet expansion. Higher rotational speeds have a measurable, but minor, effect on bullet expansion.

Some expanding bullets depend on the rotation of the sharp, exposed copper petals to enhance tissue destruction as they penetrate.

Wound Tracks

As a high-velocity bullet penetrates living tissue, it produces two kinds of deformation:

- Temporary wound cavity. The projectile's shock wave violently forces target material outward from the projectile path creating a temporary cavity. The temporary cavity may be quite large and its size is directly related to impact velocity.
- Permanent wound track. After a fraction of a second, the temporary cavity collapses, leaving a permanent wound track. This is the permanent deformation or destruction produced by the projectile as it plows through the target. The size of the permanent wound track is related to the bullet diameter and weight.

As stated, two schools of thought on bullet wounds have emerged.

Heavy, large-caliber, low-velocity bullets that penetrate deeply are best for transferring kinetic energy to the target. This group believes the permanent wound track is the most dependable mechanism for incapacitating the target.

Low-velocity bullets, such as those from revolvers and semi-automatic pistols, do not produce a large (or any) temporary wound cavity. Instead, they depend on the permanent wound track to cause damage in the target. For this reason, large-caliber handgun bullets are a better choice than small-caliber handgun bullets for hunting and self-defense as their larger diameter causes a bigger permanent wound track.

The other school of thought holds forth the belief that high-velocity, lightweight bullets that can create a large temporary wound cavity are the best mechanism for quick, dependable incapacitation of the target.

Many experts believe that the temporary wound cavity caused by the shock wave of a high-velocity bullet creates a temporary cavity large enough to cause damage at a considerable distance from the permanent wound track. This could mean tissue damage, nerve disruption or the breaking of bones that lie near but not directly in the path of the bullet.

Testing Simulated Wounds

Testing bullets for reliable expansion, penetration and weight retention can be accomplished in several ways. With bullets intended for hunting or self-defense, tissue simulants as close as possible to living tissue are chosen. The material chosen must be cheap, reliable and easy to use. Some of the materials used for bullet testing over the years include:

- modeling clay (water-based or regular)
- ductseal (heating and air conditioning)
- wet lap (paper pulp and water)
- wax (paraffin)
- soap
- bundled newspapers or telephone directories (wet or dry)
- sawdust
- cotton batting
- sand (wet or dry)
- water
- a mixture of wax and grease molded into blocks
- watermelon, grapefruit
- wood (1" sheets)
- meat
- ballistic gelatin (10 percent to 20 percent).

The consensus among expert ballisticians is that properly prepared ballistic gelatin is the cheapest, most reliable and easiest to use and prepare. The standard for most tests is 10 percent ballistic gelatin molded into transparent blocks approximately 24"x12"x12".

Using properly calibrated ballistic gelatin, it is possible to perform standardized comparisons of bullet expansion, penetration, weight retention and permanent wound tracks. With high-speed photography, the temporary cavity can also be measured.

Stopping Power

Stopping power is the general term for an attempt to quantify for comparison purposes the ability of various bullet and caliber combinations to immediately incapacitate an animal or human attacker. A popular term for this is "knockdown power."

A small-caliber rifle or pistol bullet will rarely stop or knock down a living target immediately simply by virtue of its sheer impact power. Depictions on TV and in motion pictures that show bullet impact immediately knocking a character off his feet are unrealistic. In many respects, the general perception of "stopping power" is not supported by scientific evidence. Accordingly, attempts to establish an accurate, neutral and repeatable system to measure bullet stopping power have failed.

A bullet can cause immediate incapacitation if it strikes and penetrates a critical nerve center such as the brain or spine. However, this is the result of precise bullet placement, not impact power.

Characteristics of Different Types of Ammunition

Ammunition may be classified into seven types, each of which has a different set of criteria for terminal ballistic performance.

Hunting

The terminal ballistic requirements for hunting bullets may, in turn, be subdivided into five general categories according to the type and size of the game hunted. These are: small game; varmint; medium game; large, heavy game; and dangerous game.

No single set of terminal ballistic criteria in any of the above categories will satisfy all requirements in that category. A wide variety of bullet weight, style, construction, striking velocity and accuracy may prove acceptable for any single application. This leaves plenty of room for shooter preference, experience and predjudice to come into play. For these reasons, the terminal ballistic criteria listed below must be regarded as a broad average that will accommodate most shooters, but not all.

Small Game—Animal types include rabbit, squirrel, raccoon, opossum, mink, fox, lynx, badger and raccoon. Weight typically ranges from 2 lbs. to 15 lbs. Typical range is normally less than 100 yds.

To avoid excessive meat and pelt damage, small-caliber, low-power cartridges are a popular choice for small-game hunting. For pelt hunting, non-expanding, solid-lead or full-metal-jacket bullets are used to keep damage to a minimum. For edible game, expanding lead or jacketed bullets facilitate a clean, quick kill with a minimum of lost and wounded game.

Rimfire cartridges such as the .17 Mach 2, .17 HMR, .22 LR and .22 WMR are popular choices due to low cost and wide availability. These calibers are best limited to short-range applications at a maximum of 100 yds.

In center-fire calibers, small-capacity .22s, (i.e., .22 Hornet, .218 Bee, .222 Rem. and .223 Rem.) and .25 caliber (i.e. .25-20 Win.) cartridges with soft-point or hollow-point bullets are in order. These calibers provide added range and striking energy at moderate cost.

Varmints, Pests—Animal types include coyote, jackrabbit, badger, groundhog, marmot, prairie dog, ground squirrel, rat, gopher, crow and pigeon. Weight varies from less than one to 30 lbs. Typical range extends from 100 to 400 yds.

This category of hunting animal includes both varmints and pests. Only rarely considered edible, meat damage is likely not a terminal-ballistic consideration. However, despite being small and thin-skinned, varmints can be challenging to hit and difficult to kill as ranges can be easily in excess of 300 yds. This places a premium on:

- high striking velocity
- rapid bullet expansion with minimum penetration
- match-level accuracy.

Rimfire cartridges with hollow-point bullets can be used on varmints and pests to an effective range of about 50 yds. Beyond that, however, most .22-caliber rimfire cartridges lack the striking velocity and bullet expansion needed to cleanly anchor varmints and pests, and their low noise level is an asset in some locales.

Popular modern caliber choices for hunting varmints and pests include: .17 HMR, .204 Ruger, .222 Rem., .223 Rem., .22-250 Rem., .220 Swift, .243 Win. and 6 mm Rem. The lighter-weight bullets with thin jackets and hollow-point or soft-point design are best.

Medium Game—Animal types include deer, wild sheep, antelope, javelina, feral hogs, caribou, warthog, impala and other smaller African antelope. Weight ranges from 50 to 350 lbs. Typical ranges extend from less than 50 to more than 300 yds.

Medium, thin-skinned game animals are popular quarry for modern hunters. By far the most common of these are deer. Regulations usually require that deer or medium game be hunted with a center-fire rifle cartridge of 6 mm or greater loaded with expanding soft-point or hollow-point bullets producing a minimum striking energy of a specified level at 100 yds. For this reason, non-magnum calibers of moderate power ranging in caliber from .243 Win. to .35 Rem. have been popular choices. Magnum calibers up to .30 are increasingly finding favor.

A hunting bullet suitable for medium game must be capable of reliably producing:

- penetration sufficient to reach vital organs deep inside the animal
- expansion to produce a large, permanent wound track
- retention of at least 80 percent of original weight
- enough striking energy to cleanly kill medium game at 100 yds. (approximately 1,500 ft.-lbs. or more).

In practice, this means a spitzer, flat-base bullet with a weight of 100 grains or more.

Authorities disagree on the amount of penetration needed on a game animal. One school of thought prefers that all the bullet's energy be expended inside the animal. They prefer the bullet to stop just shy of exiting. The second school of thought prefers that the bullet exit, leaving a sizeable wound and blood trail. Both schools agree that a hunting bullet for medium game must have enough penetration to reliably reach vital organs.

Target ammunition should not be used for medium-game hunting as match bullets are not designed to give reliable penetration or expansion.

Large, Heavy Game—Animal types include elk, moose, black bear, bison, musk ox, eland, zebra, kudu and crocodile. Weight ranges from 500 lbs. and up. Typical ranges extend from 50 to 300 yds.

Most large, heavy game is hunted at close range. While these animals are relatively thin-skinned, they can be very hard to kill, at times requiring more than one shot, and will frequently run long distances after a poor hit. For these reasons, heavy-game hunting places a premium on deep bullet penetration, high striking energy and reliable bullet expansion. Ballistically, this is translated into large-caliber bullets (at least .308" in diameter) weighing 180 grs. or more fired from standard or magnum calibers. Bullets for such game must be of robust construction to maintain weight and be designed to expand slowly so as to deposit maximum energy deep inside the target. These requirements call for a bullet of premium construction fired from a potent cartridge.

Dangerous Game—Animal types include lion, leopard, Cape buffalo, hippopotamus, elephant, large bears, rhinocerous and wild boar. Weight ranges from 150 lbs. (leopard) and up, often exceeding 750 lbs. Typical range is 75 yds. or less

Dangerous game such as lion, elephant, rhinoceros and Cape buffalo, as well as grizzly and polar bears, present a singular challenge in terms of ammunition. When encountered or after being hit, such animals may attack, in which case they must be stopped as quickly as possible. For this reason, powerful cartridges firing large-diameter, heavy bullets are the rule for hunting dangerous game.

For all types of dangerous game, reliable penetration and bullet weight retention to reach vital organs deep inside the animal are imperative. For large dangerous game such as elephant, hippo, rhino and Cape buffalo, heavily constructed, non-expanding bullets called solids weighing 300 to 500 grs. are a popular choice to guarantee penetration to vital areas even if the projectile has to smash through heavy bone then traverse several feet of tissue. On thinner-skinned dangerous game such as lion, leopard, bears and boar, soft-point expanding bullets with thick jackets weighing 180 to 300 grs. are a common choice to ensure deep penetration and maximum energy transfer inside the vital organs.

Self-Defense

Self-defense typically involves handgun ammunition fired from a pistol or a revolver. The fact that handguns are easy to store, easy to carry with you and handy to use makes them a popular choice for self-defense. The ballistic goal in self-defensive circumstances is to cause incapacitation of the attacker as quickly as possible with "instant incapacitation" being the ideal. In such circumstances, "incapacitation" is taken to mean that, given a fair hit, the bullet's strike causes the assailant to immediately stop all aggressive action.

To cause instant incapacitation, the ideal self-defense bullet must have design characteristics balancing these factors:

- The bullet must reliably expand to approximately double original diameter to transfer as much energy as possible and create the largest possible permanent wound cavity inside the perpetrator.
- Total penetration is ideally about 8 to 12" with no overpenetration or exit.
- The expanding bullet should not disintegrate and maintain at least 90 percent of its original weight.
- Bullet expansion must not be adversely affected by clothing penetrated before impact.
- Accuracy must be sufficient to enable the center of a silhouette (B-27) target to be hit every time at a distance of seven yds.
- Propellant should be low flash to avoid blinding the shooter in night situations.
- Striking energy should be a minimum of 220 ft.-lbs., and 300 ft.-lbs. or greater is desirable.

In case of a miss:

- The bullet should deform or disintegrate on contact with a hard surface to reduce or eliminate ricochets.
- The bullet must travel the shortest possible distance to first impact with the ground and strike with the least possible remaining energy.

Virtually all contemporary defensive ammunition makes use of jacketed hollow-point or soft-point bullets with a lead-alloy core and a copper-alloy jacket. These bullets have been designed to expand rapidly and reliably over a wide range of striking velocities.

But what caliber? Most experts who have studied this question respond by stating the the 9 mm Luger (9x19 mm Parabellum) is the smallest-caliber cartridge that should be relied upon for personal defense. And there is disagreement on this caliber with many experts condemning it as too weak. Still, there is nearly universal agreement that more powerful and larger calibers are good choices. This includes the following 11 calibers as well as 9 mm Luger:

- .38 Super Auto
- .38 Spl. +P
- .357 Mag.
- .357 SIG
- .40 S&W Auto
- 10 mm Auto
- .41 Mag.
- .44 Spl.
- .44-40 Win.
- .45 ACP
- .45 Colt.

The most popular calibers are: 9 mm Luger, .40 S&W, .45 ACP and .38 Special +P.

Many experts feel that smaller calibers such as the following lack the striking energy to be reliable self-defense calibers:

- .22 L.R.
- .22 WMRF
- .25 ACP
- 7.62x25 mm
- .32 ACP
- .32 Short, .32 Long
- .380 ACP
- 9 mm Makarov
- .38 S&W
- .38 Short Colt.

For this reason, these smaller calibers are normally considered only for "back up" or "second gun" purposes in law-enforcement circles. The most popular caliber for this purpose is the .380 ACP.

Then there are the magnum calibers. While they certainly can be used for self-defense, they produce significant recoil. These calibers include:

- .44 Mag.
- .45 Win. Mag.
- .454 Casull
- .460 S&W
- .475 Linebaugh
- .480 Ruger
- .50 AE
- .500 S&W.

Despite the considerable research done in the field of wound ballistics, experts continue to disagree in one key area. The controversy is between those who favor heavy, slow, large-caliber bullets that penetrate deeply and produce a large permanent wound track and those who favor lighter, high-velocity, smaller-caliber bullets that produce a sizable temporary cavity and a smaller permanent wound track. As bullet kinetic energy is a widely accepted standard used to compare the power of various cartridges, this controversy continues with data and experience to support the claims of both sides.

Military Ammunition

Military ammunition is not made in the same bewildering number of calibers and bullet weights and styles as civilian ammunition. Also, military ammunition is made to different pressure and velocity specifications than civilian ammunition. In general, military ammunition is made in only a few selected calibers and bullet types, but it is made in government arsenals or under contract by commercial manufactures in very large quantities far exceeding that of equivalent civilian calibers.

Military ammunition is made in a variety of different types. Many military ammunition types are designed for purposes having no equivalent in the civilian market. Here are a few of the modern types:

- ball—standard (for normal issue); heavy (for use at long ranges); penetrator (for use against body armor)
- tracer (for use by machine gunners to adjust fire)
- armor-piercing (for use against resistant targets)
- incendiary
- armor-piercing, tracer (for use against resistant targets with residual incendiary effect)
- armor-piercing, incendiary, tracer (combines effects of the three above)
- spotting (for determining range)
- match (for competition and sniping)
- short-range training, frangible (for training and practice)
- subsonic (for use in suppressed arms)
- duplex (two bullets)
- shot (for survival use)
- blank—maneuver, saluting (noise and flash); line throwing (for throwing grappling hooks or naval lines)
- grenade-launching (for launching rifle grenades)
- dummy
- proof (for gunsmith use)
- gauge (for setting and checking tolerances).

Each military type has been developed for a specific application based on many years of experience and testing. For purposes here, we will consider only the ball types.

The goal of a military ball bullet is to incapacitate enemy soldiers given a fair hit out to a specified range. The range specified varies with the caliber, bullet and tactical application from 100 yds. to 1,500 yds.

Military ball bullets are also expected to penetrate natural barriers such as sand, trees and brush. They are also expected to penetrate man-made barriers such as sandbags, walls, doors, vehicles, glass and wood. And they must do so over a range of temperatures from –40 to +125 degrees F. with a minimum of muzzle flash, smoke and residue.

In addition to all of the above, a military bullet must provide flat trajectory, maximum striking energy, low wind drift, deep penetration and reliable incapacitation. As such, most modern military ball bullets are of sharply pointed spitzer, boattail design with a heavy copper- or steel-alloy jacket and a hard-lead-alloy core with a steel insert for enhanced penetration. On impact, ball bullets normally create a large temporary wound cavity due to the shock of high-velocity impact. After penetrating 4" or 5", most ball bullets begin to yaw and tumble—frequently breaking in half at the cannelure. This creates multiple permanent wound tracks. These two events rapidly transfer energy inside the target causing damage to vital internal organs and incapacitation.

Ball bullets generally have a plain tip. Specialty bullets such as tracer and armor-piercing have a colored tip. The identifying color on the tip has different meaning in each country of service, so one cannot assume that a red tip means tracer in every instance.

In civilian use, the most practical military ammunition types are the ball, match and blank types. Military ball ammunition is an excellent choice for informal competition, practice and training while match ammo can be used for formal competition.

Law Enforcement Ammunition
Ammunition for law enforcement must meet several important criteria:
- It must reliably incapacitate the perpetrator as quickly as possible given a fair hit from 0 to 25 yds.
- Only the minimum amount of force absolutely necessary must be used to reliably incapacitate the perpetrator.
- Clothing worn by the perpetrator must not significantly degrade terminal ballistic performance.
- Accuracy must enable every shot to hit the vital center torso of a B-27 silhouette target every time from 7 to 25 yds.
- The bullet must expand to twice or more original diameter without fragmenting and retain at least 90 percent of original weight.
- Bullet must not exit the target given a fair hit to the torso.
- Propellant must be flashless with low smoke and minimal residue.
- Muzzle velocity variations (extreme spreads) must be less than 50 f.p.s.
- Ammunition must be in production and of tested, proven performance (no prototypes).
- Ammunition must be competitively priced, loaded by a manufacturer of proven quality and backed by liability insurance.

Given the above criteria, most modern law enforcement agencies. in the U.S. have selected jacketed hollow-point tactical handgun ammunition in one or more of the following popular calibers:

.40 S&W Auto (155- to 180-gr. bullet)
9 mm Luger (115- or 147-gr. bullet)
.357 SIG (124-gr. bullet)
.45 ACP (185- to 230-gr. bullet).

Note: Some departments may still use jacketed hollow-point tactical handgun ammunition in .357 Mag., .38 Spl., .41 Mag., or 10 mm.

A typical law enforcement bullet has a lead core with a tapered cavity and a copper alloy, internally tapered jacket with notches to predetermine upset points.

Competition Ammunition

Bullets for most competitions value one major criteria over all others—accuracy. The ideal is for all the bullets fired by a competitor to go through the same hole. After that, the shooter has no terminal ballistic interest in the bullet as it need penetrate only a paper target.

Beyond this, the competition shooter seeks an efficiently designed bullet offering:

- a short time of flight
- the least amount of wind drift
- minimum metal fouling buildup in barrel
- tested, proven reloading data (if reloading)
- clean neat hole in target paper (pistol wadcutters).

To comply with these criteria, most bullet and ammunition manufacturers employ a spitzer, hollow-point, boattail bullet design for center-fire rifle competition. This configuration has been proven best over many years. It is not the most efficient design, but it is the most reliable due to manufacturing procedures.

A tangent-ogive spitzer point is prefered to the more sharply pointed secant-ogive because it provides more bearing surface and is nearly as aerodynamically efficient as a secant-ogive at typical small-arms velocities.

A boattail base significantly reduces base drag which, in turn, reduces flight time, wind drift, flattens the trajectory and increases supersonic persistance.

The hollow-point tip design moves the center of gravity of the bullet rearward for better accuracy, is much easier to manufacture and helps maintain critical core/jacket concentricity for balance.

In the manufacture of match-grade bullets, bullet makers take numerous extra steps to ensure quality and accuracy, ranging from added quality checks to special procedures to special machines and tooling. The goal of a match bullet is consistency, but the shooter must still do his part.

Training Ammunition

Most ammunition manufacturers offer special handgun ammunition intended for informal competition, practice, training and qualification. As a great deal of such activity takes place on indoor ranges, the problems associated with airborne lead and lead waste disposal have become very important. There are now three types of training ammunition:

- standard ammunition with unjacketed or FMJ lead bullets for outdoor use
- ammunition with lead-free primers and lead bullets with jackets that cover the heel
- frangible ammunition with lead-free primers and lead-free bullets.

There are three major contributors to airborne lead:

- lead styphnate compounds in the primer
- lead vaporized by the hot propellant gases from the heel of the bullet
- lead dust from bullet impact on the backstop.

Indoor range operators typically reduce airborne lead levels by use of very expensive air scrubbers to remove the lead or by stipulating the use of lead-free ammunition.

In addition, waste lead from backstops is considered toxic waste and disposal is very expensive.

Ammunition makers have developed solutions to these problems at several levels with innovative new products.

- Primers are now being made with lead-free components. As lead from primers is the main contributor to airborne lead, simply switching to ammunition with lead-free primers will substantially reduce airborne lead levels—in some cases enough to meet OSHA requirements.
- Bullets are now available with copper jackets protecting the heel from propellant gases. Such bullets effectively prevent hot propellant gases from vaporizing lead off the heel of the bullet, further reducing airborne lead levels.
- Bullets with lead-free cores are becoming more prevalant.

These so-called "frangible" bullets eliminate or reduce the disposal of toxic lead waste from backstop systems as well as airborne lead. Use of frangible-bullet lead-free ammunition offers several advantages to a range operator:

- eliminates airborne lead
- eliminates expensive disposal of toxic lead waste from backstops
- reduces range upkeep expenses substantially
- complies with OSHA and EPA regulations
- eliminates need for expensive air scrubbers
- eliminates backsplatter.

There are two types of frangible bullets:

Monolithic—sintered using iron and other metals, or molded using a polymer as a binder filled with powdered metal such as copper, tungsten, iron and tin.

Jacketed—a normal copper-alloy jacket encloses a core of non-toxic bismuth, tin or iron.

On impact with a solid surface such as a steel backstop, frangible bullets are designed to disintegrate quickly into small particles that are non-toxic. Frangible bullets reduce backsplatter and ricochets. It must be noted that frangible bullets can be still lethal.

Industrial

Industrial ammunition is used in many applications for construction, testing, proving and special purposes. Some of the numerous applications are as follows:

Stud drivers are used in construction of buildings to drive anchors in concrete. Most stud drivers fire rimfire cartridges.

Kiln gun shells utlize 8-ga. shotshells loaded with lead or zinc slugs to shoot the clinkers off the walls of kilns.

Cattle killer ammunition is a center-fire cartridge designed to kill cattle quickly and humanely.

Fragment simulators are rimfire cartridges loaded with hardened-steel projectiles for testing and proving body armor.

Line throwers utlize center-fire or shotshell blanks to throw lines to or from ships.

Noise blanks are used to start and end races.

Signaling cartridges propel a pyrotechnic distress signal flare into the air.

Lock breaker shotshells with projectiles consisting of rubber bags filled with sand or small very fine lead shot are used to break door locks.

Tear gas projectiles holding CN, CS, pepper or a mixture of these are used to break up riots, barricades and flush individuals from buildings.

Shot Pellets—Impact And Penetration

When a lead pellet impacts the target, the pellet deforms slightly, increasing its frontal area and transferring energy to the target more quickly at the expense of reduced penetration. Steel and tungsten-iron shot pellets are very hard and will not deform on impact. This results in deeper penetration with slower energy transfer than lead shot. It is common for steel and tungsten-iron shot pellets to pass completely through the target. It is less common for lead shot to do the same.

Sectional density is a major factor in penetration capability. Round projectiles, regardless of diameter or type, have a very poor sectional density due to their light weight. Shotgun pellets also have a poor ballistic coefficient so they strike at relatively low velocities. For these reasons, shotgun pellets have very limited penetration capabilities.

On impact, the low striking velocity and energy of pellets can create a very small temporary cavity if any at all. Thus the main killing mechanism of pellets is the permanent cavity caused by penetration through tissue. Rarely will a single shotgun pellet of any type suffice to cleanly kill game. Rather, the lethality of shotgun pellets in directly related to pattern quality. Odds increase with dense, evenly distributed patterns that provide a high probability of the multiple hits needed to cleanly bag the game.

When hunting birds with lead shot, a phenomenon called "feather draw" is often encountered. In this instance, the deforming pellet catches and holds some of the small, fine pin feathers near the skin and may drive them though the permanent wound channel. This reduces penetration and lethality substantially. Hunters have found that copper- or nickel-plated shot addresses this problem. Apparently, the copper or nickel surface reduces friction, thereby minimizing feather draw.

There are two methods of determining which pellet sizes, pellet types and loads are best for your type of hunting.

Pattern test selected loads to determine which provide the best pattern quality. Then take the best patterning loads afield and observe the results. Select the load that offers the best combination of pattern quality and game performance. If none qualify, retest with different loads.

Study the shot size recommendation and load/choke selector charts published in ammunition manufacturers' catalogs and select an appropriate load. Based on decades of field experience, these recommendations can save you considerable time and expense.

Chapter 15
RELOADING

While many gun owners use factory ammunition exclusively, a significant number of target competitors, varminters, big-game hunters and ballistic experimenters produce their own ammunition through reloading. Reloading is defined in the *NRA Guide to Reloading* as the "reassembling, or remanufacturing, of a cartridge to its complete former state." Reloading is often called handloading, which can be thought of as the manual assembly of a functional metallic cartridge or shotgun shell from the basic cartridge components, using specialized hand tools. Specifically, reloading is a process involving the re-use of a fired cartridge case or shotgun hull, while handloading may involve either fired or new cases and hulls. Reloading can also be (and is) practiced as a large-scale commercial enterprise, using the same kind of automated equipment employed to load new ammunition, while handloading implies small-scale production by a single operator using manually operated tools. Although "handloading" better describes the activity practiced by millions of shooters worldwide, "reloading" is the more widely accepted term, and thus will be used exclusively in this chapter.

Reloading has been practiced just about as long as self-contained cartridges have been in existence. Perhaps ironically, for 19th-century shooters using muzzleloading arms and, thus, accustomed to handling percussion caps, blackpowder and bullets, reloading may not have seemed as novel as it does to contemporary gun owners who have grown up using factory-loaded ammunition. The exigencies of frontier life placed a premium on self-reliance, and gun owners often had to be able to cast their own bullets and load their own ammunition. Blackpowder cartridge reloading was both simple and relatively safe, as it was almost impossible to overcharge a case and produce excessive pressures; and in the latter part of the 19th century, in fact, many rifles came with tools for reloading such cartridges.

By the turn of the century this situation had changed. The taming of the frontier, the advent of smokeless powder (which was trickier to load than blackpowder), and the widespread availability of factory-loaded ammunition all diminished the popularity of reloading. Despite this, interest in reloading persisted, and by the early 1900s several manufacturers were publishing loading data and producing a full range of reloading equipment: tong-type loading tools, reloading presses, powder measures and bullet sizer/lubricators.

Not much changed in the reloading field for several decades. After World War II, however, there was an almost exponential growth of the reloading industry, resulting from a number of factors, including an explosion of new rifle and handgun chamberings; improved performance of modern firearms; the greater selection and quality of reloading components, particularly powders and bullets; the birth of many new types of competitive shooting disciplines, some of which are dominated by reloaded ammunition; and the development of faster, more precise, and affordable reloading tools and equipment allowing the reloader to produce better ammunition more easily. In the wake of those developments came a wide variety of magazines, books, videos, websites and other information pertaining to reloading. Today's reloader has a selection of components, tools, equipment and information unparalleled at any previous time.

Benefits of Reloading

Perhaps the single most common reason why shooters reload is economy. It is normally much less expensive to reload ammunition than to buy new, factory loaded cartridges. Depending upon the quantities in which the components are purchased, a reloader can save one-half or more of the cost of factory ammunition. Or, to look at it from the point of a dedicated shooting enthusiast, reloading makes it possible to shoot twice as much for the same amount of money.

Reloading also allows the shooter to develop a cartridge that is custom-tailored to a particular gun and its specific use for hunting or competitive shooting. Carefully constructed reloads usually give greater accuracy in a particular gun than even factory match ammunition. In this respect, the ultimate reloader is probably the benchrest shooter, whose precision cartridge-loading techniques help make possible consistent groups of less than 1/4 inch at 100 yards. Beyond accuracy, reloading also makes it possible for the shooter to create other types of cartridges not available from the major ammunition makers, such as light practice loads or hunting loads featuring premium-quality hunting bullets. Even the major commercial producers of firearms, ammunition and cartridge components use limited-production reloaded cartridges (such as proof loads) for testing and research purposes.

There are many rifles and handguns in use that are chambered for obsolete cartridges (those no longer commercially loaded), for foreign cartridges largely unavailable in the United States or for non-standard "wildcat" cartridges. Reloading is often the only way owners of such guns can continue to use and enjoy them.

For many gun enthusiasts, reloading has certain intangible benefits as well. Many technically oriented shooters are fascinated by the challenge of balancing the myriad aspects of load development to create a cartridge having the optimum combination of characteristics for a particular activity. Other shooters simply enjoy the feeling of pride and accomplishment that comes from using ammunition they have assembled. Reloading is also relaxing and fun, and is a way for parents and their shooting-age children to share their love of the shooting sports away from the range. Furthermore, those who are environmentally conscious point to the fact that their hobby helps conserve raw materials, while many reloaders provide a community service by policing up the empty cases typically found at shooting ranges.

The Reloading Process

Whether the reloader is assembling metallic cartridges or shotgun shells, the basic process is very similar. However, while a metallic cartridge consists of four components (case, primer, powder and bullet), a shotgun shell is made up of five (case or hull, primer, powder, wad and shot charge or slug). This distinction results in slightly different reloading processes for these two types of firearm ammunition.

Reloading Metallic Cartridges

Reloading metallic cartridges for rifles and handguns involves the following basic procedures:

- resizing the case (returning the case to specified dimensions)
- removing the spent primer from the case
- seating a fresh primer in the case
- recharging the empty case with the proper amount of powder
- seating a new bullet into the neck of the case to give proper cartridge length.

Each step is critical to the assembly of ammunition that is safe, reliable and accurate. In addition to the basic steps above, there are other secondary but equally necessary procedures that must be performed to prepare metallic cases for reloading:

- inspecting the case for cracks or defects
- removing dirt, grit and corrosion from the outside of the case, the inside of the case neck and the primer pocket
- measuring the case to ensure it is not overly long
- trimming those cases that exceed the maximum specified length
- chamfering and deburring the mouth of the case to facilitate bullet seating
- lubricating the case so it runs smoothly into and out of the die.

Reloading Shotgun Shells

Reloading shotgun shells involves similar procedures to those used in reloading metallic cartridges:

- resizing the case of the shotgun shell (returning the case to specified dimensions)
- removing the spent primer
- seating a fresh primer in the case

- recharging the empty case with the proper amount of powder
- seating a wad in the case, with the correct pressure
- dropping the specified amount of shot or inserting the slug into the hull
- crimping the top of the case over or around the shot load or slug.

The primary differences between reloading metallic cartridges and shotgun shells are the steps involving the seating of the wad and forming the crimp. Normally, the wad must be seated atop the powder with a certain amount of pressure; the amount of this wad pressure is often included in shotgun shell reloading data and can be set on many shotshell reloaders.

Secondary reloading steps for reloading shotgun shells include:
- inspecting the case for cracks or defects
- removing dirt, grit and corrosion from the outside of the case and primer pocket.

Finally, once a quantity of reloaded ammunition has been created and stored in ammunition boxes, each box must be labeled with the full specifications of the load for both safety and for future reference.

Equipment for Reloading Metallic Cartridges

Reloading cartridges for rifles and handguns involves specific types of equipment. The items listed and described below are what is needed to complete the basic reloading process; however, there are many additional or more sophisticated tools for the advanced techniques used to load wildcat and match-grade ammunition.

Eye Protection

Safety glasses must always be worn when working with reloading components and equipment to prevent eye damage from igniting primers, flying power granules, etc.

Reloading Press

The reloading press is the device in which the basic reloading steps are performed. Every press has mounting locations for both the cartridge case and one or more reloading dies, as well as a linkage or mechanism that allows the case to be run forcefully into the die.

There are a number of types of reloading presses. Perhaps the most common, and certainly the simplest, type of reloading press is the single-stage press, which has a single mounting position for both the case and the die. With this press, a single stroke performs one operation on one case. Another type of press, the turret press, allows several dies to be mounted but still has only one station for the case. The most sophisticated presses are progressive presses, which have multiple die stations as well as revolving platforms that hold several cases at one time. With progressive presses, a single stroke performs several different operations on several cases simultaneously. Progressive presses are used primarily for high-volume reloading. Finally,

RELOADING

loading in the field or at the range can be accomplished using portable single-stage hand presses, which are similar in principle to some of the tong-type tools used in the early days of metallic cartridge reloading.

Various designs of reloading presses are available, and are designated by the letter of the alphabet whose shape is closest to the shape of the opening in the press. Most common are "O" or "D" presses. They are strong, simple to use and offer good press leverage.

Regardless of type or design, all presses for reloading metallic cartridges perform the same functions: resizing and depriming the case, priming the case, powder charging, bullet seating, and, if required, crimping (turning in) the case mouth to retain the bullet securely in the neck. These functions are accomplished using different reloading dies.

Reloading Dies

Reloading dies are hardened steel tools that are mounted in the reloading press and used to perform various operations on the case. Most die bodies have a 7/8-14 thread to fit the threaded mounting hole in the majority of presses.

Most die sets for rifles consist of two separate dies, one for case resizing and depriming, and the other for bullet seating and case mouth crimping. Handgun die sets usually are made up of three dies, one for resizing and depriming, one for case mouth belling or flaring (to facilitate bullet seating), and one for bullet seating and crimping. Also available are some four-die sets with a separate crimp die.

Other die variations include neck sizing dies, which size only the neck portion of bottleneck cases (producing greater accuracy and longer case life), and carbide sizing dies, which have a ring of tungsten carbide that allows straight-wall cases to be sized without case lubricant.

Die adjustment is critical to produce ammunition that is safe and accurate. With bottleneck cases, adjustment of the sizing die determines cartridge headspace. Similarly, proper adjustment of the seating die controls bullet seating depth and cartridge overall length (C.O.L.), both important dimensions in relation to safe pressure levels, optimum grouping, and proper feeding from a magazine. Crimp die adjustment is also critical; too little crimp and the bullet may move upon firing or feeding, while too much can damage the bullet, cause the jacket to separate from the core and degrade accuracy. Generally, instructions for proper die adjustment are supplied by the manufacturer with the die.

Other Equipment

In addition to the reloading press and reloading dies, also required are:
- a shell holder of the proper size to retain the cartridge case in the press
- a mechanical or electronic reloading scale for measuring powder charges, bullet weights, etc.
- dial or digital calipers for measuring case length, cartridge length, and bullet diameter

- a case trimmer to cut a case stretched by firing back to its proper length
- a deburring tool to remove burrs from the outside of the case mouth and to chamfer the inside of the mouth
- a tumbler or vibratory-type case cleaning machine to remove dirt, grit and other residue from cartridge cases
- a case neck brush to remove dirt and powder residue from the inside of the case neck
- a primer pocket cleaner to remove dirt and primer residue from the primer pocket
- a case lube pad and case lube for lubricating the case
- a powder trickler or powder dribbler to deliver small amounts of powder into the pan of a reloading scale and bring the powder charge to an exact weight
- a powder measure to quickly meter out the powder charge [optional]
- a powder funnel to guide the powder charge from the scale pan or powder measure into the case mouth
- case loading blocks to organize cases in batches for more efficient reloading
- a primer flipper tray to turn primers anvil-side-up for easier insertion into the primer pocket
- a priming tool for inserting primers into the primer pocket.

Equipment for Reloading Shotgun Shells

Shotgun shells differ from metallic cartridges in several ways. For example, they operate at much lower pressures, have hulls with plastic or cardboard bodies, and come in a limited variety of sizes (gauges) and lengths. As a result, the tools used for shotshell reloading differ somewhat from those used for producing metallic cartridges.

Eye Protection

Safety glasses must always be worn when working with reloading components and equipment, to prevent eye damage from igniting primers, flying power granules, etc.

Shotgun Shell Reloader

Most modern shotgun shell reloaders incorporate into one piece of equipment all of the stations necessary to perform each operation involved in assembling a shotgun shell. Thus, there are no separate dies, as with metallic cartridge reloading. The shotgun shell reloader combines a reloading press and reloading dies in a single piece of equipment.

One major difference between metallic cartridge and shotgun shell reloading is that, in the latter process, powder and shot charges are usually metered volumetrically using either interchangeable bushings contained in a sliding charge bar, or a universal charge bar that can be adjusted to throw different charges of powder and shot. A reloading scale is still required, however, to check the weights of the powder and shot charges thrown by the bushings or universal charge bar.

Shotgun shell reloaders vary greatly in complexity, automatic features, and speed of operation. As with presses used for metallic cartridge reloading, there are single-stage shotgun shell reloaders that perform all the reloading operations on a single shell before a second shell is started, and progressive models that perform operations on several shells simultaneously with a single stroke of the handle.

Regardless of type or design, all loaders for shotgun shells perform the same functions: resizing and depriming the case, priming the case, powder charging, wad seating, charging the case with the proper weight of shot or with a slug, starting the crimp and finishing the crimp. Note that shotgun shells may have a six-segment crimp, an eight-segment crimp or a roll crimp; it is important for the shotgun shell reloader to be equipped with a die for the proper crimp.

Other Equipment

In addition to the shotgun shell reloader, also required are:

- interchangeable hollow bushings for metering out the proper amounts of powder and shot (note that different weights of powder and shot require different bushings)
- a mechanical or electronic reloading scale to verify the weights of powder and shot thrown by the bushings or universal charge bar.

Reloading Safety

As with many pastimes and recreational activities, reloading is extremely safe as long as some common sense safety rules are observed. Many of these rules apply to the process of reloading, while others pertain to the proper way in which metallic cartridge or shotgun shell components may be combined to produce safe ammunition. Finally, there are also safety rules governing the handling and storage of ammunition components and reloaded ammunition.

The following basic rules have the been compiled from several different sources, including the *NRA Guide to Reloading*; the Sporting Arms and Ammunition Manufacturer's Institute (SAAMI); and the National Fire Protection Association (NFPA). For additional safety recommendations, consult the National Reloading Manufacturers Association (NRMA).

General Reloading Safety Rules

- ALWAYS wear safety glasses when reloading.
- DO NOT SMOKE while reloading.
- Understand what you are doing and why it must be done in a specific way.
- Stay alert and concentrate on your work when reloading. Don't reload when distracted, disturbed or tired.
- Avoid reloading when you are trying to do something else, such as watching television or holding a conversation.

- If you become fatigued, stop all reloading activities.
- Never use alcohol or drugs before or during your reloading session.
- Establish a loading procedure and follow it. Don't vary your sequence of operations.
- Set up your reloading bench where powder and primers won't be exposed to heat, sparks or flame.
- Keep your reloading bench clean and uncluttered.
- Have only one canister of powder, one box of primers and one box of bullets on the bench at one time.
- Keep all reloading equipment clean and in good condition. In particular, keep all priming equipment free of primer dust (dislodged particles from the explosive primer pellet), which can ignite and cause sympathetic ignition of nearby primers.
- Clearly label components and reloaded ammunition for easy identification.
- Establish a system of checks and inspections for every step of the reloading process.
- Only use reloading components that are clearly and unmistakably identified.
- Avoid using components that are obsolete or of uncertain origin.

Safety in Assembling Loads
- Use only pressure-tested reloading data from reputable sources.
- Always follow exactly the reloading data published by reputable manufacturers.
- Always use the specific components called for in the data. Don't substitute components for those listed.
- Never exceed the powder charges listed in manufacturers' reloading data.
- Never mix powders nor substitute one powder for another.
- Never substitute smokeless powder for blackpowder or blackpowder substitutes.
- Always start loading with the minimum powder charge listed in the reloading data.
- Never use a powder charge weight less than the minimum load listed. Too-light charges of some powders in large-capacity cases are believed to result in a phenomenon known as detonation, which produces a dangerously high pressure spike capable of damaging the firearm and injuring the shooter.
- Always look for signs of high pressure and reduce the powder charge if such signs are encountered.

Safety in Handling and Storing Components and Ammunition
- Store reloading components away from heat and exposure to open flame.

- Never store powder or primers in or near the reloading bench.
- Always store reloading components in the original factory containers, which are designed to properly identify and safely contain these materials. After reloading, return any unused components to their original factory containers.
- Never store powders and primers in the same location.
- Always store all reloading components and reloaded and factory ammunition so that children and other unauthorized persons cannot have access to them.
- Don't acquire or use powders or primers that are discontinued or obsolete, or that show signs of being damaged or improperly stored.
- Store powder containers in a loosely constructed wooden box. Never store these containers in a metal box, such as a surplus ammo can.

Primer Safety

- Be extremely careful and alert when dealing with live primers. Primers are very sensitive to shock, heat, friction, pressure and even static electricity, and can cause serious damage and/or injury if accidentally ignited.
- Be aware that the ignition of one primer can cause other primers in its vicinity to simultaneously detonate as well.
- Primers differ in the amount of hot gas and white-hot particles they produce. Thus, never substitute or mix different brands or types of primers. Always use the specific primer listed in the reloading data.
- Never decap live primers. Fire the primed case in a firearm and then decap.
- Never use primers you cannot identify, or that are obsolete or have been subjected to moisture, oil, high temperature, etc.
- Never ream out or enlarge the flash hole in a primer pocket. This can increase chamber pressure.
- Keep primers in their original factory packaging until used, and return unused primers to that packaging.
- Never store primers in bulk in a jar or other similar container. The ignition of a single primer could cause mass detonation.
- If resistance is felt when seating or feeding primers, STOP and investigate. NEVER force primers.
- Store primers in a cool, dry place. High temperature causes them to deteriorate.
- Don't handle primers with oily or greasy hands. Oil contamination can adversely affect the reliability of primer ignition.
- Dispose of primers you cannot identify. Ask your local police or fire department to dispose of unserviceable or unidentifiable primers.

Powder Safety

- Never exceed maximum powder charges listed in reloading data.
- Never mix two or more powders of different types and avoid mixing different lots of the same powder.
- Store powder in a cool, dry place in original factory containers.
- If you measure powder charges by volume, initially check the weights of powder thrown using a reloading scale and recheck the charge weights at regular intervals during the reloading. Recheck the weights of powder thrown each time you begin a new reloading session.
- Return any powder you do not use to its original factory container. Do not repackage powders. Make sure any powder container is tightly closed when stored or otherwise not in use.
- Do not use powders that are not in their factory containers or whose origin is otherwise uncertain.
- Pour out only as much powder as you need for the immediate reloading work.
- Don't carry powder in your clothing. Wash your hands thoroughly after handling powder.
- Never substitute smokeless powder for blackpowder or blackpowder substitutes.
- Never salvage smokeless powder from old cartridges.

Metallic Cartridge Reloading Safety

- Examine cases before loading and discard any that are cracked, split, badly dented or corroded.
- Bullet seating depth is critical, particularly in cartridges with maximum powder charges and in small-capacity handgun cartridges. Seat bullets to the cartridge overall length (C.O.L.) specified in the reloading data.
- Always verify the powder charge thrown by a powder measure by weighing several charges on an accurate reloading scale.
- Take care to avoid double-charging a case. Put charged cases in a loading block and use a short piece of dowel rod, or visual observation with an oblique light, to verify the proper powder level in each case.

Shotgun Shell Reloading Safety

- Examine hulls before loading and discard any that are cracked, split, badly dented or corroded.
- Never interchange data between bushing selection charts.
- Always verify the shot and powder loads thrown by the shot bar or bushing by weighing several charges on an accurate reloading scale.
- Never "work up" shotgun shell loads. Always use the exact components, powder charge weights, and wad pressures listed in the reloading data.

- Never substitute steel or buffered lead shot in loads recommended for lead shot only. Steel and buffered lead shot require different components, as specified in reloading data intended for such shot.

Reloading Hygiene
- Don't eat or drink at or around a reloading bench, or while handling lead (which is toxic) or any other reloading component.
- Handle lead bullets or lead shot only in a well-ventilated area.
- ALWAYS wash hands thoroughly after handling lead.
- Always thoroughly wash your hands and face after reloading or handling cartridge components.
- Be sure there is adequate ventilation in the reloading area.
- Immediately sweep up any loose or spilled powder in the reloading area.

Disposal of Ammunition and Ammunition Components
- Ammunition that is obsolete, or that has been damaged by exposure to fire, water, solvents or improper storage conditions should be scrapped.
- Never bury defective ammunition, or dump it in a waterway, as it may be retrieved years later and could possibly pose a danger to children or uninformed persons.
- Defective ammunition may be disposed of in several ways. It can be incinerated in compliance with federal, state and local regulations or turned over to local police or fire departments for destruction. Alternately, it maybe returned to the original manufacturer (with the permission of the company).
- Small amounts of unserviceable powder may be disposed of by burning in small piles (less than one pound in any one pile) on a calm day, in accord with all relevant federal, state and local ordinances.
- Unserviceable powder may also be disposed of by dispersing it widely on a lawn, using it as fertilizer or by delivering it to local hazardous waste facility that accept such materials.

Signs of High Pressure
When working up loads for accuracy or velocity, the careful reloader will start with the minimum powder charge listed and increase the charge in small increments, never exceeding the maximum load listed. For this purpose, it is useful to consult several reloading manuals. With any given cartridge, different manuals will often list different starting and maximum charges of the same powder, even with the same case, primer and type and weight of bullet. The prudent reloader will take the lowest maximum charge listed in all the manuals as the safe limit for his or her loads.

Even with such precautions, the reloader should still watch for signs of high pressure. In a gun having a tight bore or neck, or a short throat, loads that are listed as safe in several manuals can still generate high pressures, particularly as maximum powder charges are approached. The reloader should always be aware of the signs that may denote chamber pressures that exceed safe levels.

Common signs of high pressure include:
- hard bolt lift (bolt action) or hard extraction (revolver)
- sooty ring of escaped gas around primer
- enlarged primer pocket with smudges from gas leakage, leaving primer loose
- completely open primer pocket, which frees the primer
- flattening of the primer
- primer erosion from high-pressure gas escaping around the primer
- cratering of the primer, caused by the extrusion under pressure of primer cup material into the firing pin hole
- perforation or rupture of the primer
- flowing of brass into the extractor or ejector recess
- engraving of breech face marks onto the case head
- excessive expansion of the case head.

Note that the absence of pressure signs is, in itself, no guarantee that chamber pressures are at a safe level. In most cases, signs of high pressure appear only after the maximum SAAMI pressure limit for a cartridge has been exceeded by a considerable amount. If any pressure signs appear in a series of reloaded rounds, do not fire the remaining rounds for that load. Set aside all the remaining cartridges for that load, and for loads having stiffer charges of that powder, for disassembly. Also, reduce your maximum powder charge to a weight that is at least 5 percent below the charge weight at which pressure signs first appeared.

Finally, be aware that ambient temperature may also affect chamber pressures. A maximum or near-maximum load that appears completely safe when fired at a temperature of 30 degrees F may produce significant pressure signs when used on a hot, 95-degree summer day.

REFERENCE MATERIALS

Chapter 16
FORMULAE AND TABLES

Formulae

BULLET STRIKING ENERGY IN FOOT-POUNDS (ft.-lbs.)

The striking energy of a bullet in foot-pounds.

$$E = \frac{W \times V^2}{450,400}$$

E = energy of bullet in ft.-lbs.
W = weight of bullet in grains
V = velocity of bullet in f.p.s. squared

BULLET STRIKING MOMENTUM

The impetus of the bullet as it strikes the target.

$$MS = \frac{W \times V}{225,200}$$

MS = striking energy in lb.-sec.
W = bullet weight in grains
V = striking velocity in f.p.s.

BULLET MASS

The quantity of a body as measured in its relation to inertia.

$$BM = \frac{BW \times 7,000}{32.17}$$

BM = bullet mass
BW = bullet weight in grains

SECTIONAL DENSITY OF A BULLET

The ratio of a bullet's mass in pounds
to the square of its diameter.

$$SD = \frac{WB}{DB^2}$$

SD = sectional density of bullet
WB = weight of bullet in pounds
     (weight in grains divided by 7,000)
DB = diameter of bullet in inches squared

BALLISTIC COEFFICIENT OF A BULLET

The ratio of a bullet's ability to overcome
air resistance and maintain velocity
compared to a standard.

$$BC = \frac{BW}{I \times D^2}$$

BC = ballistic coefficient
BW = bullet weight in pounds
     (bullet weight in grains divided by 7,000)
I   = form factor of bullet (see chart below)
D   = bullet diameter in inches

Approximate Form Factors

Bullet Profile	Form Factor
Very sharp	.60
Moderately sharp	.70
Moderately sharp w/small flat meplat	.85
Moderately blunt	1.00
Very blunt	1.20
* * * * * * * * * * *	
For boattail base subtract	.06
For small lead tip add	.07
For large lead tip add	.20

BULLET TIME OF FLIGHT

The time in seconds it takes for a bullet to travel
from the muzzle to the target.

$$T = \frac{2R}{VO + VR}$$

T   = bullet time of flight in seconds
R   = range to target in feet
VO = muzzle velocity in f.p.s.
VR = remaining velocity at target in f.p.s.

BULLET WIND DRIFT

Determines horizontal displacement of bullet
at target due to 90 degrees crosswinds.

$$D = W (T - TV)$$

D   = wind deflection in feet
W   = crosswind velocity in f.p.s.
T   = bullet's time of flight to target in seconds
TV = bullet's time of flight to target in vacuum
      in seconds (range to target in feet divided
      by muzzle velocity in f.p.s.)

SPEED OF BULLET ROTATION
IN REVOLUTIONS PER MINUTE (rpm)

$$BR = \frac{MV \times 60 \times 12}{RT}$$

BR = bullet rotational speed in rpm
MV = muzzle velocity in feet per second (f.p.s.)
RT = rifling twist rate in inches

RECOIL OF GUN

The "kick" of a gun measured in foot-pounds.

Step 1 — Calculate recoil impulse of gun.

$$I = \frac{(WB \times VB + 4{,}000 \times WC)}{225{,}400}$$

I   = recoil impulse of gun in ft.-lbs.
WB = weight of bullet in grains
VB = muzzle velocity of bullet
       in feet per second (f.p.s.)
WC= weight of propellant powder charge
       in grains

Step 2 — Calculate recoil velocity of gun.

$$VG = \frac{32.2 \times I}{WG}$$

VG = recoil velocity of gun in f.p.s.
I   = recoil impulse of gun in ft.-lbs.
WG= weight of gun in pounds

Step 3 — Calculate free recoil energy of gun.

$$EG = \frac{WG \times VG^2}{64.4}$$

EG = free recoil energy of gun in ft.-lbs. (kick)
VG^2 = recoil velocity of gun in f.p.s. squared
WG = weight of gun in pounds

GREENHILL'S FORMULA

Estimates proper rifling twist rate for a given bullet.

$$\text{Twist} = 150 \times \frac{D^2}{BL}$$

D = bullet diameter in inches
BL= bullet length in inches

LOCK TIME

The time it takes for the firing pin or hammer
to fall and detonate the primer.

Step 1 — Calculate S (displacement of spring at time of firing)
and S_0 (displacement of spring in cocked position).

$$S_0 = L\text{-}LC$$
$$S = L\text{-}LF$$

L = free length of spring
LC = spring length in cocked position
LF = spring length in fired position

Step 2 — Calculate spring constant (K)—the amount of force
in lbs. required to compress spring 1".

$$K = GD/8C^3N$$

G = 11.5×10^6 lb in^{-2} (for steel)
D = wire diameter of spring in inches
C = mean diameter of spring in inches
   / wire diameter of spring in inches
N = number of active coils

Step 3 — Calculate lock time.

$$T = \sqrt{W/KG} \times \cos^{-1} S/S_0$$

K = spring constant, 1 lb. in $^{-1}$
G = gravitational acceleration, 386.4 in. sec. $^{-2}$
W = weight of firing pin system in lbs.
S_0 = L-LC
S = L-LF
T = lock time

JOURNEE'S FORMULA

Estimates maximum horizontal range
of spherical lead shot pellets.

$$MR = D \times 2,200$$

MR = estimated maximum range of a spherical
     lead shot pellet in yards
D = diameter of lead shot pellet in inches

EXTREME SPREAD OF SHOTS

Measures precision of shot group.

MD - BD = ES

MD = maximum distance between the most
    widely separated shots
BD = diameter of bullet
ES = extreme spread of shot group

Group size typically three, five or 10 shots.
Normally five groups averaged together.

MEAN VERTICAL OR HORIZONTAL DEVIATION OF SHOTS

The average horizontal or vertical distance
from the group center of impact.

horizontal	**vertical**
$MA = \dfrac{E(DH)}{(N)}$	$MA = \dfrac{E(DV)}{(N)}$

MA = arithmetic mean measure of central tendency
DH = horizontal distance of each shot from center
    of impact of the group
DV = vertical distance of each shot from center
    of impact of the group
N = number of shots
E = process of successive addition (add distances together)

MAXIMUM MEAN RADIUS OF SHOTS

The average of all radial distances
from the group center of impact.

$$MR = \frac{E(DC)}{(N)}$$

MR = maximum mean radius
DC = distance of each shot from center
N = number of shots
E = process of successive addition
    (add distances together)

STANDARD DEVIATION

The variation from the average.

Step 1—Determine average velocity of all shots (or distance from the center of the group). Use as big a sample as possible (typically 20 shots).

$$AVG = \frac{E\,(V)}{(N)}$$

AVG = average velocity or distance
V = velocity or distance of each shot
N = number of shots
E = process of successive addition
      (add velocities or distances together)

Step 2—Find the difference between each shot and the average. Square each result and add together. Divide by number of shots minus one.

$$\frac{E\,(AVG - V)^2}{N\text{-}1} = S$$

AVG = average velocity or distance
V   = velocity or distance of each shot
N   = number of shots
E   = process of successive addition (add squared results together)

Step 3—Take the square root of the results of Step 2.

$$\sqrt{S} = Sd$$

S   = Step two result
Sd = standard deviation

POWER FACTOR—NRA

A calculated figure to determine handgun caliber acceptable for NRA Action Shooting.

$$V \times W = PF$$

V = velocity of bullet in f.p.s.
W = weight of bullet in grains
PF = power factor (must be 120,000 or more)

POWER FACTOR—IPSC

A calculated figure used to determine "major" caliber for IPSC competition.

$$\frac{V \times W}{1,000} = PF$$

V = velocity of bullet in f.p.s.
W = weight of bullet in grains
PF = power factor (must be 175 or more for major caliber)

HATCHER'S FORMULA FOR RELATIVE STOPPING POWER (1935)

A formula for comparing relative stopping power (RSP) of various bullets.

$$BM \times SM \times A = RSP$$

BM = bullet momentum
    (bullet mass x striking velocity)
SM = bullet shape multiplier (see chart below)
A   = bullet cross sectional area
    (radius squared x 3.1416) see chart below

Hatcher's Bullet Shape	Multipliers	Caliber	Cross Sectional Area In Inches
Jacketed round-nose	.90	.22	.039
Jacketed flat-point	1.00	.25	.049
Lead round-nose	1.00	.30	.075
Lead blunt round-nose	1.05	.32	.077
Lead flat-point	1.10	9 mm	.098
Lead wadcutter	1.25	.357 (.38)	.101
		.41	.129
		.44	.144
		.45	.159

EXPANSION RATIO

The ratio of bore volume (from the cartridge base to the muzzle) to cartridge case powder volume. Influences the amount of propellant energy that can be converted to bullet energy.

Step 1—Determine bore volume in cubic inches.

$$BV = L \times D \times .773$$

BV = bore volume in cubic inches
L = length traveled by the base of the bullet from seat to muzzle in inches
D = groove diameter of barrel in inches.

Step 2—Compute expansion ratio.

$$ER = \frac{BV + U}{U}$$

ER = expansion ratio
BV = bore volume in cubic inches
U = volume of powder chamber in cubic inches

CARTRIDGE EFFICIENCY

How efficiently a load converts stored energy in the propellant to bullet kinetic energy.

Step 1—Calculate muzzle energy.

$$ME = \frac{W \times V^2}{450{,}400}$$

ME = muzzle energy of bullet in ft.-lbs.
W = weight of bullet in grains
V = muzzle velocity of bullet in f.p.s. squared

Step 2—Calculate potential energy.

PE = PC x 180 ft.-lbs.

PE   = potential energy in propellant
PC   = weight of propellant charge in grains
180 ft.-lbs.= average power potential in one grain of propellant

Step 3—Calculate efficiency (%).

$$EF = \frac{ME}{PE}$$

EF = efficiency percentage
ME = muzzle energy in ft.-lbs.
PE = potential energy in ft.-lbs.

Conversion Formulae And Tables

The following formulae are offered for those shooters who wish to make their own conversion calculations. For those who may not wish to do this, Conversion Tables will be found below.

Conversion Formulae
VELOCITY

VELOCITY IN FEET PER SECOND TO VELOCITY IN METERS PER SECOND

Conversion of velocity in English units
to velocity in metric units.

MPS = FPS x 0.3048

MPS = velocity in metric meters per second (m.p.s.)
FPS = velocity in English feet per second (f.p.s.)

VELOCITY IN METERS PER SECOND TO VELOCITY IN FEET PER SECOND

Conversion of velocity in metric units
to velocity in English units.

FPS = MPS x 3.280840

FPS = velocity in English feet per second (f.p.s.)
MPS = velocity in metric meters per second (m.p.s)

FEET PER SECOND TO MILES PER HOUR

Bullet velocity in English feet per second
converted to speed in English miles per hour.

MPH = FPS x 0.6818

MPH = speed in English miles per hour (m.p.h.)
FPS = velocity in English feet per second (f.p.s.)

FEET PER SECOND TO MACH
(speed of sound at sea level at 59 degrees F)

Bullet velocity in English feet per second
converted to Mach.

$$M = \frac{FPS}{1,120}$$

M   = Mach
FPS = bullet velocity in English feet per second (fps)

VELOCITY IN FEET PER SECOND TO KNOTS

Conversion of velocity in English feet
per second to velocity in knots.

VK = FPS x 1.687810

VK = velocity in knots
FPS = velocity in feet per second (f.p.s.)

ENERGY

ENERGY IN FOOT-POUNDS
TO ENERGY IN JOULES

Conversion of energy in English units
to energy in metric units.

EJ = EFP x 1.355818

EJ = energy in metric Joules (J)
EFP = energy in English foot-pounds (ft.-lbs.)

ENERGY IN JOULES TO ENERGY IN FOOT-POUNDS

Conversion of energy in metric units
to energy in English units.

EFP = EJ x .7375621

EFP = energy in English foot-pounds (ft.-lbs.)
EJ   = energy in metric Joules (J)

LINEAR

INCHES TO MILLIMETERS (mm)

Conversion of English inches to metric millimeters.

LM = LI x 25.4

LM = length in metric millimeters (mm)
LI   = length in English inches (in.)

MILLIMETERS TO INCHES

Conversion of metric millimeters to English inches.

LI = LM x .0393701

LI   = length in English inches (in.)
LM = length in metric millimeters (mm)

METERS TO YARDS

Conversion of metric meters to English yards.

LY = LM x 1.093613

LY   = length in English yards (yds.)
LM = length in metric meters (m.)

YARDS TO METERS

Conversion of English yards to metric meters.

LM = LY x .9144

LM = length in metric meters (m.)
LY   = length in English yards (yds.)

WEIGHT

GRAINS TO GRAMS

Conversion of English grains to metric grams.

WGM = WGR x .0647989

WGM = weight in metric grams (gms.)
WGR = weight in English grains (grs.)

GRAMS TO GRAINS

Conversion of metric grams to English grains.

WGR = WGM x 15.43236

WGR = weight in English grains (grs.)
WGM = weight in metric grams (gms.)

KILOGRAMS TO POUNDS

Conversion of metric kilograms to English pounds.

WP = WKG x 2.204623

WP = weight in English pounds (lbs.)
WKG = weight in metric kilograms (kg.)

POUNDS TO KILOGRAMS

Conversion of English pounds to metric kilograms.

WKG = WP x .4535924

WKG = weight in metric kilograms (kg.)
WP = weight in English pounds (lbs.)

PRESSURE

PHYSICAL ATMOSPHERES (ATM)
TO POUNDS PER SQUARE INCH

Physical atmosphere is 14.7 pounds per square inch.

ATM x 14.7 = PSI

ATM = pressure in physical atmospheres (atm.)
PSI = pressure in pounds per square inch (p.s.i.)

TECHNICAL ATMOSPHERES (AT) TO POUNDS PER SQUARE INCH

Technical atmosphere is one kilogram per square centimeter or 14.223 pounds per square inch.

AT x 14.223 = PSI

AT = pressure in technical atmospheres (at.)
PSI = pressure in pounds per square inch (p.s.i.)

PRESSURE IN SHORT TONS PER SQUARE FOOT TO POUNDS PER SQUARE INCH

Converting English short tons per square foot to pounds per square inch.

PSI = TPI x 13.88889

PSI = pressure in pounds per square inch (p.s.i.)
TPI = pressure in English short tons per square foot

TEMPERATURE

TEMPERATURE IN CENTIGRADE FROM TEMPERATURE IN FAHRENHEIT

$$\frac{F - 32 \times 5}{9} = C$$

C = temperature in metric degrees centigrade (C.)
F = temperature in degrees Fahrenheit (F.)

TEMPERATURE IN FAHRENHEIT FROM TEMPERATURE IN CENTIGRADE

$$\frac{C \times 9}{5} + 32 = F$$

F = temperature in degrees Fahrenheit (F)
C = temperature in metric degrees centigrade (C)

DRAM EQUIVALENT

A dram is an English unit of weight equal to 1/16 of an ounce or 27.3 grains.

Drams were the standard unit of weight measurement for loading shotguns with blackpowder before smokeless powder became common. Today, the performance potential of smokeless-powder shotshell loads are frequently expressed in dram equivalents. Unlike blackpowder, this is *not* a measure of powder charge weight. Rather it is a gauge or guide to indicate the approximate muzzle velocity of a shot charge of a given weight propelled by smokeless powder in blackpowder performance terms. Dram equivalent numbers are therefore not direct conversion factors for loading smokeless powder shotshells.

Examples:

1.   12 ga.-2¾"- 3-dram-equiv. 1⅛-oz. shot, muzzle velocity is 1200 f.p.s.

2.   12 ga.-2¾"- 3¾-dram-equiv.1¼-oz. shot, muzzle velocity is 1330 f.p.s.

Conversion Tables
ENGLISH/METRIC

WEIGHTS

Avoirdupois	Metric
1 ounce (oz.) = 437.5 grains (grs.)	1 gram (grm.) = 1000 milligrams (mg.)
16 ounces (ozs.) = 1 pound (lb.)	1000 grams (grms.) = 1 kilogram (kg.)
7000 grains = 1 pound	
1 grain = 0.0648 grams	1 gram = 15.4324 grains / 0.03527 ounces
1 ounce = 28.3495 grams	1 kilogram = 2.2046 pounds / 35.27 ounces
1 pound = 453.5924 grams	

LINEAR

English	Metric
12 inches (in.) = 1 foot (ft.)	10 millimeters (mm) = 1 centimeter (cm)
3 ft. = 1 yard (yd.)	100 centimeters / 1000 mm = 1 meter (m)
5,280 ft. / 1,760 yds. = 1 mile (mi.)	1000 meters = 1 kilometer (km)
1 inch = 25.4 mm / 2.54 cm	1 mm = 0.03937 in.
1 foot = 304.8 mm / 30.48 cm	1 cm = 0.3937 in.
1 yard = 914.4 mm / 91.cm / 0.91 m	1 m = 39.37 inches / 3.2808 feet / 1.0936 yds.
1 mile = 1609.3 meters / 1.6093 km	1 km = 3280.8 ft / 1093.6 yds / 0.62137 mi.

VOLUME

English	Metric
1,728 cubic inches = 1 cubic foot	1 cubic inch = 163.87 cu. mm / 16.387 cu. cm
27 cubic feet = 1 cubic yard	1 cubic foot = 0.0283 cu. meter
1 cubic yard = 0.7646 cu. meter	

PRESSURE

	MEGABAR	Atmosphere (Tech)	kg/cm²	Pounds Sq. In.
MEGABAR	1	0.98692	1.01972	14.890
Atmospheres(Tech)	1.01325	1	1.03323	14.696
kg/cm²	0.98067	0.96784	1	14.223
Pounds Sq. In.	14.890	14.696	14.2234	1

ENERGY

	Joules	Kilogram-meters	foot-pounds
Joules	1	0.102	0.7373
kg./meters	9.81	1	7.2331
ft.-lbs.	1.3562	1.1383	1

Gauge

Gauge as it pertains to shotguns is the number of lead round balls of a given diameter in one pound. The abbreviated chart below is taken from the British Gun Barrel Proof Act of 1868 which is still in use.

Nominal Gauge Number	Bore Diameter in inches	
A	2.000	
C	1.875	
E	1.750	
1	1.669	Round ball weighs 7,000 grs./1 lb.
J	1.563	
L	1.438	
2	1.325	Round ball weighs 3,500 grs./ 1/2 lb.
3	1.157	
4	1.052	
6	0.919	
8	0.835	
10	0.775	Round ball weighs 700 grs.
11	0.751	
12	0.729	Round ball weighs 583.3 grs.
14	0.693	Approx. diameter of .69-cal. musket ball
16	0.662	Round ball weighs 437.5 grs./1 oz.
18	0.637	
20	0.615	Round ball weighs 350 grs.
22	0.596	

24	0.579	Approx. diameter of .577-cal. Minié ball.
26	0.564	
28	0.550	Round ball weighs 250 grs.
30	0.537	
32	0.526	
34	0.515	
36	0.506	Approx. diameter of .50-cal. BMG bullet
48	0.459	Diameter of .45-cal. rifle bullet
50	0.453	Diameter of .45-cal. pistol bullet
68	0.410	Bore diameter of .410-bore shotshell

Below 50 gauge, the labeling system switched to using bore diameter. U.S. manufacturers consider these numbers minimum with a tolerance of plus 0.020 inches. The 10 gauge is the largest shotgun size legal for hunting. Note the .410 bore is a 68-gauge shotshell.

BARREL LENGTHS

Length in Inches	Length In Millimeters
2.5	63.5
3	76.2
4	101.6
6	152.4
8	203.2
10	254
12	304.8
14	355.6
16	406.4
16.5	419.1
18	457.2
18.5	469.9
20	508
20.5	520
22	558.8
24	609.6
25	635
26	660.4
27	685.8
28	711.2
30	762
32	812.8
34	863.6
36	914.4
38	965.2
40	1,016

MUZZLE VELOCITY VS. BARREL LENGTH

Most factory muzzle velocity figures are measured from a 24"
test barrel. To estimate muzzle velocities for other barrel lengths
from 20"-26", subtract change for barrels shorter than 24" and
add for barrels over 24".

Muzzle Velocity Range (in f.p.s.)	Expected Change (in f.p.s.) Per Inch Of Barrel
up to 2,000	5
2,001-2,500	10
2,501-3,000	20
3,001-3,500	30
3,501-4,000+	40

Chapter 17
REFERENCE DATA

BALLISTICS

Newton's Three Basic Laws of Physics

- A body at rest tends to remain at rest and a body in motion tends to remain in motion at the same speed and in the same direction unless acted upon by a force.

  Explanation: Nothing starts or stops unless a force acts upon it.

- When a body is acted upon by a constant force, the resulting acceleration is inversely proportional to the mass of the body and is directly proportional to the applied force.

  Explanation: Any change in motion is proportional to the total of all forces applied.

- Whenever one body exerts a force on another, that force is equal in measure but opposite in direction.

  Explanation: For each action, there is an equal, and opposite, reaction.

Boattail vs. Flat-Base Bullet Remaining Velocity Comparison

Range in yards	.308"dia. 180-gr. Sierra spitzer flat-base Remaining Vel. (f.p.s.)	.308" dia. 180-gr. Sierra spitzer boattail Remaining Vel. (f.p.s.)	Improvement in Remaining Vel. (f.p.s.)
0	2,800	2,800	—
100	2,577	2,619	42 f.p.s./+1.6 %
200	2,369	2,446	77 f.p.s./+3.3 %
300	2,171	2,280	109 f.p.s./+5 %
400	1,983	2,120	137 f.p.s./+6.9 %
500	1,804	1,966	162 f.p.s./+9 %
600	1,638	1,820	182 f.p.s./+11.1 %
1000	1,134	1,324	190 f.p.s./+16.7 %

Note: Remaining velocity figures taken from *Sierra Bullets Reloading Manual 4th edition.*

Abridged Ballistics of
Military Rifle Ball Ammunition

		Range in meters											
	Bullet wt. in		Velocity in f.p.s.							Energy in ft.-lbs.			
Caliber	grs./style	0	100	200	300	400	500	0	100	200	300	400	500
5.45x 39 mm	53 FMJBT Type PS Ball	2952	2630	2340	2060	1804	1551	1026	815	644	499	383	283
5.56x 45 mm	55 FMJBT M193 Ball	3250	2795	2410	2055	1710	1378	1290	953	710	515	358	232
5.56x 45 mm	62 FMJBT NATO (sS109) M855A1	3050	2730	2427	2132	1883	1640	1260	1008	797	615	479	364
30 Carbine	110 FMJ M1 Ball	1988	1565	1260	1033	925	840	961	595	386	260	210	171
7.62x 39 mm	123 FMJ Type PS Ball	2330	2073	1794	1545	1310	1125	1482	1174	879	652	468	345
7.62x 51 mm	150 FMJBT M80 Ball	2750	2550	2325	2106	1896	1699	2520	2153	1788	1466	1190	955
30-'06 Sprg.	152 FMJ M2 Ball	2740	2617	2342	2083	1843	1620	2534	2273	1821	1440	1127	872

Note: All figures listed are approximate.

Rifling Twist Rates

Rifle Calibers	Twist Rate in Inches/ Millimeters per Turn	Manufacturers
.17 Rem.	9/229	
	10/254	Sako, T/C
.22 Hornet	12/305	T/C
	14/356	Kimber, Savage, Ruger
	16/406	Winchester, Browning, Anschutz
.218 Bee	12/305	
.219 Zipper	14/356	
.220 Swift	12/305	Savage, T/C
	14/356	FN, Remington, Ruger, Savage, Winchester
.221 Fireball	12/305	
.222 Rem.	14/356	

Rifle Calibers	Twist Rate in Inches/ Millimeters per Turn	Manufacturers
.222 Rem. Mag.	14/356	
.223 Rem.	7/178	Colt, Ruger, Eagle Arms, DPMS, Rock River, Bushmaster, Olympic
	9/229	Colt, Winchester, Savage, Steyr,
	10/254	Ruger
	12/305	Colt, Remington, H&R, Sako, Savage, Winchester, T/C
	14/356	Remington, Husqvarna, Savage, Weatherby
5.6x50R mm Mag.	13¾/349	
5.56x45 mm NATO	7/178	
5.7x57 mm RWS	9³/₅/244	
.22 PPC	12/305	T/C
	14/356	Sako
.22 BR	10/254	
.223 WSSM	10/254	
.224 Wby. Mag.	14/356	
.225 Win.	14/356	
.22-250 Rem.	12/305	Sako, Savage, T/C
	14/356	Browning, H&R, Husqvarna, Mossberg, Remington, Ruger, Sako, Winchester, Weatherby
6x47 mm	12/305	
6 mm PPC	10/254	T/C
	14/356	Sako
6 mm BR Rem.	14/356	
6 mm Intl.	12/305	
6 mm Rem.	9/229	Remington, Browning, Ruger
	10/254	Remington, Schultz & Larsen, Ruger, Browning
.243 Win.	9/229	Remington, Ruger
	10/254	Browning, Colt, FN, H&R, T/C Husqvarna, Mannlicher, Mossberg, Remington, Savage, Sako, Schultz & Larsen, Stevens, Savage, Winchester, Weatherby
	12/305	Steyr
.244 Win.	10/254	Remington
.240 Wby. Mag.	9/241	
.25-20 Win.	14/356	
.256 Win. Mag.	10/254	T/C
	14/356	Marlin
.25-35 Win.	10/254	

Rifle Calibers	Twist Rate in Inches/ Millimeters per Turn	Manufacturers
.250 Savage	10/254	
.257 Roberts	10/254	
.25-'06 Rem.	10/254	
.257 Wby. Mag.	9/241	
	12/305	old Weatherby
	14/356	Mannlicher-Schoenauer
.260 Rem.	9/229	
6.5x50 mm Arisaka	9/229	
6.5x52 mm Mannlicher	7¾ /197	
6.5x54 mm Mannlicher	8¼/210	
6.5x55 mm Swedish	7.9/201	Winchester
	8/203	Husqvarna, Remington, T/C
	8¼/210	Schultz & Larsen
	9/229	Remington
6.5x57 mm Mauser	8/203	
6.5x68 mm	11/279	
6.5 mm Rem. Mag.	9/229	
.264 Win. Mag.	9/229	
.270 Win.	10/254	
.270 WSM	10/254	
.270 Wby. Mag.	9/241	Weatherby
	10/254	Browning, Weatherby, Winchester
	12/305	old Weatherby
7x30 Waters	9/229	T/C
	9/241	Winchester
7mm-08 Rem.	9/229	T/C
	9/241	Browning, Sako
	10/254	Remington, Savage, Winchester
7x57 mm Mauser	8/203	Ruger
	8/216	Winchester
	9/229	Mannlicher-Schoenauer, T/C
7x61 mm Sharpe & Hart	10/254	
7x64 mm Brenneke	10/254	
7 mm Exp. Rem.	9¼/235	
7 mm STW	9/229	
7 mm Dakota	9/229	
7 mm WSM	9/241	
7 mm Rem. Ultra Mag.	10/254	
7 mm Rem. Mag.	8/203	Ruger
	9/229	Husqvarna, Remington, T/C
	9¼/235	Browning, Mossberg, Savage, Sako, Winchester, Weatherby

Rifle Calibers	Twist Rate in Inches/ Millimeters per Turn	Manufacturers
	10/254	FN, H&R, Schultz & Larsen, Browning, Weatherby
7 mm Wby. Mag.	9¼/235	Remington
	9/241	Weatherby
	10/254	old Weatherby
	12/305	old Weatherby
.280 Rem.	8/203	Ruger
	9/229	T/C
	9¼/235	Remington
	9/241	Savage
	10/254	Browning, Sako, Winchester
.284 Win.	10/254	
.30 M1 Carbine	16/406	
	20/508	Marlin, Ruger
7.62x39 mm Soviet	10/254	T/C
	12/305	Colt, Ruger
7.5x53 mm French MAS	11/279	
7.62x54R mm Russian	10/254	
7.65x53 mm Argentine Mauser	9.8/249	
7.5x55 mm Swiss	10/267	
7.7x58 mm Arisaka	9/241	
.30-30 Win.	10/254	Marlin, Remington, T/C
	12/305	Savage, Mossberg, Winchester
.30 Rem.	12/305	
.300 Savage	10/254	Remington, Savage
	12/305	Savage
.30-40 Krag	10/254	
.307 Win.	12/305	
.308 Win.	10/254	Colt, Mannlicher-Schoenauer, Marlin, Remington, Schultz & Larsen, Ruger, Savage, Weatherby, Steyr, T/C
	12/305	Browning, FN, H&R, Husqvarna, Savage, Steyr, Mossberg, Sako, Remington, Winchester
.30-'06 Sprg.	10/254	Browning, FN, H&R, Mannlicher- Schoenaur, Marlin, Remington, Schultz & Larsen, Sako, T/C, Mossberg, Weatherby, Winchester
	12/305	Husqvarna, Browning
.300 Dakota	10/254	
.300 H&H Mag.	10/254	
.308 Norma Mag.	10/254	Schultz & Larsen
	12/305	Browning, Husqvarna

Rifle Calibers	Twist Rate in Inches/ Millimeters per Turn	Manufacturers
.30-338 Wby. Mag.	10/254	
.300 WSM	10/254	
.300 Win. Mag.	10/254	
	12/305	Husqvarna
.300 Wby. Mag.	9/241	Weatherby
	10/254	Remington, Sako, Weatherby, Winchester
	12/305	Remington
.300 Rem. Ultra Mag.	10/254	
.303 British	8/203	
.32 H&R Mag.	10/254	
.32-20 Win.	10/254	
.32-40 Win.	16/406	
.32 Rem.	14/356	
.32 Win. Spl.	16/406	
8x57 mm JS Mauser	9/229	
8x68 S mm	11/279	
8 mm Rem. Mag.	10/254	
.330 Dakota	10/254	
.338 Win. Mag.	10/254	
	12/305	Browning
.338 Rem. Ultra Mag.	10/254	
.338 Lapua Mag.	10/254	
.340 Wby. Mag.	10/254	
.348 Win.	12/305	
.35 Rem.	12/305	Savage
	14/356	T/C
	16/406	Marlin, Remington
.38-55 Win.	12/305	
	18/457	Ruger
.356 Win.	12/305	
.358 Win.	12/305	
	16/406	Ruger
.35 Whelen	14/356	T/C
	16/406	Remington, Ruger
.350 Rem. Mag.	16/406	
.358 Norma Mag.	12/305	
.376 Steyr	12/305	
.375 Win.	12/305	
.375 Dakota	12/305	
.375 H&H Mag.	12/305	
.375 Rem. Ultra Mag.	10/254	
.375 Wby. Mag.	12/305	

Rifle Calibers	Twist Rate in Inches/ Millimeters per Turn	Manufacturers
.378 Wby. Mag.	12/305	
9.3x62 mm	10/254	
9.3x64 mm	14/356	
9.3x74R mm	14/356	
.405 Win.	14/356	
.416 Rigby	14/356	
.416 Dakota	12/305	
.416 Rem. Mag.	14/356	
	16/419	Ruger
.416 Wby. Mag.	14/356	
.444 Marlin	38/965	
.45-70 Gov't	14/356	T/C
	20/508	
	22/559	Navy Arms
.458 Win. Mag.	14/356	Remington, Ruger, Winchester
	16/419	Browning Savage
	18/457	Sako
.460 Wby. Mag.	16/406	
.470 Nitro Express	20/508	
.50 BMG	15/381	

Handgun Calibers	Twist Rate in Inches/ Millimeters per Turn	Manufacturers
.22 Jet	14/356	
.25 ACP	10/254	Beretta
	16/406	Colt, Sauer, Sterling
.256 Win. Mag.	14/356	
7.62x25 mm Tokarev	12/305	
7.65 mm Parabellum	11/279	
.32 ACP	16/406	Mauser, Walther
	18¾ /476	Mauser
.32 S&W Long	17/432	Charter Arms
	18¾/476	
.32 H&R Mag.	16/406	Ruger
	18¾/476	
.32-20 Win.	16/406	
.380 ACP	10/254	SIG Sauer, Taurus
	16/406	Colt, Walther, AMT
9 mm Makarov	10/254	

Handgun Calibers	Twist Rate in Inches/ Millimeters per Turn	Manufacturers
9x19 mm	10/254	Beretta, Colt, Marlin, Uzi, SIG, Glock, old S&W, Ruger, Taurus
	14/356	T/C
	16/406	Colt, Browning, Springfield Armory
	18¾/476	Colt, S&W
.38 Spl.	16/406	Ruger
	17/432	Charter Arms
	18¾/476	S&W, Dan Wesson, Ruger, Taurus
.38 S&W	18¾/476	
9 mm Largo	10/254	
.38 Auto	16/406	
.38 Super Auto	10/254	SIG Sauer
.357 SIG	16/406	
.357 Mag.	14/356	T/C, Colt, Dan Wesson,
	16/406	Marlin, Navy Arms, Ruger
	17/432	Charter Arms
	18¾/476	S&W, Dan Wesson, Ruger, Taurus, High Standard
.357 Rem. Max.	14/356	
	16/406	Ruger
	18¾/476	Dan Wesson
.375 Super Mag.	18¾/476	
.38-40 Win.	16/406	
.40 S&W Auto	10/254	Ruger
	15¾/400	Glock
	16/406	
10 mm Auto	15¾/400	Glock
	16/406	
.41 AE	13¾/349	Taurus
	18/457	
.41 Mag.	18¾/476	S&W, Dan Wesson
	20/508	Ruger
.44 Russian	20/508	
.44 Spl.	16/406	Colt
	18/457	Charter Arms
	20/508	Colt, S&W
.44-40 Win.	20/508	
.44 Mag.	18/457	
	18¾/476	Dan Wesson
	20/508	Colt, S&W, Dan Wesson, Ruger, Freedom Arms, T/C
	38/965	Browning, Marlin, Remington, Ruger, Winchester

Handgun Calibers	Twist Rate in Inches/ Millimeters per Turn	Manufacturers
.44 Auto Mag	18/457	
.44 Super Mag	18¾/476	
.45 Auto Rim	15/381	
.45 ACP	15/381	S&W
	15¼/400	Glock, SIG Sauer
	16/406	Colt, Springfield Armory
	24/610	Freedom Arms
.45 Colt	16/406	T/C, Colt, S&W, Ruger
	20/508	S&W
	24/610	Freedom Arms, Ruger
	38/965	Winchester
.45 S&W Schofield	16/406	
.45 Win. Mag.	10/254	Wildey
	16/406	
	24/610	Freedom Arms
.454 Casull	24/610	
.475 Linebaugh	18/457	
.480 Ruger	18/457	
.50 AE	19/483	
	20/508	Freedom Arms
.500 Linebaugh	20/508	
.500 S&W Mag.	18¾/476	

Ballistic Coefficient and Velocity of Selected Sizes of Lead Shotgun Pellets

Pellet Size	Pellet Dia. (in.)	Ballistic Coefficient	Velocity in f.p.s.	Energy in ft.-lbs.
9	.08	.008	74	.009
8	.09	.009	80	.014
7½	.095	.0095	83	.019
6	.11	.011	87	.032
4	.13	.013	94	.062
2	.15	.015	103	.098
BB	.18	.018	111	.235
4 Buck	.24	.025	131	.762
1 Buck	.30	.031	146	1.840
00 Buck	.33	.034	153	2.800

Note: For lead pellets alloyed with 4 percent antimony.

Sectional Density of Shotgun Pellets

Shot Size Number	Pellet Dia. (in.)	Steel	Bismuth	Pellet Material Tungsten/ Iron	Hevi-Shot	Lead
9	0.080	.0119	.0147	.0157	.0181	.0168
8½	0.085	.0126	.0156	.0167	.0189	.0178
8	0.090	.0134	.0165	.0177	.0204	.0189
7½	0.095	.0141	.0174	.0187	.0215	.0199
7	0.100	.0149	.0183	.0196	.0224	.0210
6	0.110	.0164	.0202	.0216	.0249	.0231
5	0.120	.0178	.0220	.0236	.0278	.0252
4	0.130	.0193	.0238	.0255	.0297	.0273
3	0.140	.0208	.0257	.0275	.0320	.0294
2	0.150	.0223	.0275	.0295	.0346	.0315
1	0.160	.0238	.0293	.0314	.0368	.0336
B	0.170	.0253	.0312	.0334	.0391	.0357
BB	0.180	.0268	.0330	.0353	.0419	.0378
BBB	0.190	.0283	.0348	.0373	.0437	.0399
T	0.200	.0297	.0367	.0393	.0471	.0420
TT	0.210	.0312	.0385	.0412	.0497	.0441
F	0.220	.0327	.0403	.0432	.0520	.0462
FF	0.230	.0342	.0421	.0452	.0535	.0483

ANSI Maximum Average Breech Pressures

Rifle Calibers

Cartridge	Maximum Average Breech Pressure Copper Units of Pressure (CUP)	Pounds per Square Inch (p.s.i.)
.17 Rem.	52,000	
.22 Hornet	43,000	
.218 Bee	40,000	
.221 Fireball	52,000	
.222 Rem.	46,000	50,000
.223 Rem.	52,000	55,000
.225 Win.	50,000	
.22-250 Rem.	53,000	65,000
.220 Swift	54,000	
.243 Win.	52,000	60,000
6 mm Rem.	52,000	65,000
.240 Wby. Mag.	55,100	
.25-20 Win.	28,000	

Cartridge	Maximum Average Breech Pressure	
	Copper Units of Pressure (CUP)	Pounds per Square Inch (p.s.i.)
.250 Savage	45,000	
.256 Win. Mag.	43,000	
.25-35 Win.	37,000	
.257 Roberts	45,000	54,000
.257 Roberts +P	50,000	58,000
.25-'06 Rem.	53,000	63,000
6.5x55 mm Swedish Mauser	46,000	
6.5 mm Rem. Mag.	53,000	65,000
.264 Win. Mag.	54,000	64,000
.270 Win.	52,000	65,000
7-30 Waters	40,000	45,000
7 mm-08 Rem.	52,000	61,000
7x57 mm Mauser	46,000	51,000
7 mm Rem. Mag.	52,000	61,000
7 mm Wby. Mag.	65,000	
.280 Rem.	50,000	60,000
.284 Win.	54,000	56,000
.30 Carbine	40,000	40,000
.30 Rem.	35,000	
.30-30 Win.	38,000	42,000
.300 Savage	46,000	47,000
.303 Savage	34,000	
.307 Win.	52,000	
.308 Win.	52,000	62,000
7.62x39 mm Soviet	45,000	45,000
.30-40 Krag	40,000	
.30-'06 Sprg.	50,000	60,000
.300 H&H Mag.	54,000	
.308 Norma Mag.	55,100	
.300 Win. Mag.	54,000	64,000
.300 Wby. Mag.	65,000	65,000
.32-20 Win.	16,000	
.32-40 Win.	30,000	
.32 Rem.	37,000	
.303 British	45,000	49,000
.32 Win. Special	38,000	42,000
8x57 mm Mauser JS	37,000	35,000
8 mm Rem. Mag.	54,000	65,000
.338 Win. Mag.	54,000	64,000
.348 Win.	40,000	
.351 Win. S.L.	45,000	
.35 Rem.	35,000	33,500
.350 Rem. Mag.	56,200	

Rifle Cartridge	Maximum Average Breech Pressure	
	Copper Units of Pressure (CUP)	Pounds per Square Inch (p.s.i.)
.356 Win.	52,000	
.358 Win.	52,000	
.35 Whelen	52,000	
.375 Win.	52,000	
.375 H&H Mag.	53,000	62,000
.38-40 Win.	14,000	
.38-55 Win.	30,000	
.416 Rigby	42,000	
.416 Rem. Mag.	54,000	65,000
.444 Marlin	44,000	42,000
.45-70 Gov't	28,000	28,000
.458 Win. Mag.	53,000	
.470 Nitro Exp.	35,000	

Pistol Calibers

Cartridge	Maximum Average Breech Pressure	
	Copper Units of Pressure (CUP)	Pounds per Square Inch (p.s.i.)
.25 ACP	25,000	
.30 Luger	28,000	
.32 ACP	20,500	
9x18 mm Makarov	24,100	
.380 ACP	23,000	21,500
9x19 mm Luger	33,000	35,000
.38 Auto/ACP	23,000	26,500
.38 Super Auto	33,000	
.40 S&W Auto	35,000	
10 mm Auto	37,500	
.41 AE	35,000	
.45 ACP	21,000	21,000
.45 Win. Mag.	40,000	
.50 AE	36,000	35,000

Revolver Calibers

Cartridge	Maximum Average Breech Pressure	
	Copper Units of Pressure (CUP)	Pounds per Square Inch (p.s.i.)
.32 S&W Long	12,000	15,000
.32 H&R Mag.	21,000	
.357 Mag.		35,000
.357 Rem. Max.		40,000
.38 S&W	13,000	14,500
.38 Spl.		17,000
.38 Spl. +P		18,500
.41 Mag.	40,000	36,000
.44 Mag.	40,000	36,000
.44-40 Win.	13,000	
.45 Auto Rim	15,000	
.45 Colt	14,000	14,000
.454 Casull	50,000	
.480 Ruger		36,000
.500 S&W		36,000

Shotgun Gauges

Cartridge	Maximum Average Breech Pressure Pounds per Square Inch (p.s.i.)
10 ga. 3½"	11,000
12 ga. 3½"	14,000
12 ga. 3"	11,500
12 ga. 2¾"	11,500
16 ga. 2¾"	11,500
20 ga. 3"	12,000
20 ga. 2¾"	12,000
28 ga. 2¾"	12,500
.410 bore 2½"	12,500
.410 bore 3"	13,500

Notes:

1. ANSI= American National Standards Institute
2. Copper units of pressure (CUP) are measured using copper crushers. This method is going out of use.
3. Pressure in pounds per square inch (p.s.i.) is measured by piezoelectric transducers. This method is replacing crusher-based systems.

Metallurgy of Current Shot Pellets

Type of Shot	Composition	Manufacturing Method	Density (grams/cc)
Lead	Alloy of lead with 0 to 6% antimony	Metals melted then dropped into water; larger sizes swaged	11.1
Steel	Low carbon steel	Steel wire cut, preformed, ground to size and annealed	7.9
Bismuth	Alloy of 97% bismuth and 3% tin	Metals melted then dropped into water; larger sizes swaged	9.7
Tungsten-Iron	Alloy of 40% tungsten and 60% iron	Metals in powdered form mixed, pressed together and sintered at high temperatures to harden	10.2
Tungsten-Polymer	Mix of 95.5% tungsten powder and 4.5% polymer	Powdered materials mixed and then heated to fuse together	11.2
Tungsten-Matrix	Mix of 88% tungsten, 4% nickel, 2% iron, 1% copper	Powdered materials mixed and then heated to fuse together	10.4
Hevi-Shot	Alloy of tungsten, nickel and iron	Metals melted then dropped into cold air column	12.0

Note: Shotgun pellets have also been made of tin, copper and zinc alloy.

Buckshot Pellets per Pound in Various Compositions

Pellet size	Pellet dia. (in.)	Lead (% antimony)		ST	BI	TP	TM	TI
		0.5%	6%					
No. 4	.24	338	352	479	390	338	364	371
No .3	.25	299	311	424	345	299	322	328
No. 2	.27	238	248	337	275	238	256	261
No. 1	.30	173	180	245	200	173	186	190
0	.32	143	149	203	165	143	154	157
00	.33	130	135	184	150	130	140	143
000	.36	100	104	142	115	100	108	110

Notes:
1. Pellet counts are approximate and based on weight.
2. Abbreviations: ST—steel; BI—bismuth; TP—tungsten polymer; TM—tungsten matrix; TI—tungsten iron.

Pellet Counts for Round Shot of Various Materials per Ounce

Shot Size	Pellet Dia.(in.)	Lead (% antimony) (0.5%)	(2%)	(4%)	(6%)	ST	BI	TP	TM	TI
12	0.050	2360	2374	2416	2457	3363	2723	2360	2542	2591
11	0.060	1366	1374	1398	1422	1946	1576	1366	1471	1500
10	0.070	860	865	880	895	1226	992	860	926	944
9	0.080	576	579	589	599	821	664	576	620	632
8 ½	0.085	480	483	491	500	685	554	480	517	527
8	0.090	404	407	414	421	577	466	404	435	444
7 ½	0.095	344	346	352	358	490	397	344	370	378
7	0.100	295	296	302	307	420	340	295	318	324
6	0.110	221	222	226	230	316	255	221	238	243
5	0.120	170	171	174	177	243	196	170	183	187
4	0.130	134	135	137	139	191	155	134	144	147
3	0.140	107	108	110	111	153	123	107	115	117
2	0.150	87	87	89	91	125	100	87	94	96
1	0.160	72	72	73	74	103	83	72	78	79
B	0.170	60	60	61	62	86	69	60	65	66
air rifle	0.175	55	55	56	57	78	63	55	59	60
BB	0.180	50	50	51	52	72	58	50	54	55
BBB	0.190	43	43	44	44	61	50	43	46	47
T	0.200	36	37	37	38	53	42	36	39	40
TT	0.210	31	32	32	33	45	36	31	33	34
F	0.220	27	27	28	28	39	31	27	29	30
FF	0.230	24	24	24	25	35	28	24	26	26

Notes:
1. All pellet counts are approximate and based on weight.
2. Abbreviations: ST—steel; BI—bismuth; TP—tungsten polymer; TM—tungsten matrix; TI—tungsten iron.
3. Multipliers for charge weights other than 1 oz.

To Obtain Number of Pellets per Charge For:	Multiply Pellets per Ounce by:
3/4 oz.	0.75
7/8 oz.	0.875
1$\frac{1}{16}$ oz.	1.063
1$\frac{1}{8}$ oz	1.125
1$\frac{1}{4}$ oz.	1.25
1$\frac{3}{8}$ oz.	1.375
1$\frac{1}{2}$ oz.	1.50
1$\frac{9}{16}$ oz.	1.56
1$\frac{5}{8}$ oz.	1.625
1$\frac{3}{4}$ oz.	1.75
1$\frac{7}{8}$ oz.	1.875
2 oz.	2.00
2$\frac{1}{8}$ oz.	2.125
2$\frac{1}{4}$ oz.	2.25

Shot Charge Weights English and Metric Units

grains	English ounces	metric grams
219	1/2	14.17
328	3/4	21.26
383	7/8	24.8
437.5	1	28.3
465	$1^1/_{16}$	30.1
545	$1^1/_4$	36.0
602	$1^3/_8$	39.0
656	$1\frac{1}{2}$	42.5
711	$1^5/_8$	46.1
766	$1^3/_4$	49.6
820	$1^7/_8$	53.1
875	2	56.7
984	$2^1/_4$	63.8

Shotgun Bore Diameters and Unfired Shotshell Hull Lengths

Gauge	Bore Diameter (in.)	(mm)	Length Of Unfired Shell (in.)	(mm)
10	.775	19.7	$2^5/_8$	67
10	.775	19.7	$2^7/_8$	73
10	.775	19.7	$3^1/_2$	89
12	.729	18.5	2	60
12	.729	18.5	$2^1/_2$	65
12	.729	18.5	$2^3/_4$	70
12	.729	18.5	3	76
12	.729	18.5	$3^1/_2$	89
14	.693	17.6	$2^3/_4$	70
16	.662	16.8	$2^3/_4$	70
20	.615	15.6	$2^3/_4$	70
20	.615	15.6	3	76
24	.579	14.7	$2^3/_4$	70
28	.550	14.0	$2^3/_4$	70
32	.526	13.4	$2^3/_4$	70
36	.506	12.85	$2^3/_4$	70
.410	.410	10.4	$2\frac{1}{2}$	65
.410	.410	10.4	3	76

Shotgun Choke Constriction and Expected Performance

Abbreviation	US	Choke UK	Europe	Approx. Constriction	Average Pellets in 30" Circle 40 yds.
C	cylinder	cylinder	cylinder	none	up to 40%
S	skeet	skeet	+++++	.005"	40%
IC	improved cylinder	1/4	++++	.011"	50%
M	modified	1/2	+++	.020"	60%
IM	improved modified	3/4	++	.027"	65%
F	full	full	+	.036"	70%
EF	extra full	--	--	.040"+	80%+

Notes:

1. Steel shot normally offers tightest patterns through a modified choke.
2. Skeet chokes and all .410-bore shotguns normally tested at 25 yds.

Shotshell, Choke and Shot Size Selection

Game Bird	Gauge	Choke	Shot Sizes Recommended Lead	Steel	Other
small ducks	12-2³/₄"; 20-3"	IC, M, F	--	4, 6	4, 6
medium ducks	12-2³/₄"; 20-3"	IC, M, F	--	2, 4	2, 4, 5
large ducks	12-3"; 20-3"	M, F	--	BB, 2	2, 4
medium geese	12-3"; 20-3"	M, F	--	BB, 1	BB, 2
large geese	10-3¹/₂"; 12-3¹/₂"	M, F	--	T, BB	BB, 1
turkey	12-3¹/₂"; 20-3"	F, EF	4, 5, 6	--	4, 5, 6
pheasant	12-2³/₄"; 20-3"	IC, M	4, 6	4, 6	4, 5, 6
grouse, partridge	12-2³/₄"; 16, 20-3"; 28	S, IC, M	6, 7¹/₂	4, 6	--
quail	12-2³/₄"; 16, 20, 28	S, IC, M	7¹/₂, 8	6	--
dove	12-2³/₄"; 20, 28	IC, M	7¹/₂, 8	7	--
woodcock, rail	12-2³/₄"; 16, 20, 28	S, IC, M	7¹/₂, 8	7	--
rabbit, squirrel	12-2³/₄"; 20, 28, .410-3"	M, F	6, 7¹/₂	6	--
winged pests	12-2³/₄"; 20, 28, .410	S, IC, M	7¹/₂, 8	--	--
varmints	12-2³/₄"; 20	IC, C	4B, 00B	T	--
deer	12-2³/₄"; 20	C	slug	--	slug
bear	12-3"; 20-3"	C	slug	--	slug
personal defense	12-2³/₄"; 12-3"	C	00B	--	--
trap	12-2³/₄"	IM, F	7¹/₂, 8	8	--
skeet	12-2³/₄"; 20, 28, .410	S	8, 9	8	--
sporting clays	12-2³/₄"; 20	varies	7¹/₂, 8	--	--
live pigeon	12-2³/₄"	IM, F	7, 7¹/₂	--	--

How To Test Shotgun Patterns

1. Thoroughly clean the bore of your shotgun using a suitable solvent and brush.

2. Carefully inspect the bore of your shotgun making certain there are no obstructions or damage and any choke tubes in use are securely seated.

3. Select an appropriate, factory-loaded shotshell you will use for hunting or target shooting.

4. Mount a sheet of pattern paper at least 48" in width upright on a sturdy wooden frame. Draw an aiming point in the center (a 4-6" diameter solid black circle works well).

5. Carefully measure 40 yards from the pattern frame. Place a ground marker on that spot for reference. Fire from exactly the same spot each time. Pattern skeet guns and all .410-bore shotguns at 25 yds.

6. Fire one shot on each sheet of pattern paper, remove it, and replace it with a fresh sheet. We recommend numbering each sheet and noting the barrel (if testing a double-barrel gun) and the load.

7. Determine the number of shots you need to fire for each barrel/choke/load combination using the following criteria:
- To determine choke pattern performance with 95 percent statistical certainty, fire and evaluate five shells. This is sufficient for hunting and casual target shooting purposes.
- To determine choke pattern performance to a statistically more rigorous 98-percent level of certainty, fire and evaluate 10 shells. This places your results on a firm statistical basis.
- To determine choke pattern performance to within 99 percent+ certainty, fire and evaluate 20 shells. This is necessary for engineering and research work.

8. Lay each perforated pattern sheet in turn on a white or transparent flat surface, then scribe a 30" diameter circle on each sheet in the location that will encompass the greatest number of holes. Mark the center of the circle. Disregard the aiming point. Scribe a 20" diameter circle concentrically inside the 30" circle, then draw a vertical line and a horizontal line through the center of the two circles. You now have divided the pattern into eight parts.

9. Count the number of pellet hits in each segment. Add the number of hits in both the 20" and the 30" circles. Repeat for each pattern sheet.

10. Add the total number of all hits within the 30" circles and divide by the number of pattern sheets. This will give you the average number of pellet hits inside the circle.

11. Determine pellet count by consulting the previous chart—Pellet Counts for Round Shot of Various Materials—or refer to manufacturers' specs.

12. With the above information, you are now in a position to analyze choke performance of your shotgun. Most shooters seek to determine only three factors in choke performance:

- The overall percentage of pellet hits in the 30" circle. This number is obtained by dividing the average number of pellet hits in the 30" circle by the nominal number of pellets in a shotshell.
- The evenness of pellet distribution in the 30" circle. Most shooters judge this by visually reviewing hit distribution on the pattern sheets. A statistical analysis can be made by calculating and comparing the percentage of hits in the two circles, in halves or in quarters.
- The pattern's center of impact in relation to the point of aim. In other words, does your gun pattern dead-on, high, low, left or right? Most shooters determine this by noting the position of the center of the circles in relation to the aim point.

13. Evaluate your results using the following information:

- Expected choke performance in a 30" circle at 40 yds.

cylinder	40 percent
improved cylinder	50 percent
modified	60 percent
improved modified	65 percent
full	70 percent
extra full	80 percent

- Hit distribution in the pattern:
  central thickening—compare total hits in the 20" circle vs. the 30" circle.
  hits in quadrants—compare total hits in quadrants.
  hits in segments—compare hits in one-eights segments.

- Pattern Center Point of Impact:
  field guns—most are stocked and sighted to place the pattern center slightly high at 40 yds.
  upland bird—2-4" high at 40 yds.
  migratory waterfowl—4-6" high at 40 yds.
  small game—dead-on to 2" high at 25 yds.
  target guns—
  skeet—dead-on to 2" high at 25 yds.
  trap—6-8" high at 40 yds.
  sporting clays—2-4" high at 40 yds.

Center-Fire Rifle Caliber Recommendations for Hunting

Varmints, predators, pests and rodents

Prairie dog, coyote, badger, nutria, crow, bobcat, lynx, ground hogs, rock-chucks (marmots), rats. Light, high-velocity bullets of 70 grs. or less that fragment on impact to kill game.

.204 Ruger	.220 Swift
.22 Hornet	.243 Win.
.222 Rem.	6 mm Rem.
.223 Rem.	
.22-250 Rem.	

Edible small game and furbearers

Raccoon, opossum, fox, mink, beaver, muskrat, rabbit, squirrel. Small calibers with medium-weight bullets to anchor game cleanly.

.204 Ruger	.222 Rem.
.22 Hornet	.223 Rem.

Light and medium thin-skinned game

Deer, antelope, javelina, wild sheep, caribou, black bear

For deer and javelina only, at very close range (to 100 yds.) in brush or thick cover, use big calibers firing bullets weighing 200 grs. or more with approximately 1,000 ft.-lbs. of striking energy at 100 yds.

.30-30 Win.	.44 Rem. Mag.
.348 Win.	.45-70 Gov't
.35 Rem.	.450 Marlin
.358 Win.	12-ga. shotgun slugs

For all game at normal ranges (to 200 yds.) with calibers firing bullets weighing 85-150 grs. with 1,700 ft.-lbs. of striking energy at 100 yds.

.243 Win.	7 mm-08 Rem.
6 mm Rem.	.284 Win.
.240 Wby. Mag.	.280 Rem.
.257 Roberts	7x57 mm Mauser
.260 Rem.	.30-30 Win.
.270 Win.	.30-'06 Sprg.

For black bear or other game at long ranges (beyond 200 yds.) with calibers firing bullets weighing 120 grs. or more at high velocity offering at least 1,700 ft.-lbs. of striking energy at 300 yds.

.270 Win.	7 mm Wby. Mag.
.270 WSM	.30-'06 Sprg.
.270 Wby. Mag.	.300 Win. Mag.
.280 Rem.	.300 WSM
7 mm WSM	.300 SAUM
7 mm SAUM	.300 Rem. Ultra Mag.
7 mm STW	.300 Wby. Mag.
7 mm Rem. Mag.	.338 Federal

Large, heavy game

Elk, moose, mountain goat, zebra, kudu, eland, water buffalo, musk ox, bison, grizzly bear. Magnum calibers firing bullets weighing 180 grains or more with a minimum of 2,600 ft.-lbs. of striking energy at 200 yds.

.300 Win. Mag.	.338 Win. Mag.
.300 WSM	.338 Rem. Ultra Mag.
.300 RAUM	.340 Wby. Mag.
.300 Wby. Mag.	.350 Rem. Mag.
.325 WSM	.375 H&H Mag.
8 mm Rem. Mag.	.375 Rem. Ultra Mag.

Large, dangerous game

Lion, elephant, Cape buffalo, hippopotamus, brown bear, polar bear Big magnums firing bullets weighing 300 grs. or more offering a minimum of 3,500 ft.-lbs. of striking energy at 100 yds.

.375 H&H Mag.	.416 Wby. Mag.
.375 Rem. Ultra Mag.	.458 Win. Mag.
.416 Rigby	.460 Wby. Mag.
.416 Rem. Mag.	.470 Nitro Express

Standard Blackpowder Granulation Sizes and Applications

Granulation Designation	Average Grain Size (in.)	Typical Application
Whaling	.441	Harpoon guns, historic use
Lifesaving	.131	Line-throwing cannon
Cannon	.132	Cannon over 1" bore
Fg	.069	Shotguns, large-caliber muskets
FFg	.058	Large-bore rifles, standard cartridges
FFFg	.038	Revolvers, smallbore rifles and cartridges
FFFFg	.017	Priming flintlocks, blanks, small cartridges

Effective Range of Historical Firearms

Firearm Type	Dates of Use	Effective Range (yds.)	Maximum Range (yds.)	Comments/Example
handcannon	1350-1500	25	400	fired round ball
matchlock	1450-1600	30	500	fired round ball
flintlock musket	1600-1825	50	1000	smoothbore .69 cal.
flintlock rifle	1600-1825	100	1000	rifled barrel .577 cal.
percussion rifle	1825-1870	200	1500	Enfield 1853 musket .577 cal.
breechloading rifle	1860-1885	500	3,500	Trapdoor Springfield .45-70
breechloading rifle	1885-1950	1,000	4,000	M1903 Springfield .30-'06
tactical rifle	1950-present	300	3,500	AK-47 7.62x39 mm

Chapter 18
GLOSSARY

The following are some of the more commonly used terms used in relation to firearms, ammunition and shooting. Please see *Chapter 20, Index* for references to more complete discussions of many of the terms defined below.

NRA wishes to thank the Sporting Arms and Ammunition Manufacturers' Institute (SAAMI) for permission to use definitions from its Glossary of Industry Terms.

Note that terms that are made up of two or more words are often defined under the principal word (e.g., "cut checkering" is defined under "checkering, cut"; "free rifle stock" is defined under "stock, free rifle"; etc.).

A

absorber, recoil
Any device that reduces perceived recoil of a firearm

accelerator
A device found in some semi-automatic or full-automatic firearms that, through mechanical advantage or spring energy, transfers kinetic energy from one part of the mechanism to another with the result of speeding up the action

accuracy
In firearms using single projectiles at a given distance, is the measure of the dispersion of the group of projectiles fired. The optimum would be one hole, no larger in diameter than a single projectile.

accuracy life
An estimated or empirically determined number of rounds that can be fired in a particular gun, of a particular caliber, before it fails to meet a particular accuracy specification. Wide variations may occur due to caliber, ammunition characteristics, firing schedules, maintenance and firearm design.

accurize
Common term used in conjunction with firearms that are subjected to special fitting and operations in the interest of improving accuracy

action

The combination of the receiver or frame and breech with the other parts of the mechanism by which a firearm is loaded, fired and unloaded.

action, automatic

A firearm design that continuously feeds cartridges, fires and ejects cartridge cases as long as the trigger is fully depressed and there are cartridges available in the feed system. Actuation of the mechanism may be from an internal power source such as gas pressure or recoil, or an external power source, such as electricity.

action, autoloading

Any action that extracts and ejects a fired cartridge then reloads itself

action bars(s)

A member or members, used to connect and transmit the movement of the forearm or gas system to the breech block. Often, the movement of the action bars controls or actuates other parts of the mechanism.

action, barreled

A combination of barrel and receiver or frame and breech bolt together with the other parts of the mechanism by which a firearm is loaded, fired and unloaded—usually a complete firearm less its stock

action, blow-forward

A design for semi-automatic or automatic firearms, wherein the breech block is stationary and the barrel moves forward by gas pressure to open and eject the cartridge and recycle the action

action, bolt

An action in which the breech closure is: in line with the bore at all times; manually reciprocated to load, unload and cock; and is locked in place by breech bolt lugs engaging abutments that are usually located in the receiver. There are two principal types of bolt actions: the turn-bolt and the straight-pull type.

action, DAO

An acronym used to describe semi-automatic actions that are double action only, wherein, the trigger cocks and releases the hammer without the use of a sear.

action, double

A type of handgun mechanism in which a single pull of the trigger first cocks and then releases the hammer

action, locked breech

Any action wherein the breech bolt is locked to the barrel or receiver through a portion or all of the recoiling motion

action, open breech

A type of action wherein the breech bolt is held open until the trigger is pulled. *Also known as an open bolt action.*

action, semi-automatic

A type of action in which each pull of the trigger results in a complete firing cycle from discharge through reloading. It is necessary that the trigger be released and pulled for each firing cycle.

action, sidelock

A design in which the firing mechanism is attached to a sideplate rather than being integral with the frame or trigger plate

action, single

An action design requiring the manual cocking of the hammer or striker before sufficient pressure on the trigger releases the firing mechanism.

action, single-shot

A firearm with no means for storing or loading more than a single cartridge

action, slidelock

The part of a mechanism, normally found on slide action firearms that locks the forearm/slide mechanism

action, top-break

A design in which the barrel or barrels are connected to the frame by a hinge-pin below the barrels. Upon release of the locking mechanism, usually by a top side or under lever, the barrel(s) or upper receiver rotates around the hinge pin away from the standing breech.

action, underlever

The same as a top-break mechanism except that the lever that unlocks the firearm from under the frame, allowing the barrel(s) or lower receiver to pivot and expose the breech.

adapter

1. A device used to alter the use or functioning of a firearm. Most generally, an adapter permits the use of smaller-caliber ammunition in a firearm designed for a larger caliber. See *chamber, auxiliary*.

2. A grip accessory that alters the location, size or shape of the handle portion of a pistol or revolver.

aiming

The act of aligning the sights of a firearm on a target

aiming point

A point on the target upon which the sights are aligned

air gauge

A pneumatic device for precisely measuring internal barrel diameters

airgun

A gun that uses compressed air or gas to propel a projectile. True airguns should not be confused with guns that use spring force (commonly called "BB guns") to propel projectiles. Airguns are also called "air rifles," "pellet rifles" or "pellet guns."

air resistance
The resistance of air to the passage of a projectile in flight

air space
The volume in a loaded cartridge or shotshell not occupied by the propellant or the bullet, wads or shot

alignment, sight
Centering the front sight or aperture both vertically and horizontally in the rear sight or aperature

altitude effect
The effect on velocity and, therefore, trajectory and shotshell pattern caused by changes in atmospheric density due to altitude

ammunition
One or more loaded cartridges consisting of a primed case, propellant and (with or without) one or more projectiles. *For definitions and examples of specific ammunition types not listed below, see Chapter 13, Ammunition.*

ammunition, fixed
A metallic cartridge or shotshell that is complete and ready to use

ammunition, live
Ammunition that is capable of being fired; a cartridge or shotshell that is assembled with a live primer, an appropriate propellant and projectile or shot charge

ammunition, metallic
A generic term for rimfire and center-fire ammunition, derived from their metal cases

ammunition, National Match
Ammunition produced for use at NRA National Matches by appropriate government or commercial manufacturing facilities. Cartridges are usually, but not always, head-stamped "NM" for identification purposes.

ammunition, reference
Ammunition used in test ranges to evaluate test barrels, ranges and other velocity and pressure measuring equipment. May also be used as a control sample by which other characteristics are compared, such as accuracy, patterns, etc.

ammunition, service
1. Commercially available sporting ammunition, as opposed to proof, reference, etc., or other special-use ammunition

2. Ammunition that is issued to police officers or military personnel, or that is similar in configuration

ammunition, small arms
A military term for ammunition for firearms with bores not larger than one inch

ammunition, sub-caliber

A cartridge having a projectile smaller than is standard for the firearm in which it is used

angle of departure

The angle formed between a horizontal line and the center line of the bore at the moment the projectile leaves the muzzle of the gun

angle of elevation

The vertical angle formed between the line of sight to the target and the axis of the barrel bore

Anson and Deeley

William Anson and John Deeley, inventors of a successful boxlock action design patented in 1875 that utilizes two long crosspins that retain the action within the action body

Anson fastening, fore-end

See *fore-end, Anson fastening*

anvil

An internal metal component in a cartridge primer assembly against which the priming mixture is pinched by the firing-pin blow. See *primer*.

arm

1. v. To charge or load a firearm.
2. n. A contraction of "firearm."

arms, small

Any firearm capable of being carried by a person and fired without additional mechanical support

arquebus

A smoothbore firearm of the 16th and 17th centuries that typically fires using a matchlock

autoloader

A synonym for a "semi-automatic" firearm

automatic

An expression sometimes used for an automatic firearm, or, incorrectly, an autoloading or semi-automatic firearm

B

back bored

A term used to designate a shotgun chambered for a specified gauge, whose barrel bore diameter is greater than the nominal specified for that gauge, but does not exceed SAAMI maximum

backstop

A structure intended to safely stop a fired bullet or other projectile(s)

back strap

See *strap, back*

back thrust
The force exerted on the breechblock, bolt, slide, etc. by the head of
the cartridge case during propellant burning

ball, patched
1. For modern cased ammunition, the term patched ball refers to a
full-metal-jacketed bullet (FMJ)
2. For muzzleloading, the term refers to round or conical lead
projectiles that utilize cloth or other material that acts as a gas seal or
a guide for the projectile
3. Early fixed ammunition using paper as a gas seal for the projectile

ball screw
A pointed, spiral piece of metal secured at the end of a ramrod and
used to remove a lead ball or patch from a muzzleloading gun

ballistics
The science of projectiles in motion. Usually divided into three types:
interior ballistics, exterior ballistics and terminal ballistics.

ballistic coefficient
An index of the manner in which a particular projectile decelerates
in free flight expressed mathematically. The ballistic coefficient
represents the bullet's ability to overcome the air resistance in flight.
See Chapter 16, Formulae and Tables.

ballistics, exterior
The branch of ballistics dealing with the motion of a projectile from
the muzzle of a firearm to the target

ballistics, interior
The branch of ballistics dealing with all aspects of the combustion
phenomena occurring within the gun barrel, including pressure
development and motion of the projectile along the bore of the
firearm

ballistics table
A descriptive and performance data sheet on ammunition, which
usually includes: bullet weight and type; muzzle velocity and energy;
velocity; energy and trajectory data at various ranges

ballistics, terminal
The branch of ballistics that deals with the effects of projectiles on the
target

barrel
That part of a firearm through which a projectile or shot charge
travels under the impetus of powder gases, compressed air or other
like means (may be rifled or smooth bore)

barrel band
A strip or strips of metal that encircle and hold the barrel and stock,
fore-end, magazine or other accessories together

barrel blank
An unfinished barrel in any state of completion

barrel, bulged
See *barrel, ringed*

barrel channel
A groove in a rifle stock or fore-end where the barrel fits in the assembled position

barrel corrosion
Degradation of bore and chamber surface condition due to chemical action

barrel-cylinder gap
The opening or clearance between barrel and cylinder in a revolver (also known as "cylinder gap")

barrel erosion
The wearing or physical deterioration of the bore or chamber of a firearm caused by hot powder gases or projectile passage

barrel extension
A metal projection that extends rearward from the breech end of a barrel into where the bolt locks while the firearm is in battery or firing position

barrel, fluted
A barrel with longitudinal grooves cut into the outside surface for all or some portion of the overall length

barrel guide
A ring-shaped attachment on the barrel of many shotguns that encircles the magazine tube. Sometimes called "magazine tube bracket."

barrel insert
See *Sub-caliber tube*

barrel, interchangeable
One or more barrels that may be installed on a particular action without factory fitting

barrel jacket
A tube that surrounds the barrel

barrel length
On shoulder arms and most handguns the distance between the muzzle of the barrel and the face of the breechblock or bolt. On revolvers, it is the overall length of the barrel only, including the portion within the frame.

barrel life
1. The total number of rounds that have been fired in a barrel

2. The total number of rounds fired in a barrel before it becomes unserviceable

barrel obstruction
Also called "bore obstruction." A foreign object or material in the bore of a barrel that prevents unhindered passage of the projectile(s) when fired.

barrel pressure
The pressure in a barrel developed by propelling gases when a cartridge is fired

barrel, pressure
A heavy-walled barrel fitted with instrumentation to measure pressure

barrel relining
The replacement of the interior surface of a bore by inserting and fastening a rifled tube. Usually a procedure performed on rifled barrels.

barrel, ringed
A barrel that has been fired while containing an obstruction. The resultant excessive radial pressure causes a circumferential bulge in the barrel. Also called a "bulged barrel."

barrel shank
The breech end of the barrel that fits into the action or receiver. Also called "barrel tenon."

barrel sleeving
This term usually refers to shotgun barrels. See *Barrel Relining*.

barrel step
An abrupt change in external barrel contour

barrel, test
A barrel of special dimensions used for testing ammunition

barrel threads
The screw threads found on the shank of the barrel, used to screw the barrel into the frame or receiver of the firearm

barrel time (ignition barrel time)
The elapsed time from the contact of a firing pin with a cartridge primer to the emergence of the projectile(s) from the muzzle of the firearm

barrel vent
An opening or series of openings or ports in a barrel, normally near the muzzle, through which gases pass prior to bullet exit. See *muzzle brake*.

barrel vibration
The oscillations of a barrel as a result of firing

barrel, walking
A gun barrel that changes its center-of-impact point when heated by firing

barrel wear
The gradual mechanical deterioration caused by use, i.e. firing, cleaning, etc. Also, see *Barrel Erosion*.

barrel weight
A separate weight attached to a regular barrel to change balance

barrel whip
The movement of the muzzle end of a barrel that occurs as the projectile leaves

base, high
The term commonly applied to a shotshell with a high metal cup, but properly applies to the height of the internal base wad. Often misused as a synonym for "high brass" or "high cup."

base, low
A term commonly applied to a shotshell with a low metal cup, but properly applies to the height of the internal base wad. Often misused as a synonym for "low brass" or "low cup."

base pin
See *cylinder pin*

battery
The condition where the breech of the action is in proper position for firing

battery cup
A component of a shotshell primer; a flanged metallic cup that contains and supports the primer cup and anvil

BB
The designation of spherical shot having a diameter of .180" used in shotshell loads. The term is also used to designate steel or lead rifle shot of .177" diameter. Although the two definitions cause some confusion, they have coexisted for many years.

bead sight
An aiming device usually found towards the muzzle on shotguns. Some shotguns incorporate a mid-rib bead sight that places a second bead on a rib along the middle of the barrel that offers another point of reference for aiming.

bearing surface
That portion of a bullet's outer surface that comes into direct contact with the interior surface of the barrel bore when moving through the barrel

beavertail
A term used to describe the upper part of a modern handgun's backstrap that prevents an exposed hammer in its fully cocked position to come into contact with the grip of the shooter

bedding

Refers to the fit or fitting of the metal parts of the barrel and receiver with the stock

bedding control

1. An adjustable device, which is installed in the fore-end of a rifle stock to provide pressure on a barrel

2. The pressure provided by the wood-to-metal fit

bedding screw(s)

A form of *bedding control* using machine screw(s) to produce a pressure on the underside of the barrel

benchrest

1. A table or bench specifically designed to eliminate as much human error as possible by supporting a rifle for competitive shooting or for sighting-in purposes

2. A type of shooting in which a firearm is fully supported by a rest, sandbags or other means on a table or bench

big-bore

1. In America, any firearm using a center-fire cartridge with a bullet .30" or larger in diameter

2. In shotguns, another name for "over bore"

billiard-ball effect

The divergence of shot pellets caused by collisions of pellets in the shot string as it comes into contact with the target.

blackpowder

The oldest propellant used in firearms generally composed of a mixture of potassium nitrate, carbon and sulfur

blank

1. A cartridge without a projectile
2. See *barrel blank*
3. See *stock, blank*

block

See *breechblock*

block, loading

A device containing a number of blind holes into which cases or completed ammunition are placed

block, locking

The sliding component in a firearm that secures the bolt or breechblock in the locked position when the action is closed

blowback

In ammunition, a leakage of gas rearward between the case and chamber wall from the mouth of the case (also called "blow-by")

blow, light
Insufficient firing-pin energy or protrusion. The result is erratic ignition or failure to ignite the primer.

bluing, blueing
The chemical oxidation to color ferrous metal parts various shades of blue or black

blunderbuss
A 17th-century muzzleloading firearm identifiable by the flared muzzle of the barrel. Although unpredictable, the funnel-shaped muzzle allowed for lead shot or other projectiles to be loaded and shot with greater ease.

body, case
1. The portion of the cartridge case that contains the propellant
2. In a shotshell, the tubular section that contains the propellant, wads and shot charge (if present)

bolt
1. See *breech bolt*
2. See *cylinder stop*

bolt action
A manually operated action that incorporates a rod or handle-like assembly that consist of components necessary to lock the action and fire. The firing pin, extractor and ejector are typically included in the bolt assembly of a bolt action.

bolt face
See *breech face*

bolt guides
Grooves or ridges on either bolt or receiver intended to maintain alignment or prevent over-rotation

bolt handle
A protrusion from the bolt, usually at right angles from the axis of the bolt, which is used to manually actuate the firearm's action

bolt handle, butterknife
A flat, low-profile, paddle-shaped bolt handle found on some rifles

bolt head
The forward end of the bolt containing the bolt face

bolt locking lug(s)
The protrusion or protrusions from the surface of the bolt body that lock into mating recesses in the receiver, barrel or barrel extension to resist rearward thrust of the chamber pressure. Also sometimes known as "bolt lug(s)."

bolt raceways
Longitudinal grooves in which the bolt locking lugs travel

bolt, recessed
A bolt with a counterbore in its face to accommodate the head of the cartridge case

bolt release
A device that allows the bolt to be removed from the firearm

bolt sleeve
A component at the rear end of the bolt that guides the firing pin and supports the firing-pin spring in bolt-action rifles (also "bolt plug")

bolt stop
A device that is intended to retain the bolt in the firearm during normal operation

bolt throw
The distance the bolt travels from the fully open to fully closed positions

bore
The interior of a barrel forward of the chamber

bore axis
A line through the center of the bore

bore brush
A brush used to clean the interior surface of the barrel of a firearm

bore constriction
A reduction in the internal diameter of a firearm bore

bore diameter
1. With rifled barrels, the minor interior diameter of a barrel that is the diameter of a circle formed by the tops of the lands

2. With shotgun or smoothbore musket barrels, the interior dimension of the barrel forward of the chamber but before any choke restriction or expansion at the muzzle

bore guide
A device that fits into the receiver and centers the cleaning rod in the bore to prevent contact during bore cleaning

bore sighting
A method of aligning a barrel on a target by aiming through the bore, often utilized while sighting in a firearm

bore scope
An illuminated, optical device for examining the interior of the bore of a firearm

boxlock
A lock containing the triggers, sears, hammers and respective springs within a box-shape housing found on break-open action shotguns.

brass, high
Common terminology referring to the length of the external metal cup on a shotshell (properly called high cup)

brass, low
 Common terminology referring to the length of the external metal cup on a shotshell (properly called low cup)

breech
 The part of the firearm to the rear of the chamber that provides support for the cartridge head during firing

breechblock
 A mechanism that does not operate in line with the axis of the bore, and that is intended to support, properly, the head of the cartridge

breech bolt
 The locking and cartridge head supporting mechanism of a firearm that operates in line with the axis of the bore

breech face
 That part of the breech block that is against the head of the cartridge case or shotshell during feeding and firing. Sometimes called "breechblock face."

breech pressure
 See *pressure, chamber*

breech, standing
 That part of the frame of a revolver or break-open firearm that supports the head of the cartridge when it is fired

breech plug
 In percussion or flintlock firearms, the metal part that is threaded into the breech end of the barrel

brisance
 A term describing the shattering power of high explosives

broach rifling
 The process of forming spiral rifling grooves in the barrel of a firearm by a tool having a series of cutting edges each slightly larger than the preceding

browning
 A chemical oxidation process to color metallic parts of a firearm a brownish-black shade

buckshot
 Lead pellets ranging in size from .20" to .36" diameter, normally loaded in shotshells

buffer
 In a firearm, any part intended to absorb shock, reduce impact or check recoil

bull
 A slang term for "bullseye" or "target."

bullet

A non-spherical projectile for use in a rifled barrel and sometimes contained within a sabot. (*For definitions and examples of specific bullet types not listed below, see Chapter 13, Ammunition.*)

bullet casting

A process for making lead bullets by pouring molten metal into a mold

bullet, core

The inner section of a jacketed bullet, usually lead

bullet creep, bullet popping

The movement of a bullet out of the cartridge case due to the recoil of the firearm (and the inertia of the bullet) when firing another cartridge in the firearm (also called bullet starting)

bullet crimp

The compression of the cartridge case mouth against the seated bullet to prevent movement

bullet diameter

The maximum dimension across the largest cylindrical section of a bullet

bullet engraving

1. The grooves cut into a bullet by barrel rifling

2. The forming of grooves in a bullet by the barrel rifling

bullet, gas check

A lead alloy bullet with a copper or gilding metal cup pressed over the heel

bullet jacket

A metallic cover over the core of the bullet

bullet jump

The distance that a bullet must travel from its position at rest in the cartridge case to its initial engagement of the rifling

bullet metal

The metal forming the entire bullet or bullet core. Usually an alloy of lead, antimony and/or tin.

bullet mold

A split block of metal having one or more cavities into which molten lead is poured to form a bullet

bullet ogive

The curved forward part of a bullet

bullet penetration

That distance that a bullet travels into target material

bullet plug

1. A device used in scoring bullet holes in a paper target

2. A pin inserted in a bullet mold to form a cavity in the nose or base of a bullet

bullet pull
The force required to extract a bullet from the case into which it was loaded

bullet puller
1. An instrument that measures the force required to extract a bullet from live ammunition

2. A tool used to remove bullets from live ammunition

bullet puller, inertia
A tool using impact to remove a bullet from a cartridge case

bullet stripping
A condition that occurs when the bullet fails to engage the rifling properly (also called "bullet slipping")

bullet rotation
The rotational motion imparted to the bullet by the rifling in the barrel

bullet spinner
A mechanical device used to detect the amount of eccentricity in a bullet between its rotational axis and the outer surface of the bullet

bullet stabilization
The act of steadying a bullet in flight by use of the proper rifling twist and bullet velocity

bullet tipping
The instability of a bullet in flight. Sometimes referred to as "keyholing."

bullet trap
A device that safely stops a bullet in flight. Usually found in indoor ranges behind the target area.

bullet, upset
1. In interior ballistics: the change of bullet form due to chamber pressure

2. In exterior ballistics: the expansion of a bullet upon impact with target

bullet wobble
A characteristic caused by the eccentricity or imbalance of the bullet to the axis of the bore (see *yaw*)

bull gun
See *gun, bull*

bullpup
A rifle in which the rear or barreled action is slightly in front of the buttplate

bullseye
 In target shooting, the aiming point

bullseye shooting
 A slang term used to describe the discipline of competitive shooting
 that uses a black circular target at a given range throughout a
 specified course of fire, usually involving slow, timed and rapid fire
 stages

butt
 1. In handguns: the bottom part of the grip

 2. In long guns: the rear or shoulder end of the stock

buttplate
 A metal, rubber or composition covering to reinforce and protect the
 shoulder end of a firearm stock

butt, round
 A revolver grip with a butt having a rounded shape

buttstock
 The rear or butt end of the firearm that is normally placed against the
 shooter's shoulder.

C

caliber
 1. A term used to designate the specific cartridge(s) for which a
 firearm is chambered

 2. The approximate diameter of the circle formed by the tops of the
 lands of a rifled barrel, often expressed in hundreths of an inch (.30
 caliber) or millimeters (7 mm caliber)

 3. In ammunition, a numerical term included in a cartridge name to
 indicate a rough approximation of the bullet diameter

cannelure
 1. A circumferential groove generally of corrugated appearance cut or
 impressed into a bullet or cartridge case

 2. Sometimes used to refer to an extractor groove

canister powders
 See *powders, reloading*

canting
 The tipping or tilting of a gun to one side at the time it is fired

cap-and-ball
 A muzzleloading firearm using the percussion cap ignition
 system

cap, percussion
 A small, generally cylindrical, metallic cup containing a primary

explosive that is used to ignite the powder charge in muzzleloading firearms

carbine
A rifle of relatively short length and light weight originally designed for mounted troops

carrier
A lifting mechanism in some repeating firearms that raises and positions the cartridge for feeding into the chamber. Sometimes called the "lifter."

cartouche
A French word for cartridge, this term is also used to describe various markings on a firearm

cartridge
A single round of ammunition consisting of the case, primer and propellant with or without one or more projectiles. This also applies to a shotshell.

cartridge, big bore
For target matches in the United States, cartridges utilizing bullets .30" in diameter or larger

cartridge, bottleneck
A cartridge case having a main body diameter and a distinct angular shoulder stepping down to a smaller diameter at the neck portion of the case

cartridge case
The main body of a single round into which other components are inserted to form a cartridge. This usually refers to center-fire and rimfire cartridges. Serves as a gas seal during firing of the cartridge. It's usually made of brass, steel, copper, aluminum or plastic. It's also referred to as a "shell" or "shell case."

cartridge case length
The dimensions from the face of the case head to the case mouth

cartridge, center-fire
Any cartridge intended for use in rifles, pistols or revolvers that has its primer central to the axis in the head of the case.

cartridge clip
A separate cartridge container to hold cartridges or shells in proper sequence for feeding into a specific firearm. It is a magazine charger or stripper clip, and unlike a magazine does not contain a feeding spring. Sometimes improperly called a "magazine."

cartridge cook-off
The firing of a cartridge by extreme overheating in a firearm chamber, without operation of the firing mechanism. It's usually associated with machine guns.

cartridge, dummy
An inert cartridge which cannot be fired under any circumstance. In America, an inert cartridge for gun functioning is usually black oxidized and may or may not have holes in the side wall of the case. An inert cartridge for display may be natural colored and should have a hole in the primer cup with holes in the side wall of the case optional.

cartridge feed ramp
Surface in the receiver or barrel of a repeating-action firearm along which the cartridge rides in feeding from magazine to chamber

cartridge guide
A firearm component that acts as a guide for the cartridge while it is being fed from the magazine to the chamber

cartridge, magnum
A term commonly used to describe a rimfire or center-fire cartridge, or shotshell that is larger, contains more shot or produces higher velocity than standard cartridges or shells of a given caliber or gauge. Rifles, handguns or shotguns that are designed to fire magnum cartridges or shells may also be described with the term "magnum."

cartridge, metallic
Ammunition having a metallic cartridge case

cartridge, NATO
A common designation for military cartridges produced under the specifications of the North Atlantic Treaty Organization

cartridge neck
The reduced diameter cylindrical portion of a cartridge case, extending from the bottom of the shoulder to the case mouth

cartridge, proof
A cartridge loaded to specific pressures higher than service loads. Used only for testing assembled firearms or elements of firearms that contain the primary firing pressure

cartridge, rimfire
A flange-headed cartridge containing the priming mixture inside the rim cavity. Often used to refer to .22 caliber ammunition, the most common rimfire caliber.

cartridge, rimless
A center-fire cartridge whose case head is of the same diameter as the body and having a groove turned forward of the head to provide the extraction surface

cartridge, service
A cartridge officially adopted for use by an army or military unit

cartridge, shot
A center-fire or rimfire cartridge loaded with small-diameter shot

cartridge, smallbore
General term applied in the United States to .22 caliber rimfire cartridges. Normally used for target shooting and small-game hunting

cartridge stop
See *cutoff*

cartridge, wildcat
Cartridges designed by individual inventors that have never been commercially manufactured

case
An abbreviated name for "cartridge case" or "shotshell case"

case capacity
The volume available for the propellant in a cartridge case with a fully seated bullet

case colored
The result by which a piece of metal undergoes a chemical treatment that provides the finished piece of metal with an array of distinct colors and designs

case extractor groove
An annular groove cut in rimless, semi-rimmed cartridge or belted cases, forward of the head, for the purpose of providing a surface that the gun extractor may grip to remove the case from the chamber. Also called "cannelure."

case fire-forming
A procedure used by handloaders to change the external shape of a cartridge case somewhat by firing in a gun having a chamber of the desired configuration. The case to be fire-formed must be dimensionally similar to the desired configuration, especially in the case-head area.

case gauge
A fixture used to inspect cartridge case dimensions (i.e. length, diameters, thickness, etc.) to ensure conformance to established tolerances

case hardened
The result by which a piece of metal undergoes a heat treatment that increases the surface hardness. The finished piece of metal often displays an array of distinct colors and designs.

case head expansion
An enlargement of the cartridge case head diameter on firing

case head separation
See *rupture*

case life
An expression of the number of times a case can be reloaded and fired

case mouth
The opening in the case into which the projectile or shot is inserted

case separation
Also called "case rupture." See *rupture*.

case shoulder
The angled or tapered section of a bottleneck cartridge case connecting the main body of the case to the smaller diameter neck

case split
A longitudinal rupture in the wall of a cartridge case or shotshell

case stretching
The elongation in the body of a cartridge case during firing

case taper
The gradual reduction in diameter of a cartridge case from head to shoulder or mouth

case trimmer
A device used to shorten the length of center-fire cartridge cases to proper length. The necks may stretch and lengthen as a result of repeated reloading and firing.

caseless ammunition
Ammunition that has the propellant charge attached to the bullet and not enclosed in any type of cartridge case

cast
The offset of the butt of a gun from the bore axis. "Cast-off" refers to an offset to the right for a right-handed shooter and to the left for a left-handed shooter, while "cast-on" refers to the offset of the butt of a gun to the left for a right-handed shooter and to the right for a left-handed shooter. See also *stock dimensions*.

CB cap
A low-velocity .22 caliber rimfire cartridge having a conical bullet (CB), loaded in a case shorter than the .22 short

center of impact
The center of a shot pattern or bullet group on a target

center pin
See *cylinder pin*

chamber
1. n. In a rifle, shotgun or pistol, the enlargement of the bore at the rearmost part of the barrel that has been formed to accept a specific cartridge or shell when inserted

2. n. In a revolver, the holes in the cylinder that have been formed to accept a cartridge

3. v. To insert or load a cartridge into a firearm chamber

chamber, auxiliary

An adapter that, when installed in a gun chamber for which it was designed, permits a smaller cartridge to be fired in the gun

chamber, bulge

A chamber with an abnormal enlargement

chamber cast

A cast of the chamber and/or bore of a firearm made using a special alloy or material that has a low melting point and exceptional dimensional stability. The cast is used to study the physical characteristics of the chamber or bore.

chamber, floating

A system in which a rearwardly movable chamber operates the mechanism of a firearm when fired

chamber, fluted

A chamber that has longitudinal grooves

chamber leade

The conical part of the bore between the chamber and the rifling (also called "throat" or "ball seat")

chamber reamer

One of a series of cutting tools used to form the chamber area of a barrel bore

charge

1. n. The amount, by weight, of a component of a cartridge (i.e., priming weight, propellant weight, shot weight)

2. v. To load a firearm

charge, maximum

The greatest charge weight, in grains, of a particular propellant that may be used with other specified ammunition components without exceeding the safe, maximum, allowable pressure limit for the specific cartridge or shell being loaded

charge, nominal

A typical charge weight of a specific powder for a specific combination of components

charge, powder

The amount of powder by weight in a cartridge case

charge, reduced

A less-than-nominal powder charge

charger

See *cartridge clip*.

checkering

A diamond-like pattern in the wood, plastic or metal components of a firearm for improving grip or ornamentation

checkering, cut
Checkering that is cut with a tool into the surface, either by hand or by machine, rather than impressed

checkering, French
A type of gunstock line engraving where lines are omitted at regular intervals. Also called "skip line."

checkering, hand
The process of checkering wood or metal by hand rather than using a machine

checkering, impressed
A heated die process that produces a carved effect in the gun stock or forearm

checkering, machine
The process of checkering wood or metal using a special machine

checkering line count
A method of expressing the size of the diamonds in a checkering pattern, expressed in lines per inch (l.p.i.) The higher the number, the finer the pattern; the lower the number, the coarser

checkering, runover
A wood cutting condition which occurs when any line goes beyond the border

checkering tools
The tools used for cutting a checkering pattern in wooden stocks—may be hand or machine powered

cheek, cheekpiece
A raised part of the side of the stock of a shoulder-arm against which the shooter rests his face. Usually associated with a Monte-Carlo type stock.

cherry
A tool used to cut the precise bullet configuration into the two halves of a bullet mold

chilled shot
Lead-alloy shot pellets hardened by the addition of about 3 percent antimony; so-called because of an earlier hardening process

choke
An interior constriction at or near the muzzle end of a shotgun barrel for the purpose of controlling shot dispersion

choke, cut
A choke formed by a reamer during manufacture of a shotgun barrel

choke, cylinder bore
The lack of a uniform constriction at or near the muzzle of a shotgun barrel

choke, jug
A type of shotgun barrel choke, wherein a slight recess is formed in the bore approximately one inch behind the muzzle. The recess causes the shot to gather before leaving the muzzle resulting in a denser pattern.

choke tube
A replaceable insert in the muzzle of a shotgun barrel to provide the desired amount of choke

choke, variable
An adjustable device attached to the muzzle of a shotgun in order to control the shot patterns

choke, ventilated
A shotgun choke that is slotted for the release of powder gases

chronograph
An instrument designed to measure elapsed time. When correlated with distance it is used to determine projectile velocity.

cock
To place the hammer, firing pin or striker in position for firing

cocking indicator
Any device to indicate that a firearm hammer or striker is cocked

cock-on-closing
In relation to bolt-action firearms, a mode of operation in which the striker is cocked by turning down the bolt handle

cock-on-opening
In relation to bolt-action firearms, a mode of operation in which the striker is cocked by lifting the bolt handle. This is the most common mechanical pattern seen in contemporary sporting arms.

cocking piece
1. In certain firearms, the end of a long firing pin or striker by which the firearm may be manually cocked

2. An internal portion of the cocking mechanism, which holds the firing pin or striker in its cocked position against the sear

cocking rod
A mechanical means of cocking the hammer of some firearms.

coefficient of form
A numerical term indicating the general profile of a projectile. Used to calculate the *ballistic coefficient* (q.v.).

comb
In a shoulder arm, the ridge at the upper forward part of the butt stock just in back of the grip section.

combination gun
See *gun, combination*

combustion

The chemical reaction of a fuel and oxygen, usually initiated by a heat source. When the fuel is oxidized there is an evolution of heat and often light.

compensator

A device attached to the muzzle end of the barrel that utilizes propelling gases to reduce recoil. Also, see *muzzle brake*.

cone, forcing

1. The tapered leade from the shotgun chamber diameter to the bore diameter

2. The tapered area from the bore diameter to the choke diameter

3. The tapered entrance to the bore in the rear of a revolver barrel

copper-clad steel

A composite structure of copper and steel used for the manufacture of certain bullet jackets

core

See *bullet core*

corrosive primer

A primer that, when fired, leaves a residue that attracts residue and sometimes contains traces of chlorine. If not quickly removed, this residue can easily cause rust.

crane

The part of a solid frame revolver on which the cylinder is swung out to accomplish loading and ejecting (also called yoke)

creep

See *trigger creep*

crimp, rolled

The closure of the mouth of a shotshell by inverting the mouth of the tube over a top wad or slug

crimp, star

A type of closure of the mouth of a metallic case or shotshell in which the sidewalls are folded in a star-shaped pattern. Also called "rose crimp" or "pie crimp."

crossbolt

1. A transverse operating type of lock used in some break-open type firearms (sometimes called a "Greener crossbolt")

2. A device intended to prevent stock splitting due to recoil

3. A form of manual safety that operates transversely to prevent or permit firing of a gun

crotch figure

The generally irregular grain pattern common to a stock blank cut from the crotch of a tree

crown
The radius on the muzzle end of a barrel

crowning
The act of forming the radius on the muzzle end of a barrel

crusher
A metallic cylinder that, when used in conjunction with a piston and associated equipment, can be used to measure cartridge pressures. The crusher's deformation is correlated with peak pressure.

CUP (cupper units of pressure)
A pressure value determined by means of copper crusher cylinders using SAAMI recommended procedures and equipment

cup, high
Correct term for shotshells having a high metal head type of construction

cup, low
Correct term for shotshells having a low metal head type of construction

cup, shot
See *wad, shot protector*

cup, split
A longitudinal split in the sidewall of the brass or steel cup assembled on a plastic or paper shotshell

cutoff
1. A mechanical device that is employed in firearms so that only one shell will feed into the *carrier* (or *lifter*) with each cycle of the breech mechanism. Also called "cartridge stop" or "shell stop."

2. A manually operated device to prevent the feeding of cartridges from a magazine

cyclic rate
The rate which a succession of movements repeats itself; in an automatic firearm, it is usually expressed in shots per minute that are theoretically possible to be fired, given an unlimited supply of ammunition

cylinder
The rotatable part of a revolver that contains the cartridge chambers

cylinder alignment
The relationship of the axis of the chamber in a revolver cylinder to the axis of the bore (also called cylinder indexing)

cylinder end-play
The free longitudinal movement of the cylinder in the frame

cylinder gap

In a revolver, the space between the cylinder and the barrel measured with the cylinder in the rearmost position (also called "cylinder-barrel gap" or "barrel-cylinder gap")

cylinder pin

The pin around which the cylinder of a revolver rotates. This is a feature found on revolvers in which there is no crane. Also called "axis pin," "base pin" or "center pin."

cylinder release latch

A device that permits the swinging out of the cylinder from the frame of a revolver

cylinder stop

A device to stop cylinder rotation in proper alignment with the barrel in a revolver. Sometimes called a "cylinder bolt."

cylinder stop notch

One of the machined grooves on the circumference of a revolver cylinder that is engaged by the cylinder stop in order to assure barrel and chamber alignment (also called bolt notch)

cylinder timing

In a revolver, the sequence of hammer cocking, cylinder alignment and cylinder locking. Proper timing requires that the cylinder be locked into alignment before the hammer reaches full cock.

D

Damascus barrel

A barrel formed by twisting or braiding together steel and iron wires or bars. The resulting cable is then wound around a mandrel and forged into a barrel tube. Sometimes called a laminated barrel.

datum

A reference plane, point or diameter that provides a base for calculations and measurements, such as cartridge headspace

decapper

A tool used to remove primers from cartridge cases or shells

Deeley fore-end

Unique on a shotgun, this fore-end usually possesses a catch that secures it to the barrels of a break-open shotgun and is operated by a small lever

deflagration

A rapid combustion reaction that is propagated at a subsonic rate by heat transfer into the reacting material. This reaction is accompanied by a vigorous evolution of heat and flame. The flow of reaction products is in the direction opposite that of the combustion propagation (unlike *detonation*). Deflagration is usually dependent upon having fuel and oxidizing agent in very close contact, either from having the fuel as a finely divided mixture with the oxidant, or by combining the two in the same chemical compound or mixture. Deflagration exhibits a dependence upon the surrounding gas pressure.

deflection
The variation in the normal flight path of a projectile caused by wind or other external influences

deflector
A device mounted on the receiver or frame of a firearm to change the direction of fired-case ejection

delayed fire
See *hangfire*

dent remover
A gunsmithing tool used to remove dents from shotgun barrels (also called dent raiser)

derringer
A generic term applied to many variations of small one- or two-shot pistols, using both percussion caps and cartridges. A mispelling of the last name of the original designer, Henry Deringer.

detonation
An extremely rapid exothermic decomposition reaction that proceeds at a rate greater than the speed of sound within the reacting material (unlike *deflagration*). The normal mode of initiation is shock (such as a blasting cap or a high-level mechanical shock), or from initial combustion which, due to peculiarities of confinement or other circumstances accelerates to such a degree that a shock wave is formed. Behind the shock wave is a reaction zone where material is converted to gaseous products at high temperature and pressure. The flow of the reaction is in the same direction as the propagation.

DEWAT
An acronym for *DEactivated WAr Trophy*

direct impingement
A gas system that operates using gas from a fired cartridge to operate the action without the use of a cylinder, piston or operating rod

disconnector
A device intended to disengage the sear from the trigger
1. In a manually operated firearm, it is intended to prevent firing without pulling the trigger

2. In a semi-automatic firearm, it is intended to prevent full-automatic firing

disc, paper
> A small circular piece of treated paper cut and pressed into the primer cup in contact with the priming mixture (also called "foil")

dispersion
> The greatest distance between any two bullet holes in a group on a target, normally measured center to center. Sometimes separated into horizontal and vertical dispersion.

double-barrel
> Two barrels in a firearm mounted to one frame. They can be vertically (over/under) or horizontally (side-by-side) aligned.

doll's head
> A usually round extension at the top of the barrel or rib of a shotgun that fits into a matching hole in the top of the standing breech

double-action
> See *action, double*

double-base powder
> See *powder, double-base*

double gun
> A two-barrel firearm, usually side-by-side. Also known as "double barrel" or "double." See *shotgun, double.*

double-set trigger
> See *trigger, double set*

doubling
> The unintentional firing of a second shot

dram equivalent
> Accepted method of correlating relative velocities of shotshells loaded with smokeless propellant to shotshells loaded with blackpowder. The reference blackpowder load chosen was a 3-dram charge of blackpowder, with $1\frac{1}{8}$ oz. of shot and a velocity of 1200 f.p.s. Therefore, a 3-dram-equivalent load using smokeless powder would be with $1\frac{1}{8}$ oz. of shot having a velocity of 1200 f.p.s. or $1\frac{1}{4}$ oz. of shot and a velocity of 1165 f.p.s. A $3\frac{1}{4}$-dram-equivalent load might have $1\frac{1}{8}$ oz. of shot and a velocity of 1255 f.p.s. (abbreviated "*dram equiv*").

drift
> The deviation in flight of a bullet from the center line of the bore due to the gyrational spin of the bullet imparted by the rifling

drilling
> A three-barreled long gun in which a combination of smoothbore and rifled barrels is used

drop, bullet
> The vertical distance a bullet has fallen, under the influence of gravity, at any point in its flight path. The distance is measured from a point on its path to the straight line from axis of the bore to target.

drop test, firearm

A type of safety test designed to gauge a firearm's tendency to fire when dropped or subjected to a sharp shock. It usually consists of dropping a cocked, unloaded firearm onto a specified type of surface from a specified distance and in a specified orientation.

drop test, primer

Sensitivity test for primed shells or primers

dry-fire

The release of the firing pin on an unloaded chamber of a firearm

dust cover

A cover on a firearm to reduce the possibility of foreign matter entering into the action

E

ear protection

An essential safety practice utilizing approved earplugs or muffs

effective range

See *range, effective*

ejection

The act of expelling a cartridge or fired case from a firearm

ejection port

See *port, ejection*

ejector

A device that expels cartridges or fired cases from a firearm

ejector, automatic

A mechanism in double guns that expels fired cases when the action is opened

ejector rod

The component that actuates the extractor and/or ejector. It can be manual or automatic (also called "extractor rod")

elevation adjustment

The vertical movement of a sight to compensate for vertical displacement of a bullet or bullets from the aiming point

energy, muzzle

The kinetic energy possessed by a projectile as it leaves the muzzle

energy, projectile

The kinetic energy possessed by a fired projectile, commonly expressed in foot-pounds, joules or kilogram meters. Sometimes called *bullet energy*. See *Chapter 16, Formulae and Tables*.

energy, terminal

The energy of a projectile at the time it strikes a target. Sometimes called "striking energy."

engine turning

A geometric design of overlapping circles on the metallic surfaces of a firearm (also called jeweling)

expander plug

1. A cylindrical plug of proper diameter that is inserted into the neck of a resized cartridge case to expand the diameter to its proper size. Also called "Ball Sizing Plug."

2. A tool used to remove dents in shotgun barrels

extraction

The act of withdrawing a cartridge or fired case from the chamber of a firearm

extraction groove

A groove turned in the side wall of a cartridge case just forward of the face of the head for the purpose of extraction. Also called "cannelure" or "extractor groove."

extractor

A component or device for withdrawing the cartridge or fired case from the chamber

extractor cut

A recess, usually in the barrel of a firearm, to accommodate an extractor

extractor rod

See *ejector rod*

eye protection

An essential safety practice utilizing approved safety glasses

eye relief

The distance between the eye and the rear aperture or rear sight of a firearm

F

fail-to-fire

A failure of the firearm to discharge after the trigger has been pulled. It can be one of two types: 1.) a complete misfire, or 2.) a delayed or hang-fire.

feed mechanism, automatic

A system for reloading a firearm utilizing some of the energy realized from firing a cartridge

feed ramp

See *cartridge feed ramp*

feed throat

A component or surface that guides a cartridge from the magazine to the chamber

finger lever
See *lever, operating*

firearm
An assembly of a barrel and action from which a projectile is propelled through a deflagration of propellant

fire-form
The method by which to shape a cartridge case by using the pressure from normal firing to fit a given chamber.

firing pin
The part of the firearm mechanism that strikes the primer or the rim of a cartridge to initiate ignition in order to fire the cartridge

firing pin, floating
A type of firing pin that is unrestrained by a spring or other mechanical means

firing pin indent
1. The impression made by the firing pin in the primer cup of the center-fire primer or the rim of rimfire cartridges

2. A measure of the kinetic energy delivered by the firing pin

firing pin, inertia
A type of firing pin in which the forward movement is restrained, usually by a spring, until it receives the energy from a hammer blow. It is slightly recessed in the breech face before being struck by the hammer and is shorter in length than the housing in which it is contained. Upon hammer impact, it flies forward using only its own kinetic energy to fire the primer.

firing-pin protrusion
The distance the firing pin protrudes from the breech face when it is in its most forward position

five-in-one blank
A blank cartridge that was designed for use in firearms of different calibers. It can be used in .38-40 Win., .44-40 Win. and .45 Colt revolvers and in .38-40 Win. and .44-40 Win. rifles.

flash hider
See *flash suppressor*

flash hole
1. A hole or holes pierced or drilled through the center of the web in the primer pocket of a metallic cartridge case

2. A hole or holes in the end of a battery cup primer used in shotshells

flash suppressant
A material that is added to propellant for the purpose of reducing muzzle flash

flash suppressor

A muzzle attachment designed to reduce muzzle flash (also called "flash hider")

flintlock

A muzzleloading firearm ignition system wherein a piece of flint is secured to the hammer in such a manner as to strike steel upon hammer release, causing sparks to ignite powder contained in the ignition system, for subsequent ignition of the main powder charge

floorplate

The bottom of a box magazine. It may be hinged, sliding or immovable.

fluting

1. See *oil dent*

2. Longitudinal grooves in the sidewall of a firearm chamber to aid extraction

3. Longitudinal grooves in the outside of a barrel to remove weight. See *barrel, fluted*.

flyer

1. A shot that is considerably outside the normal group on a target

2. A shot that is considerably outside the normal range with regards to velocity or pressure

follower

That part in a firearm which, through the action of a spring, forces a cartridge or cartridges to move

forcing cone

See *cone, forcing*

fore-end

The forward part of a one-piece stock. It is sometimes called "forearm."

fore-end, Anson fastening

A British term for a fastening method of the fore-end of double barreled shotguns that utilizes a spring-loaded bolt that extends beyond the tip of the fore-end.

fore-end, beavertail

A wider than normal, usually flattened, forward part of a stock

fore-end iron

On firearms with a two-piece stock, an intermediate part that holds the fore-end wood against the barrel and frame and retains the latch mechanism

form factor

See *coefficient of form*

frame

See *receiver*

frame, solid
1. In shoulder arms, a firearm in which the barrel and receiver are not designed for quick disassembly

2. In revolvers, having a frame that is not hinged

frangible projectile
A projectile that breaks up readily upon impact

free bore
A cylindrical length of bore in a firearm just forward of the chamber in which rifling is not present. It is associated with bullet jump.

free travel
See *bullet jump*

frizzen
The metal arm of a muzzleloader's lock that serves as a striking plate and guides sparks into the pan. When not in use, the frizzen also protects unfired priming powder in the pan.

full-cock
The position of the hammer or striker when the firearm is ready to fire

G

gauge, pressure
A piston or crusher system or a piezoelectric transducer system used to measure internal chamber and/or barrel pressure in a firearm or test device

gauge, star
A measuring instrument for determining internal diameters, often used to measure the inside diameter of a gun barrel

gas check
A metallic cup attached to the base of some lead alloy bullets

gas cutting
An erosive effect in a firearm caused by the high-velocity, high-temperature propellant gases

gas-operated
A type of automatic or semi-automatic firearm in which the propellant gases are used to unlock the breech bolt and then to complete the cycle of extraction and ejection. This is accomplished usually in conjunction with a spring that returns the operating parts to battery.

gate, loading
1. In revolvers: A hinged piece attached to the frame which is opened to permit loading

2. In shoulder arms: A spring-loaded cover for the loading port

gauge
> A term used in the identification of most shotgun bores (with the exception of the .410 bore.) It is related to the number of bore diameter lead balls that are required to weigh a total of one pound.

gilding metal
> A material used extensively for bullet jackets. The term refers to metal alloys of 90 to 95 percent copper and the remainder zinc (also called "commercial bronze"). Neither name is recommended by the Copper Development Association, Inc., but instead Alloy No. 220 and Alloy No. 210, respectively, are recommended.

glass bedding
> The application of a mixture of fiberglass and resin between the action and/or barrel and stock, for the purpose of improving accuracy

grain
> 1. A unit of weight (avoirdupois), with 7,000 grains per pound. The grain unit is commonly used in American and English ammunition practice to measure the weight of components.
>
> 2. A term sometimes applied to a single particle of propellant powder. More properly called a "kernel."

grip
> 1. In handguns, the handle
>
> 2. In shoulder arms, that portion of the stock to the rear of the trigger

grip adapter
> A filler piece attached to the front of the grip of a firearm

grip, bird's head
> A handgun grip that comes to a point in front, making it resemble a bird's head

grip, English
> A style of grip that features a straight wrist, typically built on light-weight shotguns

grip, pistol
> On shoulder firearms, that part of the stock behind the trigger, shaped similar to the grip of a pistol to afford a better grasp

grip, straight
> On shoulder firearms, a butt stock without a pistol grip

groove diameter
> The major diameter in a barrel that is the diameter of a circle circumscribed by the bottom of the grooves in a rifled barrel

grooves
> See *rifling*

group
> A series of consecutive shots fired at the same aiming point without changing the sight adjustments of the firearm

guard screw
> A screw that extends from the trigger guard into and sometimes through the stock

gun, bull
> A firearm built with an extra-thick, heavy barrel, used primarily for target shooting or varmint hunting

gun, combination
> A multiple barrel firearm designed to handle different sizes, calibers or types of ammunition

gun cotton
> A term for nitrated cellulose (either cotton linters, wood pulp or a mixture of the two) that is used for the manufacture of smokeless propellant. The chemical name is "nitrocellulose."

gun lock
> See *lock*

gunpowder
> A commonly used term for cartridge and muzzleloading propellant

gun, riot
> A shotgun with a short barrel designed for riot control or guard duty

gun, skeet
> A shotgun designed for use in the game of skeet. Usually made with a cylinder bore or similarly open choke.

gun, trap
> A shotgun specifically designed for the game of trap shooting

H

half cock
> The position of the hammer, when about half retracted and held by the sear, intended to prevent release of the hammer by a normal pull of the trigger. This is the safe or loading position on many guns.

hammer
> A spring-powered component of a firing mechanism which strikes the firing pin, primer or percussion cap

hammer block
> A device intended to isolate the hammer from the firing pin except when the trigger is pulled

hammer forging
> A process used to produce a barrel or receiver by hammering the part around a mandrel into its final shape

hammerless
Any firearm having a concealed hammer or striker

hammer nose
That part of the hammer that serves as a firing pin

hammer rebound
A feature of some firearms, usually external-hammer guns, wherein the hammer, after striking the firing pin, retracts slightly before coming to rest

hammer spur
The knob or extension on an exposed hammer that acts as a cocking or decocking aid

hammer, target
A firearm hammer having a wider spur designed for convenient and rapid cocking

hand
The lever that rotates a revolver cylinder. Sometimes called a "pawl."

handgun
A firearm, usually with a short barrel, designed to be held and fired with one hand

handle, operating
The handle of a semi- or full-automatic firearm used to cycle the firearm without firing. Also called "charging handle," "cocking handle" or "cocking knob."

handloading
The process of manually reassembling a fired cartridge case with a new primer, propellant and bullet or wads and shot. See *reloading*.

hangfire
Any delay in firing of an abnormal duration. Also called a "delayed fire," the term implies that firing does eventually occur.

hardball
A slang term for full-metal-jacketed pistol ammunition

head
The end of the cartridge case in which the primer or priming is inserted and the surface upon which the headstamp identification is imprinted

head clearance
The distance between the head of a fully seated cartridge or shell and the face of the breech bolt when the action is in the closed position. It is commonly confused with *headspace*.

headspace
The distance from the face of the closed breech of a firearm to the surface in the chamber on which the cartridge case seats

headspace gauge
A device used in a firearm to determine the distance between the

breech face and the chamber surface on which the cartridge seats (also called "breeching plug")

headstamp
Numerals, letters and symbols (or combinations) stamped into the head of a cartridge case or shotshell to identify the manufacturer, caliber or gauge and other additional information

heel
1. The part of a rifle or shotgun stock at the top of the butt end

2. The rear portion of a bullet

heel cavity
A recess in the base of a bullet

high brass
Common terminology referring to the length of the external metal head on a shotshell. Properly called "high cup."

highpower
A term often to refer to formal competition bullseye-target shooting with center-fire rifles

hinge pin
A cylindrical member at the forward end of a frame about which the barrel or barrels pivot (also called a "joint pin")

hull
A slang term for a cartridge or shotshell case

I

ignition barrel time
See *barrel time*

ignition time
The elapsed time from moment of firing-pin contact on the primer to the point on the X (time) axis of the pressure-time curve that indicates that propellant burning has initiated

in battery
A firearm is said to be in battery when the breeching mechanism is in the proper position for firing

in-line
A firearm design that places the firing mechanism substantially in line with the longitudinal axis of the barrel. Ignition gases are typically induced concentric to the bore with this design.

inertia block
1. A device intended to function during recoil to set the fire control mechanism to fire a second barrel

2. A device intended to function during recoil to prevent doubling on some double-barrel shotguns

J

jacket

The envelope enclosing the lead core of a compound bullet

jam

A malfunction of a firearm that prevents the action from operating; this may be caused by faulty parts, ammunition, improper maintenance or improper use of the firearm

jeweling

See *engine turning*

joint

A place where two or more parts join so as to permit motion. The term is sometimes used in reference to the pivot point of a hinged action.

joint pin

See *hinge pin*

jump

The upward and rearward recoiling movement of a firearm when it is fired (also, see "bullet jump, recoil")

K

keeper

A loop or clip made of leather, metal or plastic that holds together straps or cords, as on a gun sling

kernel

A single particle of propellant powder

keyhole

An oblong or oval hole in a target that is produced by an unstable bullet striking the target at an angle to the bullet's longitudinal axis

kicker

The part that draws back a rod that forces home a cartridge on some recoil-operated firearms. Also refers to some break-open shotgun ejectors.

knurling, knurl

1. A series of regular ridges or rectangles on a tool handle or gun component (such as a trigger, hammer, bolt handle, etc.) to help prevent slipping

2. Infrequently, a cartridge case or bullet cannelure

L

land, lands

The uncut surface of the bore of a rifled barrel

land diameter

See *bore diameter*

lanyard
A strap or cord that is attached to a firearm (usually handgun) and worn around the neck or shoulder to prevent loss of the firearm

lap, lapping
The process of polishing a metal surface, such as the interior of a barrel or the rails of a receiver, with a fine abrasive substance

leade
That section of the bore of a rifled gun barrel located immediately ahead of the chamber in which the rifling is conically removed to provide clearance for the seated bullet (also called "throat" or "ball seat")

leading
The accumulation of lead in the bore of a firearm from the passage of lead shot or bullets (also called "metal fouling")

length, overall
1. In firearms: The dimension measured parallel to the axis of the bore from the muzzle to a line at right angles to the axis and tangent to the rearmost point of the buttplate or grip

2. In ammunition: The greatest dimension of a loaded cartridge, i.e., from face of the head to the tip of the bullet for center-fire or rimfire or to the crimp for shotshells or blanks (not to be confused with the uncrimped length in a shotshell). It is abbreviated *OAL*.

lever
A projecting piece used to operate a mechanism, as the lever of a lever-action firearm

lever action
An action that cycles a cartridge during the loading, locking and unloading process by means of a lever, located below the receiver and usually serves as a trigger guard

lever, cocking
A manually operated, external lever for the hammer or striker of some firearms

lever lock
A device intended to hold the lever closed on some lever-action guns

lever, operating
On lever-action firearms, that part operated by the hand to open and close the breech

lever, rebound
A rotating device designed to move the hammer into a position in which there is no contact of either hammer and firing pin or firing pin and primer. It may also be used to position a safety device between the hammer and firing pin or primer.

lifter
See *carrier*

line engraving
A form of engraving in which the entire pattern or design consists of shallow line cuts as opposed to engraving done in bas-relief. This type of engraving is often found on the metal parts of firearms.

line of bore
See *bore axis*

line of departure
The direction in which a projectile is moving when it leaves the muzzle of a firearm—also defined as the tangent to the trajectory at the muzzle. See *trajectory*.

line of sight
A straight line drawn from the shooter's eye, passing through the sights of a firearm and extending from the firearm to a target

load
1. n. The combination of components used to assemble a cartridge or shotshell
2. v. The act of putting ammunition into a firearm

load, brush
A shotshell load specifically designed to provide a wide spread pattern at a close range in a choked gun. Also called "spreader load," "scatterload," "brush load" or "thicket load."

load, duplex
1. A cartridge case containing two projectiles with a single powder charge

2. A cartridge case containing a single projectile with two types of powder.

load, field
A shotshell loaded for hunting small-game animals and birds

load, proof
See *cartridge, proof*

load, squib
A cartridge or shell that produces projectile velocity and sound substantially lower than normal—may result in projectile and/or wads remaining in the bore

loading density
The relationship, in a cartridge, of the volume of the propellant to the available case volume. It is usually expressed as a percentage.

lock
1. A general term referring to the total firing mechanism in a firearm

2. Range command sometimes used to indicate engagement of a manual safety ("*lock* your firearms")

3. An externally applied device intended to help secure a firearm

lock energy
The amount of energy delivered to the primer from the firing-pin blow

lock frame
A device incorporated into the mechanism of some firearms in which the barrel and the bolt assembly recoil upon firing. The lock frame acts to absorb the shock of the recoiling parts prior to the bolt unlocking and opening.

lock plate
A metal plate mounted on the stock of a gun to provide for mounting of, or access to, the firing mechanism

lock, rebounding
A type of firing mechanism, wherein the hammer or striker after forward movement retracts slightly to a rest position

lock time
The time interval between sear release and the firing pin striking the primer

longrifle
1. Originally the term was used in reference to long-barreled flintlock rifles

2. The name given to one type of a .22-caliber rimfire cartridge

lug, barrel
A general term for any projection extending at right angles to the barrel

lug, recoil
A block or plate on the bottom of a receiver and/or barrel to transfer the recoil to the stock

lump
One of several projections located on the underside of the barrel or barrels on top-break-action guns, which serves to secure the barrels to the action or receiver. See *lug, barrel.*

lump, chopper
A type of lump that is integral with the barrel. See *lump.*

lump, hook of
A notch machined into a lump used to mate with the hinge pin

lumps, bifurcated
A type of lump found mainly on expensive over/under shotguns. The bifurcated or divided lumps are mounted on each side of the lower barrel, as opposed to under it, which serve to reduce the overall height of the receiver-barrel assembly.

LUP (lead units of pressure)
A pressure value determined by means of lead crusher cylinders. In firearms, used mainly to measure chamber pressure of shotgun shells.

M

machine gun

1. n. A fully automatic firearm that loads, fires and ejects continuously when the trigger is held to the rear until the ammunition is exhausted or pressure on the trigger is released

2. v. To fire continuously, in the manner of a machine gun; also known as "firing full-automatic."

machine rest

A mechanical apparatus used for holding a firearm in a precisely controlled, repeatable position for testing the accuracy of the ammunition or the firearm

magazine

1. A building for the storage of either ammunition or its components

2. A receptacle for a firearm that holds a plurality of cartridges or shells under spring pressure preparatory for feeding into the chamber. Magazines take many forms, such as box, drum, rotary, tubular, etc. and may be fixed or removable.

magazine, blind box

A magazine having a permanently closed bottom. Loading and unloading are accomplished through the same opening.

magazine, box

A rectangular receptacle attached to or inserted into a firearm that holds cartridges stacked on top of one another ready for feeding into the chamber

magazine catch

The device that retains or releases the magazine in a firearm—also known as a "magazine latch" or "magazine release"

magazine-fed

Said of a repeating firearm in which the ammunition for subsequent firing is fed from a magazine

magazine follower

A spring-actuated device to move cartridges in a magazine into the feeding position

magazine, Mannlicher

A type of rotary magazine

magazine plug

1. A part inserted in a magazine to reduce its capacity

2. A part in the end of a tubular magazine that closes the end and retains the spring

magazine, rotary

A form of magazine in which the cartridges are arranged about a central rotating spindle or carrier. See also *magazine, Mannlicher.*

magazine safety
A type of safety magazine that prevents the firing of a semi-automatic firearm when the magazine is removed, even if there is a round in the chamber

magazine spring
The spring in a magazine that exerts its thrust against the follower

magazine, tubular
A metal tube that contains cartridges or shells end to end

magnum
A term commonly used to describe a rimfire or center-fire cartridge, or shotshell, that is larger, contains more shot or produces higher velocity than standard cartridges or shells of a given caliber, or gauge. Rifles, handguns or shotguns that are designed to fire such cartridges or shells may also be described with the term "magnum."

mainspring
The mechanical energy storage device (usually a coil or leaf spring) that operates the striker or hammer of a firearm

malfunction
Failure of a firearm to perform properly due either to the firearm or the ammunition

master eye
The eye that controls both eyes when pointing toward or picking out an object. Sometimes called the dominant eye.

match ammunition
A high-grade of ammunition geared to competitive shooting

matchlock
A muzzleloading firearm's lock that utilizes a smoldering match held by an s-shaped piece of metal under spring tension when cocked. When used, the match falls forward igniting the priming powder in the pan.

matte finish
A dull, non-reflecting metallic surface

maxi-ball
An elongated, heavy weight bullet, usually incorporating annular exterior grooves to hold lubricant. Designed to be loaded and fired without a patch; its major diameter being slightly larger than bore diameter causing engraving by the rifling upon loading.

meplat
A term for the blunt tip of a bullet, specifically the tip's diameter

metal fouling
Metallic bullet material left in the bore after firing

Metford rifling
A form of rifling with shallow grooves that are arcs of less than half of the groove diameter

mid-range
1. A term that defines a specific point in the trajectory of a projectile that is half the distance between the firearm and the target

2. A reduced velocity, center-fire cartridge, used principally in target shooting

mil
An abbreviation for "milradian," it is the angle subtended by one unit at 1,000 units (e.g., the angle subtended by one yd. at 1,000 yds.)

Minié ball
A conical nosed lead bullet, slightly under bore diameter, incorporating a hollow base, designed to expand into the rifled bore upon firing for gas-sealing purposes without the use of a patch

minute of angle (m.o.a.)
An angular measurement method used to describe accuracy capability. A minute of angle is 1/60 of a degree, and subtends 1.047" at 100 yds., which for practical shooting purposes is considered to be one inch. A minute-of-angle group, therefore, equals slightly more than one inch at 100 yds., two inches at 200 yds., etc.

miquelet lock
A sidelock action developed in Spain at the end of the 16th century that uses flint to ignite blackpowder in the pan. This lock is usually recognized by the unique large ring on the cock jaw screw.

mirage
A visual phenomenon that appears to displace a target from its true position through a shimmering effect. It is caused by heated air that deflects light rays.

misfeed
Any malfunction during the feed cycle of a repeating firearm resulting in the failure of a cartridge or shell to enter the chamber completely (also known as "failure to feed")

misfire
A failure of the priming mixture to be initiated after the primer has been struck an adequate blow by a firing pin or the failure of the initiated primer to ignite the powder

monobloc
The solid section at the breech end of some multi-barrel guns into which the barrels are inserted

mount, offset
A mount for telescopes or iron sights affixed to the gun in such a manner, that the line of sight is to the side and above the receiver or barrel

mount, scope
A device to hold a telescopic or optical sight on a firearm

mount, see-through
> A scope mount arrangement which has a hollowed-out base through which the iron sights may be seen and used (also called a "tunnel mount")

mouth
> The open end of a cartridge case or shotshell, from which the projectile or shot charge is expelled in firing

mushroom
> A descriptive term for the desirable tendency of a hollow-point, soft-point or other type of hunting bullet to expand upon hitting the target and thus greatly increase its frontal area.

musket
> An unrifled military firearm with a long barrel and a fore-end or forearm that extends nearly to the muzzle

musket cap
> The ignition source for most military muzzleloading rifles of the Civil War era, usually consisting of a copper alloy cup containing the priming mix. They are larger than percussion caps and typically incorporate a continuous or segmented flanges (wings) at the cup mouth for ease of handling.

muzzle
> The end of a gun barrel from which the bullet or shot emerges

muzzle blast
> The resultant noise that occurs at the muzzle of a firearm when the projectile leaves the muzzle and hot gases are released

muzzle brake
> Device at the muzzle end usually integral with the barrel that uses the emerging gas behind a projectile to reduce recoil. See also *compensator*.

muzzle cap
> A cover put on the muzzle end of a barrel to keep out foreign matter

muzzle energy
> A projectile's energy at the time it leaves the muzzle of a gun

muzzle flash
> The illumination which is the result of the expanding gases from the burning propellant particles emerging from the barrel behind the projectile and uniting with oxygen in the air

muzzle guard
> A device put on the end of a barrel with a hole concentric with the bore to admit a cleaning rod and keep the rod from wearing the rifling in this critical area. Not used on guns cleaned from the breech end.

muzzle jump
> The generally upward motion of the muzzle of a firearm which occurs upon firing

muzzleloader
> A firearm which can be loaded with powder and projectile(s) only through the muzzle or front end of a cylinder in the case of a muzzleloading revolver

muzzle velocity
> The velocity of a projectile as it exits the muzzle of a firearm

muzzle wave
> The shock wave that moves out radially from the muzzle of a firearm upon firing

N

neck
> See *cartridge neck*

neck annealing
> A heating process used in cartridge case manufacture intended to relieve internal stresses in the neck area caused by cold working

neck clearance
> The dimensional difference between the diameter of the neck of a loaded cartridge case and the chamber

neck split
> A longitudinal rupture in the neck of a metallic cartridge case

neck tension
> The circumferential stress that the case neck exerts on the seated bullet, as a result of the interference fit provided by the case neck inside diameter and the bullet outside diameter

necking-down
> The use of case-forming dies to reduce the diameter of a cartridge case neck

nipple
> A hollow, cone-shaped part of a percussion firearm upon which a percussion cap or musket cap is placed. The hole in the nipple directs the flame or flash of the cap to the powder charge.

nitrocellulose powder
> See *powder, nitrocellulose*

nitroglycerine
> The common term for the nitric acid ester of glycerine, i.e., glyceryl nitrate. It is incorporated with nitrocellulose smokeless powder formulations to make double-base propellant powders. See *powder, double-base.*

non-corrosive
> A term applied to primers that contain no chemical compounds that could produce corrosion or rust in gun barrels, but does not necessarily protect from corrosion or rust

nose
The point or tip of a bullet

NRA
An acronym for the National Rifle Association

nutcracker tool
See *tong tool*

O

obturation
The momentary expansion of a cartridge case against chamber walls which minimizes the rearward flow of gases between the case and the chamber wall when the cartridge is fired

ogive
The curved portion of a bullet forward of the bearing surface

ogive, secant
A projectile nose with the curvature not tangent to the cylindrical bearing portion

ogive, tangent
A projectile nose with the curvature that is tangent to the cylindrical bearing portion

oil dent
A defect in a brass cartridge case, usually in the form of a shallow indentation caused by excessive oil present in dies during case manufacture, or in re-sizing dies during handloading operations, or in a chamber during firing (also called "fluting")

open point
A type of bullet having a cavity in the tip or nose

out-of-battery
A firearm is said to be out-of-battery when the breeching mechanism is not in proper position for firing

over-under, over/under, over-and-under
A firearm having two barrels placed one above the other

over-bore
A shotgun whose barrel bore diameter is greater than the SAAMI maximum for that gauge

over-bore capacity
A cartridge case containing more powder than can be efficiently burned in that bore diameter and volume. Most *magnum* cartridges are of over-bore capacity.

overtravel
The additional rearward motion of the trigger after sear or hammer release

P

Parkerizing

A non-reflecting, rust-resistant finish used on metal surfaces of some firearms (also called "phosphatizing" or "phosphate coating")

passive firing pin block

A small piece of metal that blocks the forward path of a firing pin and is lowered or raised when a part of the action is worked, usually the trigger

patch

1. A piece of cloth used with a rod to clean the bore of a firearm

2. A piece of paper wrapped around lead bullets to prevent leading of the barrel and to improve the gas seal

3. In muzzleloading firearms, the piece of cloth surrounding the bullet or ball to improve the gas seal

Patridge sight

Named after E.E. Patridge, a rear sight on pistols or revolvers having a flat top with a square notch used with a broad flat-topped front sight.

pattern

The distribution of shot fired from a shotgun. Generally measured as a percentage of pellets striking in a 30" circle at 40 yards. Some skeet guns are measured with a 30" circle at 25 yards.

pattern, blown

A pattern usually with a low percentage of pellets and of erratic distribution. Also known as "doughnut pattern" or "cartwheel pattern" depending on its overall shape and distribution.

pattern, doughnut

A pattern whose central area has no pellet hits. Sometimes called a "cartwheel pattern."

pellet

1. A common name for the small spherical projectiles loaded in shotshells

2. A non-spherical projectile used in some airguns

pepperbox

An early form of a revolver with a number of barrels bored in a piece of metal resembling a cylinder. Functioning much like a modern revolver, each pull of the trigger rotated a barrel into position for firing. Pepperbox pistols did not become widely popular until the invention of the percussion cap in the early 19th century.

percussion cap

The ignition source for several types of muzzleloading firearms, usually consisting of a copper alloy cup containing the priming mix. It is placed on the nipple.

piezoelectric pressure transducer
A pressure-sensing device that operates by means of a crystal which generates an electrical charge that is proportional to the pressure applied to it

pinfire cartridge
An early self-contained cartridge identifiable by a small-shaped pin protruding from the side of the cartridge at the base above the primer.

pistol
A generic term for a hand-held firearm. Often used more specifically to refer to a semi-automatic handgun.

pistol, air
A handgun with the same principle of operation as an airgun (also called "pellet pistol." See *airgun*

pistol, automatic
A common but improperly used term applied to autoloading pistols in use today. Almost all current "automatic" pistols are actually semi-automatic in function. See *semi-automatic*.

pistol-grip adapter
An accessory made to attach to the front of a revolver grip to afford a better grasp

piston, gas
The component in a gas-operated firearm upon which the gas impinges to operate the action

piston ring
A sharp-edged ring mounted on the piston of gas operated automatic and semi-automatic firearms which makes a close seal between the piston and cylinder wall, and by a scraping action reduces the accumulation of carbon in the cylinder

pitch
1. In regard to rifling, the distance a bullet must travel in the bore to make one revolution

2. In regard to handguns, the angle that the front of the handgun grip makes with the line of sight

3. A component used in making clay targets

4. See *stock pitch*

plinking
Informal target shooting at inanimate objects (usually other than paper targets), often located at arbitrary or indefinite distances from the firing point

plug screw
Screw used to fill holes for sight or telescopic sight mounting when not in use. Also used to fill access holes to internal pins (also called "dummy screw").

point-blank range
Very close range

point of aim
The exact point on which the shooter aligns a firearm's sights

port, gas
An opening in the wall of a barrel to allow gas to be harnessed in order to operate a mechanism or reduce sensible recoil

port, ejection
The opening in the slide or receiver of a semi-automatic arm through which fired cases are ejected

port, loading
The opening in a receiver where a cartridge may be placed in the firearm either directly into the chamber or the magazine

powder
Commonly used term for the propellant in a cartridge or shotshell

powder, ball
A type of smokeless propellant powder with the kernels formed in the shape of a sphere or flattened sphere

powder, black
The earliest form of propellant, reputed to have been made by the Chinese or Hindus before the remote beginnings of history. First used for guns in the 13th century. It is a mechanical mixture of potassium or sodium nitrate ("saltpeter"), charcoal and sulfur.

powder bridging
The wedging action of powder in the feed tube of a *powder measure,* causing stoppage of normal flow

powder burning rate
The speed with which a propellant burns. It is affected by both physical and chemical characteristics, as well as conditions under which it is burned.

powder, canister
See *powder, reloading*

powder charge
The amount of powder by weight in a cartridge case

powder deterioration
The chemical decomposition of modern smokeless propellant. It can be accelerated by improper storage conditions.

powder, double-base
A propellant composed of nitrocellulose and nitroglycerin as its base, as opposed to single-base powder which has nitrocellulose only as its base material. The percentage of nitroglycerin ranges from 3 to 39 percent.

powder, flake
A type of smokeless propellant in the form of thin discs or cut squares

powder fouling
The powder residue left in firearms after firing

powder, IMR
The abbreviation for "Improved Military Rifle" powder. A single-base, tubular, smokeless propellant

powder measure
A device used in cartridge manufacture or reloading that measures out powder charges volumetrically

powder, nitrocellulose
A smokeless propellant for ammunition whose principal ingredient is nitrocellulose. The nitrogen content of the nitrocellulose is usually between 13.1 and 13.2 percent (also known as "single-base powder").

powder, non-hygroscopic
Smokeless powder that resists water absorption

powder, progressive burning
A smokeless propellant in which the burning rate is controlled by physical and/or chemical means

powders, reloading
Propellant powders offered to individual consumers for loading small-arms ammunition (also called canister powders)

powder scale
A balance or weighing instrument for accurately weighing powder charges

powder, single-base
That powder which has nitrocellulose as its main ingredient, and contains no other major energy producing component. See *powder, double-base* for comparison.

powder, smokeless
A propellant containing mainly nitrocellulose (single-base) or both nitrocellulose and nitroglycerine (double-base)

powder, triple-base
A propellant composed of nitrocellulose, nitroglycerine and nitroguanidine. Generally used in large-caliber military ammunition.

press, reloading
A mechanical device for handloading metallic cartridges or shotshells

pressure
In a gun or cartridge, the force imparted to various components by the expanding gases generated by the deflagration of the propellant upon firing

pressure, average
The arithmetic mean of a number of rounds tested for pressure

pressure barrel
A heavy-walled barrel made to minimum chamber and bore dimensions and fitted with instrumentation to measure chamber pressure. See *pressure, chamber.*

pressure, chamber
That pressure inside the chamber and bore of a firearm that is generated by the expanding propellant powder gases after ignition. Normally measured by means of piezoelectric transducers or crusher gauges. Also sometimes called "breech pressure."

pressure curve
A graph of the relationship of chamber pressure to time or bullet travel in a firearm when a cartridge or shell is fired

pressure gauge
A device used to measure internal barrel pressure in a firearm or test device, usually by means of a piston and crusher or a piezoelectric transducer

pressure, peak
The highest value that the chamber pressure reaches during propellant burning

pressure, residual
The pressure level that remains in the cartridge case or the shell within the firearm's chamber, and in the bore, after the projectile leaves the muzzle of the firearm

pre-travel
The initial distance the trigger moves prior to sear movement. Also known as "trigger take-up" or "slack." Not the same as *trigger creep.*

primer
A cartridge ignition component consisting of brass or gilding metal cup, priming mixture, anvil and foil disc, which fires the cartridge when struck with sufficient force

primer, American
See *primer, Boxer*

primer, battery cup
1. A flanged metal cup having a flash hole at the bottom end
2. An ignition component using a battery cup as a holder for the other elements, usually found in shotshells

primer, Berdan
An ignition component consisting of a cup, explosive mixture and covering foil. The anvil is an integral part of the cartridge case head in the bottom center of the primer pocket. One or more flash holes

are drilled or pierced through the bottom of the primer pocket into the propellant cavity of the base. Commonly found in European cartridges.

primer, blanked

A fired primer in which the firing-pin indent in the cup has been punched out by internal gas pressure

primer, blown

A primer that is separated completely from the cartridge or shotshell after firing due to severe expansion of the primer pocket and head

primer, Boxer

An ignition component consisting of a cup, explosive mixture, anvil and covering foil or disc which together form the completed primer ready for assembly into the primer pocket of a cartridge case. One central flash hole is pierced through the bottom of the primer pocket into the propellant cavity of the case. Used in modern commercial center-fire ammunition made in Canada and the United States.

primer, center-fire

A cartridge initiator which is assembled central to the axis of the head of the cartridge case and which is actuated by a blow to the center of its axis, as opposed to a rimfire primer, which must be struck on the circumference of the cartridge head

primer, corrosive

A priming mixture that contained compounds of chlorine and oxygen, generally used in military ammunition made before 1952. The residues are hygroscopic and, therefore, promote rusting.

primer cratering

A circumferential rearward flow of metal surrounding the indentation of a firing pin in a fired primer cup

primer cup

The brass or copper cup which contains the priming mixture

primer flash

The illumination produced by the extremely hot gases which result from the rapid build-up of pressure and temperature when the priming mixture detonates

primer, flattened

1. A condition where the normally rounded corners of a fired primer cup are squared due to internal pressures

2. A primer cup configuration in which the crown is flattened to alter sensitivity

primer leak

The escape of gas between the primer cup and head of the cartridge case, or shotshell head

primer, loose
A primer that does not fit properly in the primer pocket of a cartridge case or shotshell

primer, non-corrosive
A primer that does not contain chemical compounds that could produce corrosion or rust in gun barrels. It does not by itself prevent corrosion or rust.

primer, non-mercuric
A primer that does not contain compounds of mercury

primer pellet
The explosive component of a primer

primer, pierced
A fired primer that has been perforated by the firing pin

primer pocket
A cylindrical cavity formed in the head of a metallic center-fire cartridge case, or in the head of a shotshell, to receive an appropriate primer or battery cup primer assembly

primer, rimfire
A type of primer found in the circumferential cavity or rim of rimfire ammunition. Usable only with rimfire guns. See *primer, center-fire.*

primer seating
The insertion of a center-fire primer or battery cup in the head of a cartridge case or shotshell. Properly seated, it should be flush or slightly below the face of the head.

primer setback
The condition when a primer, or battery cup primer assembly, moves partially out of its fully seated position in the primer pocket of a metallic cartridge or shotshell during firing

priming mixture
A combination of explosive and/or pyrotechnic type ingredients, that, when pressed into a cup or spun into the rim cavity of a rimfire shell, will explode or deflagrate from the impact of a firing pin and ignite the propellant in a cartridge or shotshell

projectile
An object propelled from a firearm by the force of rapidly burning gases or other means

projectile, disintegrating
A projectile that breaks up after leaving the muzzle and before it hits the target

projectile, frangible
A projectile that breaks up readily upon impact with the target to minimize ricochets or over penetration

projectile rotation
  The spinning motion that is imparted to a projectile due to engagement with the rifling in the barrel of a firearm, as it is driven down the barrel. The rate of rotation is dependent upon the rate of twist of the rifling and the velocity. The barrel twist (left or right) determines the direction of the rotation.

projectile, round ball
  A spherical projectile, usually of lead

projectile, saboted
  A sub-caliber projectile centered in a lightweight carrier (sabot) to permit the sub-caliber projectile to be fired in a larger-caliber gun

proof mark
  A stamp applied at or near the breech or other stressed component of a firearm after it has passed a proof test

proof test
  The test of an assembled firearm or individual components by firing a proof cartridge. See *cartridge, proof*

propellant
  In a firearm, the chemical composition which, when ignited by a primer, generates gas. The gas propels the projectile. Also called "powder," "gunpowder," "smokeless powder" and "blackpowder."

pull, length of
  See *stock length of pull*

pull-through
  A flexible device pulled through the barrel of a firearm to clean the barrel

pump action
  A manual action that uses a moveable forearm that usually sits parallel to the barrel. Sliding, or pumping, the action to the rear opens the action and empties the breech once a cartridge has been fired. When the forearm is moved forward, a new cartridge can be loaded into the chamber as the action moves forward and locks.

R

radius, mean
  One method used to measure ammunition and/or firearm accuracy capability. To determine the mean radius, the center of the group is located, and the distance to the center of each shot from the group center is measured and recorded. The sum of these measurements divided by the number of shots is the mean radius.

radius, neck
  The curvature at the junction of the neck and the shoulder of a cartridge case

radius, shoulder
>The curvature at the junction of the body and the shoulder of a cartridge case

ramp, loading
>A platform or cut placed in the bottom of the receiver that aids in guiding a cartridge into the chamber as the action is closed

ramp, sight
>A sight base having a sloping rear surface

ramrod
>A rod used in seating a load in muzzleloading firearms

range
>1. An area equipped for testing firearms and ammunition
>
>2. The horizontal distance between the firearm and the target

range, effective
>The maximum distance that a projectile can be expected to be useful

range, maximum
>The greatest distance a projectile can travel when fired at the optimum angle of elevation of the gun barrel

rate of twist
>The distance required for the rifling to complete one revolution

rebarrel
>The replacement of a barrel with another barrel

receiver
>The basic unit of a firearm that houses the firing and breech mechanism and to which the barrel and stock are assembled. In revolvers, pistols and break-open guns, it is called the "frame."

receiver bridge
>That part of the receiver on bolt-action rifles that arches over the rear of the bolt hole. If cut to allow the passage of the bolt handle it is known as a "split bridge."

receiver ring
>The front part of the receiver on bolt-action rifles into which the barrel is fitted

receiver, universal
>A heavy duty test receiver in which special barrels may be installed for testing ammunition, pressure, etc.

rechamber
>The cutting of a new chamber in a barrel to accommodate a cartridge of the same bore diameter

recoil
>The rearward movement of a firearm resulting from firing a cartridge or shotshell. Sometimes informally called "kick."

recoil-operated

Said of an automatic or semi-automatic type firearm in which the force of recoil is used to unlock the breech bolt and then to complete the cycle of extracting, ejecting and reloading

recoil pad

A buttplate, usually of rubber, to reduce the felt recoil of shoulder firearms

recoil pendulum

A device for measuring free recoil energy, in which a firearm is suspended from fixed points so as to allow it to swing freely while the barrel remains horizontal

recoil plate

1. Steel insert in the frame of a revolver immediately surrounding the firing-pin hole; also called firing-pin bushing

2. See *lug, recoil*

recoil shield

On a revolver, a lateral extension of the standing breech, to each side, to prevent fired or unfired cartridges from coming out of the chambers and to protect the otherwise exposed primers of unfired cartridges

recoil shoulder

Another name for *recoil lug*

recoil spring

The spring which returns a semi-automatic firearm to battery

regulation of barrels

The adjustment of the barrels of multi-barreled firearms so as to make the points of impact of the barrels coincide

relief engraving

The carving of raised scenes to produce three-dimensional figures

reloading

The process of manually reassembling a fired cartridge case with a new primer, propellant and bullet or wads and shot (also called *handloading*)

reloading components

Primers, propellant powder, bullets or shot and wads, used with fired cases to load ammunition

reloading data

A description of recommended relationships of reloading components

reloading dies

Tools which hold and/or reform cartridge cases or shotshells during a reloading operation

repeater
  Any firearm equipped with a magazine that holds more than one shot without reloading

resizing, full-length
  The operation of reforming a fired cartridge case to approximately its original dimensions

rest
  A device to support a firearm during firing

rest, palm
  An adjustable support for a target rifle extending downward from the fore-end

reticle
  The aiming reference marks seen when looking through an optical sight

revolver
  A firearm, usually a handgun, with a cylinder having several chambers so arranged as to rotate around an axis and be discharged successively by the same firing mechanism through a common barrel

revolver, double-action
  A type of revolver in which the rotation of the cylinder, cocking and firing are performed by a single pull of the trigger. Most double-action revolvers can also be fired in the single-action mode by manually cocking the hammer.

revolver, single-action
  A type of revolver in which the hammer must be cocked manually to rotate the cylinder for each shot. The firearm is then discharged by a pull of the trigger. The process is repeated for each shot.

rib
  A raised surface used as a sighting plane. Ribs may be either solid or ventilated. See *rib, ventilated.*

rib extension
  The protrusion of a rib beyond the breech end of a barrel

rib, solid
  A solid raised surface above a barrel or barrels that functions as a sighting plane

rib, ventilated
  A raised sighting surface that is separated from the barrel by means of posts that allow air to circulate around it. Its purpose is to minimize heat waves in the line of sight (also called "bridge rib").

ricochet
  The glancing rebound of a projectile after impact

rifle
  A firearm having spiral grooves in the bore and designed to be fired from the shoulder

rifle, automatic

A fully automatic shoulder firearm that starts firing when the trigger is pulled and continues until the trigger is released or ammunition is exhausted. The term should not be used in conjunction with "semi-automatic" firearms.

rifle, benchrest

A rifle designed for optimum accuracy while being shot from a fully supported position on a shooting bench, usually off a front tripod rest and rear sandbag

rifle, long

1. Originally, the term was used in reference to long-barreled flintlock rifles

2. The name given to one type of a .22-caliber rimfire cartridge

rifle, musket

A smoothbore, shoulder-fired, muzzleloading rifle with a typically long barrel and stock that extended to or near the muzzle

rifle, varmint

A sporting rifle with a heavy barrel, designed for long range small game hunting, firing high velocity, flat trajectory projectiles

rifling

The spiral grooves formed in the bore of firearm barrel to impart rotary motion to a projectile

rifling broach

A tool having a series of cutting edges of slightly increasing height used to cut the spiral grooves in a rifle barrel

rifling, button

A process wherein a hardened steel disc or button with a rifling cross-section configuration is pushed or pulled through a drilled and reamed barrel so as to cold form the rifling grooves to the desired depth and twist

rifling, cut

A process of forming the spiral grooves in the bore of a rifle barrel by a cutting tool which has a hook shape (also called "hook rifling")

rifling, hammer forged

The formation of the spiral grooves in the bore of a rifle barrel by means of an internal mandrel and external hammers (sometimes called "swaged rifling")

rifling head

That part of the hook or cut rifling tooling that holds the cutter and the mechanism for deepening the cut as the operation progresses

rifling pitch

The distance the projectile must move along a rifled bore to make one revolution; usually expressed as "one turn in x inches (or millimeters)"

rim

The flanged portion of the head of a rimfire cartridge, certain types of center-fire rifle and revolver cartridges and shotshells. The flanged portion is usually larger in diameter than the cartridge or shotshell body diameter and provides a projecting lip for the firearm extractor to engage so that the cartridge or shotshell may be extracted from the chamber after firing. In a rimfire cartridge the rim provides a cavity into which the priming mixture is charged.

rim seat

A counterbore in the rear end of a chamber or bolt face to support the head of a rimmed cartridge

round

One complete small-arm cartridge

runovers

Checkering or engraving lines that go beyond the border of the pattern

rupture

A generally circumferential separation in the side wall of a cartridge case—may be complete or partial

S

SAAMI

The acronym for the "Sporting Arms and Ammunition Manufacturers' Institute"

sabot

A carrier in which a sub-caliber projectile is centered to permit firing the projectile in a larger bore firearm

saddle ring

A ring usually attached to the receiver of a firearm designed to be carried by a horseback rider

safe

An incorrect generic term for "safety"

safety

A device on a firearm intended to help provide protection against accidental or unintentional discharge. When the safety is *on*, firing is prevented; when *off*, the firearm may be discharged.

safety, automatic

A safety device on some firearms intended to return to the *on* position when the action is opened

safety, cross bolt

A type of manual firearm safety operated by a lateral force on a button usually located in the trigger guard (also called "push-button safety")

safety, grip
An auxiliary device on the grip of some handguns that is intended to prevent firing until depressed

safety, gun
Precautions taken by firearm users to help provide protection against accidental or unintentional discharge

safety, half-cock
See *half cock*

safety, manual
A safety device on some firearms that must be manually engaged and subsequently disengaged to permit normal firing

safety, sliding
A manual safety mechanism on a firearm that is operated by a longitudinal sliding motion

safety, tang
A type of safety in which the external control component is mounted on the upper receiver tang of a firearm

safety, thumb
A type of manual safety in which the external control component is located for convenient operation by the thumb of the trigger hand

safety, wing
A manual safety found on some bolt-action rifles, usually mounted at the rear of the bolt assembly, which pivots in an arc at right angles to the bore line

schnabel
A German term for a hook shaped knob at the forearm tip of a stock

schuetzen buttplate
An extremely concave metal buttplate with a rearward extension usually at the bottom used mostly on certain types of target rifles for offhand (standing) shooting

screw, strain
A screw that bears against a leaf spring and by its movement in or out will change the tension of the spring

screw, tang
The screw or screws passing through either one or both tangs by which the stock or trigger guard is attached to the receiver or frame

sear
An action component that retains the hammer or striker in the cocked position; when released, it permits firing

seating
The positioning of a primer or bullet in a metallic cartridge case or a wad in a shotshell

seating depth
The longitudinal position of a bullet, primer or wad in a cartridge case

sectional density
The ratio of bullet weight to the square of its diameter, given by the formula: SD=weight/(projectile diameter)^2

selective fire
At term used to describe a firearm that has multiple methods of firing. Typically, this term is applied to firearms that have the option to fire a given number of rounds for each pull of the trigger or to fire continuously until the trigger is released.

selector
1. In a double-barreled gun, a device to allow the shooter to choose which barrel is to be fired by the first pull of the trigger

2. A lever that enables the shooter to choose the type of fire, semi-auto or full-auto, with high or low rate of automatic fire

semi-automatic
Firearm that fires, extracts, ejects and reloads once for each pull and release of the trigger (also called "self-loading" or "autoloading")

serration
Narrow parallel grooves cut into a surface to provide a gripping surface or to break up light reflections

shell
A colloquial term for a cartridge, cartridge case or shotshell

shell catcher
A device for catching fired shells

shell holder
1. A device for holding the head of a cartridge case in a reloading tool

2. A type of turnbolt action in which the bolt head holds the cartridge in the manner of a shell holder (def. 1). The bolt must be completely withdrawn from the receiver to load or unload.

shell, paper
Shotshells which are constructed with a body made from paper tubing

shocking power
A colloquial term used to describe the ability of a projectile to dissipate its kinetic energy effectively in a target

shock wave
The disturbance of air surrounding and behind the bullet caused by a compression of the air column directly in front of the bullet

shoe
1. A metallic adapter fastened to a trigger to widen the surface

2. A metallic insert in the forearm of a side-by-side double barreled

shotgun by which the forearm is attached to the barrels (also called "fore-end iron" or "fore-end plate")

shooting glasses
Eye protection and sight improvement specifically designed for, and which should always be used, when shooting firearms

shot
Spherical pellets used in loading shotshells. Commonly formed from lead but may be made from steel, tungsten, bismuth or other materials.
For definitions and examples of specific shot types not listed below, see Chapter 13, Ammunition.

shot, balled
The fusing together of several pellets in a shotshell load, usually caused by hot propellant gases leaking past the wadding and fusing the shot while the shot is still in the barrel. See *shot, fused.*

shot bridging
A wedging action of shot pellets in a tube causing a stoppage of flow in a shotshell loading operation

shot-collar
A plastic or paper insert surrounding the shot charge in a shotshell to reduce distortion of the shot when passing through the barrel

shot column
The length of the shot load in a shotshell

shot diverter
A device attached to the muzzle of a shotgun to provide oval shot patterns

shot, fused
Two or more shot pellets joined together during the process of manufacturing or during firing

shot, size
A numerical or letter(s) designation indicating the average diameter of a pellet

shot string
The distance between the leading and trailing pellets of a shot charge in flight

shot tower
A tall building in which molten lead alloy is dropped through a colander near the top of the tower into a tank of water at the bottom to produce spherical pellets

shotgun
Smoothbore shoulder firearm designated to fire cartridges containing numerous pellets or a single slug

shotgun, double-barrel
A shotgun with two barrels adjacent to each other in the horizontal plane. If arranged vertically, it is usually termed an "over/under shotgun."

shotshell
A round of ammunition containing multiple pellets for use in a shotgun

shotshell, one-piece
1. A shotshell component having the body and base wad as a single unit with a metallic cup (sometimes called "unibody shell")

2. A complete round of ammunition having the body and base wad as a single unit without a head of a different material

shotshell, plastic
A complete round of ammunition having a plastic body, a basewad that may or may not be a single unit and a metallic head

shoulder
1. v. Act of placing a shotgun or rifle to a shooter's shoulder, in order to properly align the sights and fire at a target

2. n. The sloping portion of a metallic cartridge case that connects the neck and the body of a bottleneck-type cartridge

3. The square or angular step between two diameters on a barrel, pin, stud or other part commonly used in sporting firearms

shoulder arm
Any firearm fitted with a stock and designed to be used while held with both hands and supported by a shoulder

sidearm
A pistol or revolver

side-by-side
A firearm with two barrels arranged adjacently in the horizontal plane. Often used to describe a type of "double-barrel shotgun."

side-hammer
A firearm with the hammer located externally on the side of the frame as contrasted to an internally pivoted hammer

side-lock
A form of firearm construction that has the firing mechanism mounted on detachable plates on the side

side-plate
A removable plate in the frame or receiver to allow access to internal parts or upon which some internal parts are mounted

sight
Any of a variety of devices, mechanical or optical, designed to assist in aiming a firearm. *For definitions and examples of specific sight types not listed below, see Chapter 10, Sights & Optics.*

sight, adjustable
Usually taken to mean a rear sight that is adjustable for windage or elevation or both; however, adjustable front sights are sometimes used on target firearms

sight, aperture
A form of metallic sight, front or rear, containing an aperture or disc with a hole. See *Sight Aperture*. Also called "peep sight" or "receiver sight" (if mounted on receiver).

sight aperture
The hole in the disc of a peep or aperture sight

sight base
That part of a sight that is usually attached to a gun

sight bead
The small cylindrical top portion on some forms of front sights

sight blade
Thin, flat metal post used as the front sight on some firearms

sight cover
Protective metal cover fastened about a sight to guard it from being moved out of adjustment from jars or blows (sometimes called a "sight hood" or "hooded sight")

sight disc
That part of an aperture (peep) sight that contains the hole. May have either a fixed orifice or contain an iris diaphragm to vary its size.

sight elevation
The height to which a rear sight is set to zero-in the firearm for any specific range

sight extension
A device that increases the distance between the sights

sight, front
Any form of sighting device at or near the muzzle of a firearm

sight hood, front
A cover to protect the front sight from damage

sight inserts
Metal or plastic discs with either apertures or posts for use in globe front sights

sight, iron
See *sight, metallic*

sight, laser
Any sight that utilizes a laser mounted in alignment with the bore axis to assist in aiming

sight leaf
The vertical portion of a metallic rear sight containing the notch

sight, metallic
Any sight, front or rear, not containing optical magnifying elements. It may be fixed or adjustable (also called "Iron Sight").

sight, micrometer
A sight with a mechanism for adjusting windage and elevation settings controlled by cylindrically calibrated knobs, usually with detents to control and indicate setting intervals

sight, middle
A second, smaller bead sight near the middle of the barrel or barrels of some shotguns

sight, notch
An open rear sight having either a "V", "U" or square-shaped cut on its upper edge

sight, open
A rear sight having a notch through which the front sight is aligned for aiming

sight, optical
Any sight that utilizes optical elements of glass or plastic to assist in aiming. See *sight, red-dot* and *sight, telescopic.*

sight, Patridge
A rear sight on pistols or revolvers having a flat top with a square notch used with a broad flat-topped front sight. Named after E. E. Patridge.

sight, peep
Common, popular term for an *aperture* rear sight

sight picture
The visual image observed by the shooter when the firearm sights are properly aligned on the point-of-aim

sight radius
The distance between the rear sight and the front sight on a firearm

sight ramp
A front sight that is mounted atop a ramp

sight, rear
Any metallic sight used in conjunction with a metallic front sight located anywhere between the shooter eye and the front sight

sight, receiver
Any rear sight fitted to the receiver of a firearm, but usually refers to an *aperture* or *peep* sight

sight, red-dot
A type of optical sight that projects an illuminated colored dot (usually but not always red) onto the focal plane of the target. Red-dot sights may or may not produce magnification of the target.

sight, telescopic
A sight containing optical elements which magnify or enlarge the target

sight tube
A metal tube that contains the rear sight

sights, target
Sights designed for use in competitive shooting

sighting-in
The procedure of adjusting the sights so as to bring the point of impact to coincide with the point of aim

sighting shot
Shot(s) fired to determine point of impact

silencer
See *suppressor*

six o'clock hold
A sight picture where the top of the sight is tangent to the bottom of the bullseye

sizing
1. The reduction in diameter of a bullet by forcing it through a die of smaller diameter than the bullet

2. The reduction in diameter of a cartridge case by forcing it into a die of smaller diameter than the case

sizing die
A tool used to form a cartridge case or bullet to proper dimensions

sizing, full-length
The operation of reforming a fired cartridge case to approximately its original dimensions

sizing, neck
The operation performed by reloaders to reduce or restore the original neck diameter of a fired cartridge

skeet gun
A shotgun with an open choke specifically designed for skeet shooting or close range hunting

skeet shooting
A shotgun target sport in which shooters move around a semi-circle and fire at clay targets thrown at specified angles and from a high and a low house, each containing a target trap

skeleton buttplate
A metal buttplate forming only a border for the butt

skid marks
Longitudinal rifling marks formed on the bearing surface of bullets as they enter the rifling of the barrel before rotation of the bullet starts

skip-line checkering
See *checkering, French*

sleeve
1. A tube installed in the bore of an old or damaged shotgun barrel

2. A tube surrounding the receiver of a target rifle to improve rigidity

slide
A component attached to, and reciprocating with, the breech block

slide, rebound
A reciprocating device found in some double-action revolvers that moves the hammer into a position in which there is no contact of either hammer and firing pin or firing pin and primer. It can also be used to position a safety device between hammer and firing pin or primer in such revolvers.

slide stop
A component designed to retain the slide in an open position

sling
A strap detachably fastened to a firearm to assist in carrying or to steady it during firing

sling, swivel
A metallic loop to which the sling is attached

slug
A term applied to a single projectile for shotgun shells; also slang term for bullet

slug, Brenneke
A formed rifled slug with a wad assembly attached to its base by a screw for use in shotguns

slug, rifled
Single projectile with spiral grooves and hollow base, intended for use in shotguns

slugging (bore)
A process of determining the interior dimensions of a rifled barrel by measuring a lead ball or plug which has been expanded to fill the bore

small arms
Firearms capable of being carried by a person and fired without mechanical support; usually have a bore diameter of less than one inch

small-bore
In America, any firearm or ammunition of the rimfire type with a lead alloy bullet not over 0.23" in diameter

smokestack jam
A type of jam in which a fired case (or, less frequently, a live cartridge) becomes caught in the ejection port, protruding vertically

smoothbore

A firearm with unrifled bore, typically a shotgun

snap-cap

A protective device to permit dry-firing without damage to the firing-pin

snaphaunce lock

A sidelock action developed in mid-to-late 16th century as an alternative to the wheellock. The ease of manufacture and reliable spark helped this sidelock replace the matchlock and wheellock-type of firearms.

speed of rotation (spin)

The rate of spin of a projectile fired from a rifled barrel

split, shoulder

A longitudinal rupture in the side wall of the shoulder of a bottlenecked cartridge case

sporterize

The act or process of converting a military small arm to a sporting firearm, usually by removing unneeded accessories, and altering the barrel and/or stock

sporting clays

A clay target game designed to simulate field shooting

spread, extreme

The distance between the centers of the two shots which are the farthest apart of a group of shots on a target

spring, recoil

A spring used to close the action in automatic and autoloading firearms (also called "counter recoil spring" or "operating spring")

square butt

The handle of a revolver with a flat or squared end

squib

See *load, squib.*

standard deviation

A quantified statistic that indicates the dispersion of various samples around the mean of a given set of data

stippling

The roughening of wood or metal with a pointed tool. It is normally performed to provide a gripping or decorative surface (also called "matting").

stock

The wood, plastic or metal component to which the metal parts of a firearm are attached to enable the shooter to hold the firearm. In the plural form, refers to the flattened wood, plastic or metal components that attach to the sides of a handgun grip frame. *For definitions and examples of specific stock types not listed below, see Chapter 7, Stocks.*

stock, blank
A rough sawed piece of wood having the approximate external outline of a stock prior to final shaping

stock bolt
A bolt which passes through a buttstock lengthwise to secure it to the receiver or frame

stock cast
The lateral displacement of the centerline of the buttplate (pad) from the centerline of the bore. For a right-handed shooter, when the centerline of the buttplate is to the left of the bore, it is expressed as cast-on and to the right as cast-off. The opposite is true for left-handed shooters.

stock drop
The vertical distance from the line of sight to the comb, Monte Carlo or heel of the stock. It is measured from an extension of a straight line drawn from the top of the front sight through the top surface of the open rear sight adjacent to the notch (or, for a shotgun, from the base of the front bead sight across the highest point on the frame or receiver). The drops for target rifles are usually measured from the centerline of the bore.

stock, free rifle
A target rifle stock used for position shooting matches. The word "free" refers to the fact that there are no restrictions on its configuration or weight.

stock finish
The protective and often ornamental coating applied to most gun stocks, particularly those made of wood. Common wood finishes include oils, lacquer/varnish and polyurethane and other synthetic preservatives. Final appearance ranges from glossy (high luster) to matte.

stock girth
The smallest circumferential dimension at the pistol grip

stock, half
A rifle stock with a fore-end that extends approximately to the midpoint of the barrel

stock(s), handgun
The grip panels fitted to the frame of a pistol or revolver. Most often made of wood, rubber or synthetic material. See *grip*.

stock, laminated
A stock that is made from two or more pieces of wood which have been glued together longitudinally

stock, length of pull
The distance from the center of the trigger to the center of the rear buttplate or recoil pad

stock, Mannlicher
A full-length rifle stock that extends from the butt to the muzzle

stock, Monte Carlo
A stock with a raised comb to bring the eye in alignment with the sight

stock, offset
A curved buttstock for use by a shooter who wishes to use the left eye when shooting right handed or vice versa (also known as a "cross-over stock")

stock, pistol grip
A stock or buttstock having a downward extension behind the trigger guard somewhat resembling the grip of a pistol. Often found on target rifles.

stock pitch
The angle at which the buttplate or recoil pad slopes in relation to the bore axis. For method of measuring, see *Chapter 7, Stocks.*

stock screw
A screw used for attaching the stock to the receiver or frame of a firearm. More than one may be used per firearm.

stock, semi-finished
The term for a stock which has been rough shaped and partially or completely inletted

stock, semi-inletted
A firearm stock that has been machine inletted and requires additional hand fitting to achieve proper fit (also called "rough inletted")

stock, small of the
That portion of the stock between the rear of the action and the comb, which has the smallest circumference

stock, straight
1. A stock with no pistol grip

2. A stock with less than the normal amount of drop. See *Chapter 7, Stocks*

stock, thumbhole
Any stock having a contoured hole in the grip area to accommodate the thumb of the trigger hand

stock, Whelan
A rifle stock developed by Colonel Townsend Whelan that features a forward sloping comb and cheekpiece

stop, hand
An attachment beneath the fore-end or forearm of a target rifle to restrict the forward movement of the hand. Often also used to attach a target sling.

stoppage
> This term is used when a firearm stops firing due to a malfunction of either the gun mechanism or ammunition. This term is normally used in connection with semi-automatic or full-automatic firearms. Also called "jam."

stove-piping
> A failure to eject where the fired case is caught in the ejection port by the forward motion of the bolt. The case protruding upward out of the ejection port is said to resemble an old fashioned stove pipe.

straight-pull
> A bolt-action firearm in which the bolt need not be rotated to open or close the action but is reciprocated by a straight backward and forward motion of the bolt handle

strap, back
> The exposed metal strip at the rear of a pistol or revolver grip

strap, front
> The exposed metal strip at the front of a pistol or revolver grip

strap, top
> That portion of a revolver frame which passes over the cylinder

striker
> A rod-like firing pin or a separate component that impinges on the firing pin and strikes the primer to fire a cartridge

strip
> To disassemble a firearm in order to clean, repair or transport it. *Field stripping* is simple disassembling for cleaning; *detail stripping* is a complete disassembly of the firearm into its components.

stripping
> 1. The act of disassembling a firearm
>
> 2. The act of transferring cartridges from a loading ("stripper") clip to the magazine
>
> 3. Failure of a bullet to engage the rifling properly

subcaliber
> An adaptation to a firearm to enable the firing of smaller or lower powered ammunition for which it was originally intended

subcaliber tube
> A tube placed in the bore of a firearm to enable the firing of smaller or lower-powered ammunition

submachine gun
> A full-automatic firearm that utilizes ammunition usually associated with handguns

suppressor
A device attached to the muzzle of a firearm to reduce the noise of discharge. Sometimes incorrectly called a "silencer." It was heavily regulated under the 1934 National Firearms Act.

swivel, quick detachable
A two-part sling swivel which has a stud that is attached to the stock or barrel and a bow portion which is mounted on a spring plunger arrangement. The plunger passes through a hole in the stud for attachment of the bow to the firearm. They allow for quick mounting and dismounting of a sling from a firearm.

T

take down
Describing a type of firearm designed for ease of disassembly and transportation

tang
A rearward projecting tongue on a receiver or frame to which the buttstock is attached. Some parts of the operating mechanism of a firearm may also pass through the tang. A gun may have either or both an upper and lower tang.

target, clay
A circular, domed, frangible disc used as an aerial target for shotgun shooting games. Originally formed out of clay, modern clay targets are generally made from a formulation of pitch and limestone. Dimensions and weights are regulated by skeet and trap shooters' associations (also called "clay bird" or "clay pigeon").

tarage table
A tabulation of values relating the compressed length of a crusher cylinder to the chamber pressure

targeting
The act of shooting a firearm to align sights. See *sighting in.*

target rifle
Any rifle designed and equipped for match or target shooting

target shooting
The act of shooting at inanimate objects. Formal target shooting is done at specified distances at targets designated for scoring. Informal target shooting is done at varying distances at impromptu targets for practice. See *plinking.*

T-bolt
A patented reciprocation and locking system for use on a rimfire rifle. Sometimes used to describe *straight-pull* bolt-action rifles with a horizontally protruding straight bolt handle.

telescopic sight
A type of optical sight in which the optical elements magnify the apparent target size

temperature of ignition
The lowest temperature to which the surface of material must be raised for the combustion of the material to become self-sustaining

tenon
1. The projecting part of a stock that fits into the receiver or frame

2. With ammunition, that portion of a rimfire bullet which fits into the cartridge case, from bullet base to bottom of band (also called "heel")

throat
See *leade*.

thumbpiece (cylinder release)
A latch used on some revolvers to release the cylinder. Sometimes called a "thumb latch."

thumb rest
A ledge in the grip area of a rifle or handgun on which to rest the thumb of the trigger hand

time of flight
The total elapsed time that a projectile requires to travel a specific distance from the muzzle

toe
The bottom (lower) end of a buttplate and adjacent portion of the stock on a shoulder firearm

tong tool
An unmounted, portable handloading tool using a "nutcracker" or plier action for handloading center-fire cartridges (also called "nutcracker tool")

top-break
The term used for any firearm on which the barrel or barrels are allowed to tip down at the muzzle (up at the breech) exposing the chamber or chambers for loading or unloading

top extension
A projection which extends behind the breech end of the barrels on some break-action firearms. When the gun is closed, it fits into a corresponding recess slot in the frame and is used for locking purposes.

trajectory
The curved path of a projectile from muzzle to target

trajectory, flat
A relative term for minimal arching in the flight of a projectile. Generally, the faster the speed of the projectile, the flatter its trajectory.

trajectory, mid-range
> The distance, measured in inches, that a projectile travels above the line of sight at a specific point in the trajectory that is half the distance between the firearm and a target

trajectory table
> A computed table describing the downrange trajectory of a projectile or of shotshell pellets, buckshot or rifled slugs

transfer bar
> A piece of metal that transfers energy from one moving part, usually a falling hammer, to an object at rest, usually a firing pin

trap
> A clay target throwing device. Traps are generally of two types: *hand-operated traps* and *mechanically operated traps.*

trap-door action
> An action that incorporates a top-hinged breechblock that pivots up and forward to open. Locking occurs by a cam located at the rear of the breechblock that fits into a mating recess when the action is closed

trap-door buttplate
> A type of buttplate with a hinged closure plate in the butt-end of a firearm. Opening of the trap door exposes a recess in the stock which can be used for storage.

trapshooting
> A shotgun target sport in which clay targets are thrown away from the shooters by a reciprocating *trap* located forward of the firing line

trigger
> That part of a firearm's mechanism which is movable by the finger to cause the firearm to discharge. *For definitions and examples of specific trigger types not listed below, see Chapter 9, Triggers.*

trigger, adjustable
> Any trigger mechanism that has features (such as weight, overtravel, etc.) that can be adjusted

trigger bar
> A connecting piece between the trigger and the sear

trigger creep
> The sensible movement of the trigger after pretravel or slack has been taken up, but before sear release. Creep refers specifically to the movement of the sear on the striker, firing pin or hammer.

trigger, crisp
> A trigger that releases without sensible movement

trigger, double
> A term used for firearms having two barrels and a separate trigger for the discharge of each. This term does not apply to firearms with double-set triggers

trigger, two-stage (double pull)
A trigger which has two distinctive pull characteristics. The first or take-up stage is usually long and light in pull force; the second stage having a short but distinct increase in the pull force required to discharge the firearm.

trigger, double-set
An arrangement of two triggers in which the actuation of one trigger presets the second resulting in a lighter pull of the latter

trigger guard
A rigid loop that partially surrounds the trigger to reduce the possibility of accidental discharge

trigger, hair
A slang term for a trigger requiring very low force to actuate. Sometimes used to describe the light pull of a second trigger in a double-set trigger mechanism

trigger, hinged
A trigger that is hinged to fold forward

trigger, inertia
The term used for firearms having two barrels and a single trigger wherein the inertia resulting from the recoil forces of firing one barrel causes the trigger sear to switch to the unfired barrel. A second pull of the trigger can then fire the second barrel.

trigger lock
1. An accessory for blocking unauthorized trigger movement during gun storage. Must never be applied to a loaded firearm.

2. A form of firearm safety blocking trigger movement

trigger mechanism
Those parts which, when pressure is applied to the trigger, release the hammer or striker

trigger, non-selective single
A single trigger on double-barrel guns which fires the barrels in a fixed sequence

trigger pull
The average force which must be applied to the trigger of a firearm to cause sear or hammer release with the force applied approximately parallel to the bore line

trigger pull scale
A device for measuring trigger release force

trigger, release
An unconventional mechanism generally found only in some trap shotguns in which the firearm is fired by the release of, rather than the pull of, the trigger

trigger, selective single
An arrangement on double-barrel firearms having a single trigger which enables the shooter to choose the barrel he wishes to fire first. The mechanism will then subsequently switch to the unfired barrel, which a second pull of the trigger can then fire.

trigger, set
Either a single or double trigger arrangement on which the required trigger pull force can be made very light by means of a "setting" mechanism. May be either a *double-set trigger* or *single-set trigger*.

trigger, sheath
A trigger which has a minimum projection from the action and is not usually surrounded by a trigger guard (also called "spur trigger")

trigger shoe
An accessory which is attached to the trigger to give a much larger trigger-finger bearing surface

trigger, single
A trigger mechanism for multiple barrel firearms wherein repeated pulls of one trigger fires the barrels successively

trigger, single-stage
1. A trigger mechanism in which the trigger travel is relatively short and there is no significant sensible change in pull force from the beginning of movement up to the point of firing
2. A trigger which releases with a single pull

trigger squeeze
A gradual increase of pressure on a trigger until it releases

trigger stop
1. A device to prevent certain firearms from being fired until the finger lever is closed
2. A device to prevent over-travel of the trigger

trigger, stud
A button-type trigger, the end of which is pressed to fire the firearm

trigger take-up
See *pre-travel*

trigger, target
1. A trigger mechanism which provides for adjustment of such characteristics as pull force, travel or overtravel
2. A trigger which provides a large bearing surface for the trigger finger
3. A relatively light, crisp trigger designed to assist in accurate shooting

trigger, twin-single
A double trigger arrangement used on some double-barrel firearms, wherein one or both triggers will, with each pull, fire the barrels sequentially. They are non-selective.

triggers, single-double

A type of trigger mechanism found on some double-barrel or over-under shotguns consisting of two triggers. The front trigger functions as a conventional non-selective single trigger, while the rear trigger will fire only the barrel with the tighter choke.

try gun

A shoulder firearm having a stock that is fully adjustable for length of pull; drop at comb, Monte Carlo and heel; pitch and cast. Used for fitting of custom firearms to a specific shooter's physical characteristics.

tube

1. The cylindrical body of a shotshell

2. Colloquial term for a shotgun barrel

3. A barrel insert to allow firing of a smaller-gauge shotshell

tumbling

1. The end-over-end rotation of an unstable projectile in flight. Sometimes referred to as "bullet tipping" or "keyholing."

2. The act of case preparation in handloading that involves a case(s) being turned against a cleaning or polishing media.

turnbolt

A bolt assembly that incorporates a bolt head that works in conjunction with the bolt body or bolt carrier. The bolt head usually consists of multiple locking lugs that must first unlock before the bolt body can move rearward.

twist

The distance required for one complete turn of rifling usually expressed as a ratio, e.g., 1 in 10 inches

twist, gain

Barrel rifling in which the rate of twist is faster at the muzzle than at the chamber end. Also called progressive rifling.

U

underbolt

The moveable lock of some break-open firearms. It normally engages the barrel lug (underlug) and is actuated by the top lever.

underlug, underlugs

The downward-projecting lug or lugs at the breech end of a break-open firearm used for locking the action and positioning the barrel in the frame (also called "lumps")

V

velocity

The speed of a projectile at a given point along its trajectory

velocity, instrumental
> The velocity of a projectile, or a shot charge, that is recorded by suitable instrumentation located a predetermined distance from the muzzle of a test barrel or a firearm

velocity, remaining
> Velocity that a projectile retains at any specific location along its trajectory path

velocity, standard
> An industry term to denote rimfire ammunition loaded to a velocity level below that of high velocity rimfire ammunition

velocity, striking
> The velocity of a projectile at the point of impact

velocity, terminal
> The remaining velocity of a projectile at maximum range

vent, gas
> 1. Any hole in the action of a firearm to allow the escape of gases from the breech
>
> 2 A hole in the gas cylinder of a firearm to bleed off gas
>
> 3. In ammunition, the *flash hole*
>
> 4. See *barrel vent*

vierling
> A rare four-barreled gun that possesses two shotgun barrels and two rifle barrels originating in Germany and Austria

W

wad, base
> A cylindrical component that is assembled into the head end of a shotshell.

wad, card
> A thin card-like disc placed over a shot load or powder. See also *wad, overpowder.*

wad column
> The wads between propellant and shot pellets in a specific shotshell

wad, cup
> A powder and shot separator of a shallow cup design which when loaded with lips down acts to help seal powder gases and so protect the rear of the shot column

wad, filler
> Discs of various shapes and thicknesses used to adjust the volume of the contents of a shotshell

wad, integral base
A misnomer. See *shotshell, one-piece.*

wad, nitro
An unlubricated, overpowder wad made of cardboard or felt. It is used with smokeless powder (also called "nitro card wad").

wad, overpowder
Various designs of separators, made of various materials and used between the propellant powder and the shot pellets

wad pressure
The force applied to a wad column as it is seated firmly against the propellant

wad, shot protector
Various designs of shot cups made of plastic and designed to reduce pellet deformation during barrel travel

wad, top
The closure disc over the top of the shot column held in place by a rolled crimp

wadcutter
A cylindrical, sharp-shouldered bullet designed to cut a round hole in a paper target for score in competition

water table
The flat portion of the frame on break-open firearms which extends forward from and is approximately at right angles to the standing breech face. It is the surface on which the barrel flats rest when the gun is closed.

weapon
An instrument used in combat. The term is never used when referring to target or sporting firearms.

web
1. The solid portion of a brass center-fire cartridge case between the inside of the case at the head and the bottom of the primer pocket

2. The smallest dimension of a smokeless powder kernel

wheelgun
A slang term used to describe a revolver

wheellock
A muzzleloading firearm's lock that utilizes a wheel with serrated edges. When cocked, the wheel is wound against a spring. When the lock is released, the wheel spins against a block of iron pyrite creating a shower of sparks into the pan used to ignite the priming powder in the pan.

windage adjustment
The transverse movement of a sight to compensate for the horizontal displacement of a bullet or bullets from the aiming point

windage knob
  The knob on some iron and telescopic sights that is turned in either direction to adjust the horizontal setting of the notch, aperture or reticle of the sight

wingshooting
  A slang term applying to all forms of bird hunting or shotgun shooting at flying clay targets

witness mark
  A line on each of two mating parts used to indicate proper alignment. Also known as an "index mark"

wrist
  See *stock*

Wundhammer swell
  A bulge or swelling in the pistol grip of a stock to fit the palm of the trigger hand. Named after inventor Louis Wundhammer

X

X-ring
  A circle inside the highest scoring ring on a target, used to break ties in shooting matches. The shooter with the most X-ring hits wins.

Y

yaw
  The angle between the longitudinal axis of a projectile and a line tangent to the trajectory through the center of gravity

yoke
  See *crane*

Z

zero, zero-in
  See *sighting-in*

ABBREVIATIONS

automatic Colt pistol	ACP
armor-piercing	AP
boattail	BT
Bureau of Alcohol, Tobacco, Firearms & Explosives	BATFE
copper units of pressure	CUP
double-action	DA
double-action-only	DAO
Federal Firearms License	FFL
full-metal-case	FMC
full-metal-jacket	FMJ
foot-pounds	ft.-lbs.
feet per second	f.p.s.
gauge	ga.
grain	gr.
gram	gm.
hollow-point	HP
high velocity	HV
improved cylinder (choke)	Imp Cyl
improved modified (choke)	Imp Mod
improved military rifle powder	IMR
jacketed hollow-point	JHP
jacketed soft-point	JSP
long rifle (type of rimfire cartridge)	LR
lead units of pressure	LUP
model or mark	M, MK, Mk
magnum	Mag.
muzzle energy	ME
millimeters	mm
minute of angle	m.o.a., MOA
modified (choke)	Mod

mid-range trajectory	MRT
muzzle velocity	MV
North Atlantic Treaty Organization	NATO
National Rifle Association	NRA
National Reloading Manufacturers Association	NRMA
National Shooting Sports Foundation	NSSF
over-under	o/u
pounds per square inch	p.s.i., lb/in^2
pointed soft point	PSP
rimfire	RF
round-nose	RN
round-nose lead	RNL
semi-wadcutter	SWC
single-action	SA
Sporting Arms and Ammunition Manufacturers' Institute	SAAMI
soft point	SP
muzzle velocity	MV
wadcutter	WC

Chapter 19
SOURCES

Manufacturers and Importers of Firearms

A-Square
205 Fairview Ave.
Jeffersonville, IN 47130
812-283-0577
www.a-squarecompany.com

Accu-Tek
4510 Carter Ct.
Chino, CA 91710
909-627-2404
www.accu-tekfirearms.com

ADCO Sales
4 Draper St.
Woburn, MA 01801
800-775-3687
www.adcosales.com

Alexander Arms
U.S. Army Radford Arsenal
P.O. Box 1
Radford, VA 24141
540-639-8356
www.alexanderarms.com

American Derringer
127 N. Lacy Dr.
Waco, TX 76705
254-799-9111
www.amderringer.com

J.G. Anschutz
Daimlerstrasse 12
D-89079 Ulm
GERMANY
www.anschutz-sporters.com

AR-7 Customer Accessories
998 N. Colony Rd.
Meriden, CT 06450
203-238-2200
www.ar-7.com

Ares Defense Systems
P.O. Box 10667
Blacksburg, VA 24062
540-639-8633
www.aresdefense.com

ArmaLite
745 S. Hanford St.
Geneseo, IL 61254
800-336-0184
www.armalite.com

Armi Chiappa
Via Milano, 2
25020 Azzano Mella
Brescia, ITALY
www.armisport.com

Arms Corporation of the Philippines
Armscor Ave., Fortune
Marakina City 1800
PHILIPPINES
www.armscor.com.ph

Armscorp USA
4424 John Ave.
Baltimore, MD 21227
301-775-8134
www.armscorpusa.com

Arnold Arms Co.
P.O. Box 1011
Arlington, WA 98223
800-371-1011

Armory USA & Global Trades
7311 Galveston Rd., Ste. 260
Houston, TX 77034
713-944-3351
www.globaltrades.com

Ata AV Tufekleri ve Tic
Imes Sanayi Sitesi B-blok 201
Sok N. 8 Yukan Dudullu
TR-34788 Umraniye/Istanbul
TURKEY
www.ataarms.com

Atlantic Research Marketing Systems
230 W. Center St.
West Bridgewater, MA 02379
508-584-7816
www.armsmounts.com

Auto-Ordnance Corporation (Thompson)
P.O. Box 220
Blauvelt, NY 10913
845-652-8535
www.tommygun.com

AyA, Aguirre y Aranzabal
Avda. Otaola 25-3 Planta
Eibar 20600
SPAIN
www.aya-fineguns.com

BWE Firearms
407-592-3975
www.bwefirearms.com

Ballard Rifle and Cartridge
113 W. Yellowstone
Cody, WY 82414
866-997-4353
www.ballardrifles.com

Bansner's Ultimate Rifle
P.O. Box 839
Adamstown, PA 19501
717-484-2370
www.bansnersrifle.com

Barrett Firearms
P.O. Box 1077
Murfeesboro, TN 37133
615-896-2938
www.barrettrifles.com

Breda Meccanica Bresciana
Via Lunga, 2
25126 Brescia
ITALY
www.bredafucili.com

Benelli USA
17603 Indian Head Hwy.
Accokeek, MD 20607
301-283-6981
www.benelliusa.com

Beretta
Via Pietro Beretta, 18
25063 Gardone Val Trompia
Brescia, ITALY

17601 Beretta Dr.
Accokeek, MD 20607
301-283-0189
www.berettausa.com

Bernardelli Vincenzo
Via Grand, 10
25030 Torbole Casaglia
Brescia, ITALY
www.bernardelli.com

Bersa
Magallanes 775
(B1704FLC) Ramos Mijfa
Prov. de Buenos
ARGENTINA
www.bersa-sa.com.ar

Bill Hanus Birdguns
P.O. Box 533
Newport, OR 97365
541-265-7433
www.billhanusbirdguns.com

Blaser Jagdwaffen
Ziegelstradel im Allgau
D-88316 Isny
GERMANY
www.blaser.de

Bobcat Weapons
P.O. Box 21017
Mesa, AZ 85277
480-832-0844
www.bobcatweapons.com

Bond Arms
P.O. Box 1296
Granbury, TX 76048
817-573-4445
www.bondarms.com

Boss & Co.
16 Mount St.
London W1K 2RH
ENGLAND
www.bossguns.com

Bowen Classic Arms
P. O. Box 67
Louisville, TN 37777
865-984-3583
www.bowenclassicarms.com

BrazTech International
16175 NW 49th Ave.
Miami, FL 33014
305-474-0401
www.rossiusa.com

Briley Manufacturing
1230 Lumpkin Rd.
Houston, TX 77043
800-331-5718
www.briley.com

Browning Arms
One Browning Pl.
Morgan, UT 84050
800-333-3288
www.browning.com

BSA Imports
3911 SW 47th Ave. Ste. 914
Ft. Lauderdale, FL 33314
954-581-5822
www.bsaoptics.com

BUL Transmack
Rival St.
Tel-Aviv 67778
ISRAEL
www.bultransmark.com

Bushmaster Firearms
999 Roosevelt Trail
P.O. Box 1479
Windham, ME 04062
207-892-8068
www.bushmaster.com

Cabela's
1 Cabela Dr.
Sidney, NE 69160
800-237-4444
www.cabelas.com

Calico Light Weapon Systems
1498 Greg St.
Sparks, NV 89431
775-358-6000
www.calicolightweaponsystems.com

Century Arms
236 Bryce Blvd.
Georgia, VT 0545
802-524-5268
www.centuryarms.com

Century International Arms
430 S. Congress Ave., Ste. 1
Delray Beach, FL 33445
800-527-1252
www.centuryarms.com

Caesar Guerini USA
700 Lake St.
Cambridge, MD 21613
410-901-1131
www.gueriniusa.com

Ceska Zbrojovka (CZ)
Svatopluka Cecha 1283
688 27 Uhersky Brod
CZECH REPUBLIC

P.O. Box 171071
Kansas City, KS 66117
800-955-4486
www.cz-usa.com

Champlin
P.O. Box 3191
Enid, OK 73702
580-237-7388
www.champlinarms.com

Chapuis Armes
Z.1 La Gravoux
F-42380 St. Bonnet le Chateau
FRANCE
www.chapuis-armes.com

Charles Daly
P.O. Box 6625
Harrisburg, PA 17112
866-325-9486
www.charlesdaly.com

Charter Arms
273 Canal St.
Shelton, CT 06484
203-922-1652
www.charterfirearms.com

CheyTac Associates
363 Sunset Dr.
Arco, ID 83213
208-527-8614
www.cheytac.com

Christensen Arms
192 E. 100 N.
Fayette, UT 84630
435-528-7999
www.christensenarms.com

Cimarron Firearms
P.O. Box 906
Fredericksburg, TX 78624
830-997-9090
www.cimarronfirearms.com

Cobb Manufacturing
P.O. Box 88
Dallas, GA 30132
770-505-3080
www.cobb50.com

Cobra Enterprises of Utah
1960 S. Milestone Dr., Ste. F
Salt Lake City, UT 84104
801-908-8300
www.cobrapistols.com

Colt's Manufacturing
P.O. Box 1868
Hartford, CT 06144
860-236-6311
www.coltsmfg.com

Connecticut Shotgun Manufacturing
P.O. Box 1692
New Britain, CT 06053
860-225-6581
www.connecticutshotgun.com

Connecticut Valley Arms (CVA)
Blackpowder Products Inc.
5988 Peachtree Corners E.
Norcross, GA 30071
770-449-4687
www.cva.com

Cooper Arms of Montana
P.O. Box 114
Stevensville, MT 59870
406-777-0373
www.cooperfirearms.com

Cosmi Americo & Figlio
Via Flaminia, 307
60020 Torrette
Ancona, ITALY
www.cosmi.net

DSA
P.O. Box 370
Barrington, IL 60011
847-277-7258
www.dsarms.com

DPMS/Panther Arms
3312 12th St. SE.
St. Cloud, MN 56304
800-578-3767
www.dpmsinc.com

Dakota Arms
1310 Industry Rd.
Sturgis, SD 57785
605-347-4686
www.dakotaarms.com

Dan Wesson
5169 Hwy. 12 S.
Norwich, NY 13815
607-336-1174
www.danwessonarms.com

Daudsons Armoury
Kohat Road
Peshawar 25210
PAKISTAN
www.daudsons.org

Detonics USA
115 Enterprise Dr. , Ste. B
Pendergrass, GA 30567
866-759-1169
www.detonicsusa.com

Dixie Gun Works
P.O. Box 130
Union City, TN 38281
800-238-6785
www.dixiegunworks.com

Doublestar
P.O. Box 430
Winchester, KY 40391
859-745-1757
www.star15.com

Downsizer
P.O. Box 710316
Santee, CA 92072
619-448-5510
www.downsizer.com

Dumoulin Herstal
Rue du Tige 13
B-4040 Herstal
BELGIUM
www.dumoulin-herstal.com

EGE Silah Sanayi Ticaret
Ulucak Beldest, Kirovasi Mevkii
TR-Kemalpasa/Izmir
TURKEY
www.egesulah.com

EMF
1900 E. Warner Ave., Ste. 1-D
Santa Ana, CA 92705
949-261-6611
www.emf-company.com

Eagle Firearms
10107 W. 37th Pl.
Wheat Ridge, CO 80033
303-432-2255
www.eaglefirearms.net

Eagle Imports
1750 Brielle Ave., Unit B-1
Wanamassa, NJ 07712
732-493-0333
www.bersa-llama.com

Ed Brown
P.O. Box 492
Perry, MO 63462
573-565-3261
www.edbrown.com

Effebi snc di F. Beretta
Via Rossa, 4
25060 Concesio
Brescia, ITALY
www.effebi.org

Entreprise Arms
5321 Irwindale Ave.
Irwindale, CA 91706
626-962-8712
www.entreprise.com

Euroarms of America
P.O. Box 3277
Winchester, VA 22601
540-662-1863
www.euroarms.net

European American Armory
P.O. Box 560746
Rockledge, FL 32956
321-639-4842
www.eaacorp.com

Excel Industries
4510 Carter Ct.
Chino, CA 91710
909-627-2404
www.excelarms.com

Essex Arms
P.O. Box 959
Hardwick, VT 05843
802-472-3215
www.essexarms.com

Fabbrica Armi Isidoro Rizzini (FAIR)
Via Gitti, 41
25060 Marcheno
Brescia, ITALY
www.fair.it

F.A.P. Pietta
Via Maldolossa, 102
25064 Gussago
Brescia, ITALY
www.pietta.it

Fabarm (Lion)
Via Averolda, 31
25039 Travagliato
Brescia, ITALY
www.fabarm.com

Fabrique Nationale USA
P.O. Box 697
McLean, VA 22101
703-288-1292
www.fnhusa.com

Falco
Via Gitti, 60
25060 Marcheno
Brescia, ITALY
www.falcoarms.com

Fanzoj Jagdwaffen
Griesgasse 1
9170 Ferlach
AUSTRIA
www.fanzoj.com

Fausti Stefano
Via Martiri dell' Indipendenza, 70
25060 Marcheno V.T.
Brescia, ITALY
www.faustistefanoarms.com

Feather USA
600 Oak Ave.
P.O. Box 247
Eaton, CO 80615
970-206-1948
www.featherusa.com

Feinwerkbau
Neckarstrasse 43
D-78727 Oberndorf a. N
GERMANY
www.feinwerkbau.com

FERLIB di Tanfoglio Ivano
Via Parte, 33
25060 Marcheno
Brescia, ITALY
www.ferlib.com

Franchi USA
17063 Indian Head Highway
Accokeek, MD 20607
301-283-6981
www.franchiusa.com

Freedom Arms
314 Highway 239
Freedom, WY 83120
307-883-2468

Fulton Armory
8725 Bollman Pl. #1
Savage, MD 20763
301-490-9485
www.fulton-armory.com

Gamba-Societa Armi Bresciane
Via Artigiani, 91-93
25063 Gardone V.T.
Brescia, ITALY
www.renatogamba.it

Glock
Nelkengasse 3, POB 9
A-2232 Wien
AUSTRIA

6000 Highlands Pkwy.
Smyrna, GA 30082
770-432-1202
www.glock.com

Griffin & Howe
33 Claremont Rd.
Bernardsville, NJ 07924
908-766-2287
www.griffinhowe.com

Grulla Armas
13 Avda. Otaola
E-20600 Eibar
SPAIN
www.grullaarmas.com

GSI
P.O. Box 129
Trussville, AL 35173
205-655-8299
www.gsifirearms.com

H-S Precision
1301 Turbine Dr.
Rapid City, SD 57703
605-341-3006
www.hsprecision.com

H&R 1871
60 Industrial Rowe
Gardner, MA 01440
978-630-8220
www.hr1871.com

Hatsan Arms
TURKEY
www.hatsan.com.tr

Harris Gunworks
11240 Cave Creek Rd., Ste. 104
Phoenix, AZ 85020
602-582-9627
www.harrisgunworks.com

Hartford Armory
100-B Main St.
Collinsville, CT 06019
860-693-8932
www.hartfordarmory.com

Heckler & Koch
21480 Pacific Blvd.
Sterling, VA 20166
703-450-1900
www.hk-usa.com

Henry Repeating Arms
110 8th St.
Brooklyn, NY 11215
718-499-5600
www.henryrepeating.com

Heritage Manufacturing
4600 NW. 135th St.
Opa Locka, FL 33054
305-685-5966
www.heritagemfg.com

Heym Waffenfabrik AG
Am Aschenbach 2
98646 Gleichamberg
GERMANY
www.heym-waffenfabrik.de

Hi-Point Firearms
8611-A N. Dixie Dr.
Dayton, OH 45414
877-425-4867
www.hi-pointfirearms.com

High Standard Mfg.
5200 Mitchelldale, Ste. E-17
Houston, TX 77092
713-462-4200
www.highstandard.com

Holland & Holland
31-33 Bruton St.
London W1J 6HH
ENGLAND
www.hollandandholland.com
10 E. 40th St., Ste. 1910
New York, NY 10016
212-752-7755

Howa Machinery
Sukaguichi, Shinkawa-cho
Nishikasugai-gun, Aichi 452
JAPAN
www.howa.co.jp

Huglu
Tufekleri
Antalya Cad. No. 58
TR-42710 Huglu
TURKEY
www.huglu.com.tr

1247 Rand Rd.
Des Plaines, IL 60016
847-768-1000
www.armsco.net

IAR
33171 Camino Capistrano
San Juan Capistrano, CA 92675
877-722-1873
www.iar-arms.com

Import Sports
1750 Brielle Ave., Unit B-1
Wanamassa, NJ 07712
732-493-0333
www.bersa-llama.com

Inter Ordnance
3305 Westwood Industrial Dr.
Monroe, NC 28110
704-225-8843
www.interordnance.com

Interstate Arms
6 Dunham Rd.
Billerica, MA 01821
800-243-3006
www.interstatearms.com

NRA FIREARMS SOURCEBOOK

Intrac Arms International
5005 Chapman Hwy.
Knoxville, TN 37920
865-573-0065
www.intracarms.com

Investarm
Via Zanardelli, 210
25060 Marcheno
Brescia, ITALY
www.investarm.com

Iver Johnson Arms Inc.
1840 Baldwin St., Ste. 7
Rockledge, FL 32955
321-636-3377

Izhevsky Mekhanichesky Zavod (Baikal)
3 Derjabin Pr., Izhevsk
RUS-426006 Udmurt Republic
RUSSIA
www.baikalinc.ru

Izhmash Concern Russia (Saiga)
3 Proezd. Deryabin St.
RUS-426006 Ishevsk
RUSSIA
www.izhmash.ru

Jarrett Rifles
383 Brown Road
Jackson, SC 29831
803-471-3616
www.jarrettrifles.com

John Rigby & Co.
500 Linne Road, Ste. D
Paso Robles, CA 93446
805-227-4236
www.johnrigbyandco.com

Jonathan Arthur Ciener
8700 Commerce St.
Cape Canaveral, FL 32920
321-868-2200
www.22lrcpnversions.com

KBI
P.O. Box 6625
Harrisburg, PA 17112
866-325-9486
www.charlesdaly.com

KBP Instrument Design Bureau
Shcheglovskaya Zaseka St.
RUS-300001 Tula
RUSSIA
www.home.tula.net/tularms

KDF Inc.
2485 Hwy. 46 N.
Seguin, TX 78155
800-533-4867

Kahr Arms
130 Goddard Memorial Dr.
Worcester, MA 01603
508-795-3919
www.kahr.com

Kel-Tec
1475 Cox Rd.
Cocoa, FL 32926
800-515-9983
www.kel-tec.com

Kemen Armas
Ermuarenbide 14 Apartado no. 6
E-20870 Eigoibar (Guip.)
SPAIN
www.sport-kemen.com

Khan Shotguns
Yali Mh, Maresal Fevzi
Cakmak Cd. M. Caglar Apt. No. 11/1
Maltepe/Istanbul
TURKEY
www.khanshotguns.com

Kimber
One Lawton St.
Yonkers, NY 10705
800-880-2418
www.kimberamerica.com

Knight's Manufacturing
701 Columbia Blvd.
Titusville, FL 32780
321-607-9900
www.knightarmco.com

Knight Rifles
21852 Hwy. J46
Centerville, IA 52544
641-856-2626
www.knightrifles.com

Kolar
1925 Roosevelt Ave.
Racine, WI 53406
262-554-0800
www.kolararms.com

Korth Germany
Robert Dosch Strasse 11
Ratzeburg 23909
GERMANY
www.korthwaffen.com

Kreigeskorte Handels (Krico)
Nurnberger Strasse 6
D-90602 Pyrbaum
GERMANY
www.krico.de

Kreighoff
P.O. Box 26 10
D-89016 Ulm
GERMANY
www.kreighoff.de

Kroko
Hybesova 46
CZ-60200 Brno
CZECH REPUBLIC
www.korabrno.cz

KY Imports
P.O. Box 22446
Louisville, KY 40252
502-244-4400
www.kyimports.com

Lanber Armas
3 Zubiaurre
E-48250 Zaldibar-Vizcaya
SPAIN
www.lanber.net

L.A.R. Manufacturing
4133 West Farm Rd.
West Jordan, UT 84088
801-280-3505
www.largrizzly.com

Laurona Armas Eibar
25 Avda. Otaola
E-20600 Eibar (Guip.)
SPAIN
www.laurona.com

Lazzeroni Arms
P.O. Box 26696
Tucson, AZ 85726
888-492-7247
www.lazzeroni.com

Leitner-Wise Rifle
1033 N. Fairfax St., Ste. 110
Alexandria, VA 22314
703-751-8500
www.leitner-wise.com

Lebeau-Courally
386 Rue Saint Gilles
B-4000 Liege
BELGIUM
www.lebeau-courally.com

Legacy Sports International
4750 Longley Ln., Ste. 208
Reno, NV 89502
703-548-4837
www.leagacysports.com

Les Baer Custom
29601 34th Ave. N.
Hillsdale, IL 61257
309-658-2716
www.lesbaer.com

Ljutic Industries
732 N. 16th Ave. Ste. 22
Yakima, WA 98902
509-248-0476
www.ljutivgun.com

Llama Gabilondo Y Cia.
Portal De Gamarra 50 Vitoria Alava
E-01080 Victoria
SPAIN

Mag-na-port International
41302 Executive Dr.
Harrison Township, MI 48045-1306
586-469-6727
www.magnaport.com

Magnum Research
7110 University Ave. NE.
Minneapolis, MN 55432
800-772-6168
www.magnumresearch.com

Magtech Ammunition
6845 20th Ave. S., Ste. 120
Centerville, MN 55038
800-466-7191
www.magtechammunition.com

Manu Arm
43 Ave. de la Liberation
F-42340 Veauche
FRANCE
www.manuarm.fr

Marlin Firearms
100 Kenna Dr., P.O. Box 248
North Haven, CT 06473
203-239-5621
www.marlinfirearms.com

Marocchi Armi
C.D. Europe srl
Via Galilei, 6
25068 Sarezzo
ITALY
www.marocchiarms.com

Matsan A.S.
Halitpasa cad. No.9
TR-34130 Gazi O.P. Istanbul
TURKEY
www.diamond-gun.com

Mauser Jagdwaffen
1 Ziegelstadel
D-88316 Isny
GERMANY
www.mauser.com

Maverick Arms
7 Grasso Ave.
North Haven, CT 06473
203-230-5452
www.maverickarms.com

McMillan Bros. Rifles
1638 W. Knudsen, #102
Phoenix, AZ 85027
623-582-3713
www.mcbrosrifles.com

Merkel
7661 Commerce Ln., P.O. Box 129
Trussville, AL 35173
205-655-8299
www.gsifirearms.com

Millenium Designed Muzzleloaders
RR 1, Box 405
Maidstone, VT 05905
802-676-3311
www.mdm-muzzleloaders.com

Mitchell Manufacturing
P.O. Box 9295
Fountain Valley, CA 92728
800-274-4124
www.mitchellsales.com

MKS Supply/Hi-Point Firearms
8611-A N. Dixie Dr.
Dayton, OH 45414
877-425-4867
www.mkssupply.com

MOA
2451 Old Camden Pike
Eaton, OH 45320
937-456-3669

Montana Rifle
3172 Montana Hwy. 35
Kalispell, MT 59901
406-755-4867
www.montanarifleman.com

Morini Competition Arm
Via Ai Gelsi 11
CH-6930 Bedano
SWITZERLAND
www.morini.ch

Molot JSC
135 Lenin
RUS-612960 Viatskie Poliany
RUSSIA
www.molot.biz

Navy Arms
219 Lawn St.
Martinsburg, WV 25401
304-262-9870
www.navyarms.com

New England Arms
6 Lawrence Ln.
Kittery, ME 03905
207-439-0593
www.newenglandarms.com

New England Custom Gun
438 Willow Brook Rd.
Plainfield, NH 03781
603-469-3450
www.newenglandcustomgun.com

New England Firearms
60 Industrial Rowe
Gardner, MA 01440
978-630-8220
www.hr1871.com

New Ultra Light Arms
P.O. Box 340
Granville, WV 26534
304-292-0600
www.newultralight.com

Norinco
12A Guang An Men Nan Jie, Beijing,
CHINA
P.O. Box 2932 Beijing
www.norinco.com

North American Arms
2150 S. 950 E.
Provo, UT 84606
800-821-5783
www.northamericanarms.com

North West Arms
26884 Pearl Rd.
Parma, ID 83660
208-722-6771

Nosler
P.O. Box 671
Bend, OR 97709
800-285-3701
www.nosler.com

Nowlin Custom Manufacturing
20622 S. 4092 Rd.
Claremore, OK 74019
918-342-0689
www.nowlinguns.com

O.F. Mossberg & Sons
7 Grasso Ave.
North Haven, CT 06473
203-230-5300
www.mossberg.com

Ohio Ordnance Works
310 Park Dr., P.O. Box 687
Chardon, OH 44024
440-285-3481
www.ohioordnanceworks.com

Olympic Arms
624 Old Pacific Hwy. SE.
Olympia, WA 98513
800-228-3471
www.olyarms.com

P.W. Arms
8525 152nd Ave. NE.
Redmond, WA 98052
452-882-1161
www.russianammo.com

Pacific Armament
4813 Enterprise Way, Unit K
Modesto, WA 95356
209-545-2800
www.pacificarmament.com

Para-Ordnance
980 Tapscott Rd.
Toronto, Ontario M1X 1C3
CANADA
416-297-7855
www.paraord.com

Pardini Armi
Via Italica, 154/A
55043 Lido di Camaiore
Lucca, ITALY
www.pardini.it

**Parker Reproduction
Shotguns**
115 U.S. Hwy. 202
Ringoes, NJ 08551
908-284-2800

Pedersoli Davide & Co. SNC
Via Artigiani, 57
25063 Gardone Val Trampia
Brescia, ITALY
www.davide-pedersoli.com

Perazzi Armi
Via Fontanelle, 1-3
25080 Botticino Mattina
Brescia, ITALY

1010 West 10th St.
Azusa, CA 91702
(626) 334-1234
www.perazzi.com

Peters Stahl
GERMANY
www.peters-stahl.com

Phillips & Rogers
100 Hilbig #C
Conroe, TX 77301
409-435-0011

Phoenix Arms
4231 E. Brickell St.
Ontario, CA 91761
909-437-6900

Powell & Son (Gunmakers)
35 - 37 Carrs Lane
Birmingham B4 7SX,
UNITED KINGDOM
www.william-powell.co.uk

Precision Small Arms
9272 Jeronimo Rd., Ste. 121
Irvine, CA 92618
949-768-3530

RPM
15481 N. Twin Lakes Dr.
Tucson, AZ 85739
520-825-1233

Remington Arms
P.O. Box 700
Madison, NC 27025-0700
336-548-8700
www.remington.com

Rifles, Inc.
3580 Leal Rd.
Pleasanton, TX 78064
www.riflesinc.com

Rizzini
Via 2 Giugno, 7/7Bis
25060 Marcheno
Brescia, ITALY
www.rizzini.it

1140 McDermott, Ste. 103
West Chester, PA 19380
610-344-7730
www.rizziniusa.com

The Robar Companies
21438 N. 7th Ave.
Phoenix, AZ 85027
623-581-2648
www.robarguns.com

Robinson Armament
P.O. Box 16776
Salt Lake City, UT 84116
801-355-0401
www.robarm.com

Rock River Arms
1042 Cleveland Rd.
Colona, IL 61241
309-792-5780
www.rockriverarms.com

Rocky Mountain Arms
1813 Sunset Pl., Unit D
Longmont, CO 80501
800-375-0846
www.bearcoat.com

Rogue Rifle
1140 36th St. N., Ste. B
Lewiston, ID 83501
877-743-4355
www.roguerifle.com

Rohrbaugh Firearms
P.O. Box 785
Bayport, NY 11705
800-803-2233
www.rohrbaughfirearms.com

Rossi
143 Rua Amadeo Rossi
P.O. Box 28-CEP 93030-220
Sao Leopoldo RS
BRAZIL

16175 NW 49th Ave.
Miami, FL 33014
305-474-0401
www.rossiusa.com

Sabatti
Via A.Volta, No. 90
25063 Gardone Val Trampia
Brescia, ITALY
www.sabatti.com

Sabre Defence Industries
Sabre House, Belvue Road
GB-Northolt, Middlesex UB5 5QJ
UNITED KINGDOM

450 Allied Dr.
Nashville, TN 37211
615-333-6229
www.sabredefence.com

Safari Arms
P.O. Box 1825
Seaford, NY 11783
516-826-7516
www.safariarms.com

Sako
FIN-11100 Riihimaki
FINLAND
www.sako.fi
www.berettausa.com

Samco Global Arms
6995 NW 43rd St.
Miami, FL 33166
800-554-1618
www.samcoglobal.com

SAM Arms
Via al Lido 5, CP 534
CH-6962 Lugano-Viganello
SWITZERLAND
www.samarms.ch

Sarco
323 Union St.
Stirling, NJ 07980
908-647-3800
www.sarcoinc.com

Sarsilmaz Silah Sanayi
Nargileci Solnk No. 1
34450 Merkezi, Istanbul
TURKEY
www.sarsilmaz.com

Sauer & Sohn
Sauerstrasse 2-6
D-24340 Eckernforde
GERMANY
www.sauer-waffen.de

Savage Arms
118 Mountain Rd.
Suffield, CT 06078
866-233-4776
www.savagearms.com

S.G.S. Importers
1750 Brielle Ave., Ste. B-1
Wanamassa, NJ 07712
732-493-0333
www.bersa-llama.com

C. Sharps Arms
100 Centennial, Box 885
Big Timber, MT 59011
406-932-4353
www.csharparms.com

Shiloh Rifle Manufacturing
P.O. Box 279
Big Timber, MT 59011
406-932-4454
www.shilohrifle.com

SIG Arms
Industrie Platz
CH-8212 Neuhausen am Rhinefall
SWITZERLAND

18 Industrial Dr.
Exeter, NH 03833
603-772-2302
www.sigarms.com

Silma
Via 1 Maggio, 74
25060 Zanano di Sarezzo
Brescia, ITALY
www.silma.net

Sisk Rifles
400 County Rd. 2340
Dayton, TX 77535
936-258-4984
www.siskguns.com

SKB (New) Arms
JAPAN
www.shirstone.com/skb

SKB Shotguns
4325 S. 120th St.
Omaha, NE 68137
800-752-2767
www.skbshotguns.com

Smith & Wesson
2100 Roosevelt Ave.
Springfield, MA 01104
800-331-0852
www.smith-wesson.com

Sphinx Systems
12 Gsteigsrasse
CH-3800 Matten /Interlaken
SWITZERLAND
www.sphinxarms.com

Springfield Armory USA
420 W. Main St.
Geneseo, IL 61254
800-680-6866
www.springfieldarmory.com

Steyr Mannlicher
1 Mannlicherstrasse
4442 Kleinraming Steyr
AUSTRIA
www.steyr-mannlicher.com

STI International
114 Halmar Cove
Georgetown, TX 78628
512-819-0656
www.stiguns.com

Stoeger Industries
17603 Indian Head Hwy., Ste. 200
Accokeek, MD 20607
301-283-6300
www.stoegerindustries.com

Strayer-Voigt
3435 Roy Orr Blvd., Ste. 200
Grand Prairie, TX 75050
800-928-1911
www.sviguns.com

Sturm, Ruger & Co.
1 Lacey Pl.
Southport, CT 06890
203-259-7843
www.ruger.com

Suhler Jagd und Sportwaffen
26 Schutzenstrasse
D-98527 Suhl
GERMANY
www.merkel-waffen.de

Tanfoglio Fratelli
Via Valtrompia, 39-41
25063 Gardone
Brescia, ITALY
www.tanfoglio.it

Tar-Hunt Slug Guns
101 Dogtown Rd.
Bloomsburg, PA 17815
570-784-6368
www.tar-hunt.com

Taurus International Manufacturing
16175 NW 49th Ave.
Miami, FL 33014
305-624-1115
www.taurususa.com

Taylor's & Co.
304 Lenoir Dr.
Winchester, VA 22603
540-722-2017
www.taylorsfirearms.com

Tennessee Guns
P.O. Box 9689
Knoxville, TN 37940
865-977-9707
www.tnguns.com

Thompson/Center Arms
P.O. Box 5002
Rochester, NH 03866
603-332-2333
www.tcarms.com

Tikka
2 Sakonkatu
FIN 11100 Riihimaki
FINLAND
www.tikka.fi
www.berettausa.com

TJF Jagdwaffen in Suhl
D-98528 Suhl
GERMANY
www.tjf-jagdwaffen.de

Traditions Performance Firearms
P.O. Box 776
Old Saybrook, CT 06475
860-388-4656
www.traditionsfirearms.com

Tristar Sporting Arms
1816 Linn St.
North Kansas City, MO 64116
816-421-1400
www.tristarsportingarms.com

Truvelo Manufacturers
P.O. Box 14183
ZA-0140 Lyttleton
SOUTH AFRICA
www.truvelo.co.za

Uberti
Via Artigiani, 1
25063 Gardone
Brescia, ITALY

17603 Indian Head Hwy., Ste. 200
Accokeek, MD 20607
301-283-6300
www.ubertireplicas.com

Ugartechea
Ignacio, Chonta 26
Eibar, SPAIN

UMAREX Sportwaffen
P.O. Box 2720
D-59717 Arnsberg
GERMANY
www.umarex.de

Unique/M.A.P.F.
10 Les Allees
F-64700 Hendaye
FRANCE

Uselton Arms
1249 Northgate Business Park, Ste. 8
Madison, TN 37115
615-865-0006
www.useltonarms.com

United States Fire Arms Manufacturing
P.O. Box 1901
Hartford, CT 06144
877-227-6901
www.usfirearms.com

Valkyrie Arms
120 State Ave, NE., Ste. 381
Olympia, WA 98501
360-482-4036
www.valkyriearms.com

Valtro
Via Capretti, 12
25136 Brescia
ITALY
info@valtroeurope.it

24800 Mission Blvd.
Hayward, CA 94544
510-489-8477
www.valtrousa.com

Verney-Carron
54 Boulvard Thiers-BP 72
F-42002 St. Etienne
FRANCE
www.verney-carron.com

Voere Kufsteiner Geratebau- und Handelsges
56 Untere Sparchen
A-6330 Kufstein
AUSTRIA
www.voere.com

Valor Corp
1001 Sawgrass Corporate Pkwy.
Sunrise, FL 33323
954-377-4925
www.valorcorp.com

Volquartsen Custom
24276 240th St.
Carroll, IA 51401
712-792-4238
www.volquartsen.com

Walther
P.O. Box 2740
D-59757 Arnsberg
GERMANY

2100 Roosevelt Ave.
Springfield, MA 01102
800-372-6454
www.waltheramerica.com

Weatherby Inc.
3100 El Camino Real
Atascadero, CA 93422
805-466-1767
www.weatherby.com

Weihrauch Sport
11 Industriestrasse
D-97638 Mellrichstadt
GERMANY
www.weihrauch-sport.de

Westley Richards & Co.
40 Grange Rd.
Birmingham B29 6AR
UNITED KINGDOM
www.westleyrichards.com

Wichita Arms
923 E. Gilbert
Wichita, KS 67211
316-265-0661
www.wichitaarms.com

Wildey
45 Angevine Rd.
Warren, CT 06754
860-355-9000
www.wildeyguns.com

Wild West Guns
7100 Homer Dr.
Anchorage, AK 99518
800-992-4570
www.wildwestguns.com

Wilson Combat & Scattergun Technologies
2234 CR 719
Berryville, AR 72616
800-955-4856
www.wilsoncombat.com

Winchester Firearms
275 Winchester Ave.
Morgan, UT 84050
800-333-3288
www.winchesterguns.com

Zabala Hermanos
P.O. Box 97
E-20690 Elgueta-Guipuzcoa
SPAIN
www.zabalahermanos.com

Zastava Oruzje
4 Trg Topolivaca
YU- 34000 Kragujevac
YUGOSLAVIA
www.zastava-arms.co.yu

Zbrojovka Brno
7 Lazarenti
CZ-61500 Brno
CZECH REPUBLIC
www.zbrojovkabrno.com

Zoli Antonio
Via G. Zanardelli, 39
25063 Gardone
Brescia, ITALY
www.zoli.it

Manufacturers and Importers of Airguns

Aeron CZ
Svitavske Nab. 27
CZ-60200 Brno
CZECH REPUBLIC
www.aeron.cz

Air Arms
Hailsham Industrial Park
Diplocks Way
East Sussex
BN27 3JF
ENGLAND
www.air-arms.co.uk

Air Gun
9320 Harwin Dr.
Houston, TX 77036
713-780-2415
www.airrifle-china.com

Airforce Airguns
P.O. Box 2478
5058 Brush Creek Rd.
Fort Worth, TX 76113
877-247-4867
www.airforceairguns.com

J.G. Anschutz
Daimlerstrasse 12
D-89079 Ulm
GERMANY
www.anschuetz-sport.com

Arms Corporation of the Philippines
6/F Strata 100 Bldg.
F. Ortigas Jr. Rd., Ortigas Ctr.
Pasig City, 1605
PHILIPPINES
www.armscor.com.ph

Bruni
Via Como, 50-52
20037 Palazzolo Milanese
Paderno-Dugano
Milano, ITALY
www.bruniguns.com

BSA Guns
Armoury Rd. Small Heath
Birmingham, B11 2PP
ENGLAND
www.bsaguns.com

Beeman Precision Airguns
5454 Argosy Dr.
Huntington Beach, CA 92649
800-227-2744
www.beeman.com

Crosman
7629 Routes 5 & 20
East Bloomfield, NY 14443
800-7AIRGUN
www.crosman.com

Daisy Manufacturing
400 West Stribling Dr.
P.O. Box 220
Rogers, AR 72757
800-643-3458
www.daisy.com

Daystate
Birch House Ln.
GB-Cotes, NR Stone
Staffordshire ST1 OQQ
ENGLAND
wwwdaystate.com

Dianawerk
Karlstrasse 34
Rastatt BW 76437
GERMANY
www.diana-airguns.com

Drulov, Vyrobni druzstvo
Smetanovo namesti 81
CZ-57001 Litomysl
CZECH REPUBLIC
pragueoffice@volny.cz

Dynamit Nobel/RWS
81 Ruckman Rd.
Closter, NJ 07624
201-767-1995
www.dnrws.com

Falcon Pneumatic Systems
Unit 5-6, Hailsham Industrial Park
Diplocks Way, Hailsham
East Sussex BN27 3JF
ENGLAND
www.falcon-airguns.co.uk

Fegarmy Arms Factory
Soroksari St. 158
H-1095 Budapest
HUNGARY
www.fegarmy.hu

Feinwerkbau
Neckarstrasse 43
D-78727 Oberndorf a. N
GERMANY
www.feinwerkbau.com

Gamo
P.O. Box 16
E-08830 Sant Boi de Llobregat-
Barcelona, SPAIN

3911 SW 47th Ave., Ste. 914
Ft. Lauderdale, FL 33314
954-581-5822
www.gamo.com

Gun Power
P.O. Box 567
Ashford, Kent TN23 5FP
ENGLAND
www.gunpower.org.uk

Hammerli
Industrieplatz
CH-8212 Neuhausen am Rheinfall
SWITZERLAND
www.haemmerli.ch

Hatsan Arms
Izmir-Ankara Karayolu 28. Km.
No. 289 Org. San Bol.
Kemalpasa-Izmir 35170
TURKEY
www.hatsan.com.tr

Izhevsky Mekhanichsky Zavod (Baikal)
Promyschlennaya St. 8
RUS-426063 Izhevsk
RUSSIA
www.baikalinc.ru

Janz-Labortechnik
Lutjenburger Strasse 84
D-23714 Malente
GERMANY
www.jtl.de

Kimar
Via Milano, 2
25020 Azzano Mella
Brescia, ITALY
www.kimar.com

Manu Arm
43 Avenue de la Liberation
F-42340 Veauche
FRANCE
www.manuarm.fr

Marksman Products
5482 Argosy Ave.
Huntington Beach, CA 92649
714-898-7535

Matsan
Halitpasa cad. No.9
Gaziosmanpasa
34130 Istanbul
TURKEY
www.diamond-gun.com

Morini Competition
Via Ai Gelsi 11
CH-6930 Bedano
SWITZERLAND
www.morini.ch

Norica-Farmi
16 Otaola
E-20600 Eibar-Guipuzcoa
SPAIN
www.norica.es

Productos Mendoza
Prol. Constitucion No. 57
Col. Santiago Tepalcatlapon
MEXICO D.F.
www.productosmendoza.com

Rohm
50 Heinrich-Rohm Strasse
D-89567 Sontheim
GERMANY
www.roehm-rg.de

SAM Arms
Via al Lido 5, CP 534
CH-6962 Lugano Viganello
SWITZERLAND
www.samarms.ch

Shanghai Airgun Factory
625 Yao Hua Road, Pu Dong
VRC-200126 Shanghai
CHINA
www.airrifle-china.com

Steyr Sportwaffen
40 Hauptstrasse
A-4432 Ernsthofen
AUSTRIA
www.steyr-sportwaffen.com

UMAREX Sportwaffen
P.O. Box 2720
D-59717 Arnsberg
GERMANY
www.umarex.de

Walther
P.O. Box 2740
D-59757 Arnsberg
GERMANY

2100 Roosevelt Ave.
Springfield, MA 01102
800-372-6454
www.waltheramerica.com

Webley & Scott
Frankley Industrial Park
Tay Road, Rubery
GB-Birmingham B45 OPA
UNITED KINGDOM
www.webley.co.uk

Weihrauch Sport
11 Industriestrasse
D-97638 Mellrichstadt
GERMANY
www.weihrauch-sport.de

Zastava Oruzje
4 Trg Topolivaca
YU- 34000 Kragujevac
YUGOSLAVIA
www.zastava-arms.co.yu

Manufacturers and Importers of Ammunition and Reloading Components and Tools—Bullets, Brass, Powder, Primers, Wads and Shot

Accurate
P.O. Box 158
Miles City, MT 59301
406-234-0422
www.accuratepowder.com

Alliant Powder
Route 114, Bldg. 229
P.O. Box 6
Radford, VA 24143
800-276-9337
www.alliantpowder.com

Aguila, Industrias Tecnos
Km. 6 Carretera Cuernavaca a
Tepoztlan
Cuernavaca, Morelos Cp. 62000
MEXICO
www.itecnos.com.mx

American Ammunition
3545 NW. 71st Street
Miami, FL 33147
888-28AMERC
www.a-merc.com

497

American Pioneer Powder
20423 State Rd. 7 F6-268
Boca Raton, FL 33498
888-756-7693
www.americanpioneerpowder.com

Ammo Load Inc.
1560 E. Edinger, Ste. E
Santa Ana, CA 92705
714-558-8858

Arms Corporation of the Philippines
6/F Strata 100 Bldg.
F. Ortigas Jr. Rd., Ortigas Ctr.
Pasig City, 1605
PHILIPPINES
www.armscor.com.ph

Armusa
La Calzada de Zubiete 6
E-48192 Gordexola-Vizcaya
SPAIN
www.carmusa.com

Azot
1 Rdultovskogo Sq.
Krasnozavodsk RUS-141321
RUSSIA
www.azot-patron.ru

BSN di Ballabio
Via Guido Rossa, 46-52
25060 Cellatica
Brescia, ITALY
www.bsn.it

Ballard Rifle and Cartridge
113 West Yellowstone
Cody, WY 82414
866-99-RIFLE
www.ballardrifle.com

Ballisti-Cast
3305 4th Ave. NW
Minot, ND 58703
701-857-6366
www.ballisti-cast.com

Ballistic Products
P.O. Box 293
Hamel, MN 55340
888-273-5623
www.ballisticproducts.com

Barnaul Machine-Tool Plant
28 Kulagina St.
Barnaul 656002
RUSSIA
www.ab.ru/~stanok

Barnes Bullets
P.O. Box 215
American Fork, UT 84003
800-574-9200
www.barnesbullets.com

Baschieri & Pellagri
1241 Ellis St.
Bensenville, IL 60106
800-683-0464
www.bandpusa.com

Battenfeld Technologies
5885 W. Van Horn Tavern Rd.
Columbia, MO 65203
877-509-9160
www.battenfeldtechnologies.com

Bell Reloading
1725 Harlin Ln. Rd.
Villa Rica, GA 30180

Berger Bullets
4275 N. Palm St.
Fullerton, CA 92835
714-447-5456
www.bergerbullets.com

Berry's Manufacturing
401 N. 3050 E.
St. George, UT 84790
800-269-7373
www.berrysmfg.com

Bertram Bullet
P.O. Box 313
Seymour, Victoria 3660
AUSTRALIA

Big Bore Express
2316 E. Railroad St.
Nampa, ID 83687
800-376-4010
www.powerbeltbullets.com

Bismuth Cartridge
7155 Valjean Ave.
Van Nuys, CA 91406
818-909-4742
www.bismuth-notox.com

Black Hills Ammunition
3050 Eglin St.
Rapid City, SD 57703
605-348-5150
www.black-hills.com

Bornaghi
Via dei Livelli
24047 Treviglio
Bergamo, ITALY
www.bornaghi.it

Brenneke
P.O. Box 1646
D-30837 Langenhagen
GERMANY

P.O. Box 1481
Clinton, IA 52733
800-773-9733
www.brennekeusa.com

Browning International
Parc Industriel des Hauts Sarts
3eme Ave., 25
B-4040 Herstal
BELGIUM
www.browningint.com

Buffalo Arms
660 Vermeer Ct.
Ponderay, ID 83852
208-263-6953
www.buffaloarms.com

Buffalo Bullet
12637 Los Nietos Rd., Unit A
Santa Fe Springs, CA 90670
800-423-8069

Bumar
ZPS Pionki
11 Al Jana Pawla II
00-828, Warszawa
POLAND
www.phzbumar.com.pl

Cabela's
One Cabela Dr.
Sidney, NE 69160
800-243-6626
www.cabelas.com

CCI Ammunition
2299 Snake River Ave.
Lewiston, ID 83501
208-746-2351
www.cci-ammunition.com

Camdex
2330 Alger
Troy, MI 48083
248-528-2300
www.camdexloader.com

Cartuchos Saga
14, Balmes 5
25006 Lleida
SPAIN
www.saga.es

Casull Arms
P.O. Box 1629
Afton, WY 83110
307-886-0200

CH4D
P.O. Box 889
Mt. Vernon, OH 43050
740-397-7214
www.ch4d.com

Cheddite France
99 Route de Lyon
Bourg-les-Valence 26500
FRANCE
www.cheddite.com

CheyTac Associates
363 Sunset Dr.
Arco, ID 83213
208-527-8614
www.cheytac.com

Claybuster Wads & Harvester Bullets
309 Sequoya Dr.
Hopkinsville, KY 42240
800-922-6287
www.claybusterwads.com

Clever
Via A. Da Legnago, 9
37033 Ponte Florio Montorio
Verona, ITALY
www.clevervr.com

Companhia Brasileira de Cartuchos
Av. Humberto de Campos, 3220
CEP: 09426-900, Guapitba Ribeirao
Pires-SP
BRAZIL
www.cbc.com

Collin Tech
Muhlenstrasse 2
86551 Aichach
GERMANY
www.collin.de

Cor-Bon/Glaser
1311 Industry Rd.
Sturgis, SD 57785
800-626-7266
www.corbon.com

Dakota Arms
1310 Industry Rd.
Sturgis, SD 57785
605-347-4686
www.dakotaarms.com

Delta Frangible Ammunition
P.O. Box 2350
Stafford, VA 22555
800-339-1933
www.dfafrangible.com

Dillon Precision Products
8009 E. Dillons Way
Scottsdale, AZ 85260
800-762-3845
www.dillonprecision.com

Dionisi Cartridge
Via Bonifica, 34
63040 Maltignano
Ascoli Piceno, ITALY
www.dionisi.com

Dynamit Nobel/RWS/Norma
81 Ruckman Rd.
Closter, NJ 07624
201-767-1995
www.dnrws.com

EDB Engineering
Rue de la Legende, 51A
B-4141 Louveigne (Sprimont)
BELGIUM
www.edb.be

Eley Hawk
Selco Way
Minworth Industrial Estate
Sutton Coldfield
West Midlands B76 1BA
ENGLAND
www.eleyhawkltd.com

Eley Limited
Selco Way
Minworth Industrial Estate
Sutton Coldfield
West Midlands B76 1BA
ENGLAND
www.eley.co.uk

Environ-Metal (Hevi-Shot)
1307 Clark Mill Rd.
Sweet Home, OR 97386
541-367-3522
www.hevishot.com

Estate Cartridge
900 Ehlen Dr.
Anoka, MN 55303
800-322-2342
www.estatecartridge.com

Explosia
Pardubice-Semtin, PSC 532 17
CZECH REPUBLIC
www.explosia.cz

Extreme Shock Ammunition
Route 2
P.O. Box 304-N
Clintwood, VA 24228
877-337-6772
www.extremeshockusa.com

FAM-Pionki
ul. Zakladowa 7.
PL 26-670 Pionki
POLAND
www.fam-pionki.pl

Federal Cartridge
900 Ehlen Dr.
Anoka, MN 55303
800-322-2342
www.federalcartridge.com

Fiocchi
Via Santa Barbara, 4
23900 Lecco
ITALY

6930 Fremont Rd.
Ozark, MO 65721
417-725-4118
www.fiocchiusa.com

Forster Precision Products
310 E. Lanark Ave.
Lanark, IL 61046
815-493-6360
www.forsterproducts.com

Gamebore Cartridge
Great Union St.
GB-Hull HU9 1AR
ENGLAND
www.gamebore.com

Garrett Cartridges
www.garrettcartridges.com

Glaser Safety Slug
1311 Industry Rd.
Sturgis, SD 57785
800-626-7266
www.safetyslug.com

GOEX
P.O. Box 659
Doyline, LA 71023
318-382-9300
www.goexpowder.com

Golden West Bullets
2458 Rosemead Blvd.
S. Elmonte, CA 91733
626-454-4585
www.goldenwestbrass.com

Gualandi & Co.
Via Emilia Levante, 480
40068 Idice
Bologna, ITALY
www.gualandi.it

Haendler & Natermann Sport
Kasseler Strasse 2
D-34346 Hann. Munden
GERMANY
www.natermann.de/sport

Hirtenberger
Leobersdorfer Straße 31-33
A-2552 Hirtenberg
AUSTRIA
www.hirtenberger.at

Hodgdon Powder
P.O. Box 2932
Shawnee Mission, KS 66201
913-362-9455
www.hodgdon.com

Hornady Manufacturing
P.O. Box 1848
Grand Island, NE 68802
800-338-3220
www.hornady.com

Hull Cartridge
Bontoft Avenue, National Avenue
Hull HU5 4HZ
ENGLAND
www.hullcartridge.co.uk

Huntington Die Specialties
P.O. Box 991
Oroville, CA 95965
866-735-6237
www.huntingtons.com

Igman International
2499 Main St.
Stratford, CT 06615
203-375-8544
www.igman.co.ba

Impala Europa
Dr. Karl Renner Strasse 2b
A2353 Guntramsdorf Osterreich
AUSTRIA
www.impalabullets.at

IMR Smokeless Powder
6231 Robinson
Shawnee Mission, KS 66202
913-362-9455
www.imrpowder.com

Indusys Technologies
Burgemeester van de Mortelplein 42
5037 PJ Tiburg
P.O. Box 484
5000 AL Tiburg
BELGIUM
www.indusys.com

Ingear Outdoor Optics
Rm. 901, No.12 Jia Yi St., Yi Le Rd.
Guangzhou
CHINA
www.ingear-outdoor.com

International Cartridge
2273 Route 310
Reynoldsville, PA 15851
877-422-5332
www.internationalcartridge.com

ITD Enterprise
3533 N. 70th St., Ste. 104
Scottsdale, AZ 85251
602-392-7671
www.itdenterpriseinc.com

J. Dewey Manufacturing
P.O. Box 2014
Southbury, CT 06488
203-264-3064
www.deweyrods.com

Kent Cartridge
P.O. Box 849
Kearneysville, WV 25430
888-311-5368
www.kentgamebore.com

Krasnozavodsk Chemical Factory
1 Rdutlovskogo Sq.
141321 Krasnozavodsk/Moscow
RUSSIA

Kynoch Ammunition
The Old Railway Station
Station Road
Mildenhall
Suffolk IP28 7DT
ENGLAND
www.kynochammunition.co.uk

Lapua
P.O. Box 5
62101 Lapua
FINLAND
www.lapua.com

1241 N. Ellis
Bensenville, IL 60106
800-683-0464
www.kaltron.com

Lawrence Brand Shot
1200 16th St.
Granite City, IL 62040
618-451-4400
www.metalico.com

Lazzeroni Arms
P.O. Box 26696
Tucson, AZ 85726
888-492-7247
www.lazzeroni.com

Lee Precision
4275 Hwy. U
Hartford WI 53027
262-673-3075
www.leeprecision.com

Lightfield Ammunition
P.O. Box 162
Adelphia, NJ 07710
570-784-6557
www.lightfieldslugs.com

Lyalvale
Express Estate
Fisherwick, NR Whittington
Litchfield
WS13 8XA, ENGLAND
www.lylevaleexpress.com

Lyman Products
475 Smith St.
Middletown, CT 06457
860-632-2020
www.lymanproducts.com

**Hungarian Ammunition
Manufacturing**
H-3332 Sirok, P.O. Box 9
HUNGARY
www.mfs2000.hu

MK Ballistic Systems
2707 Santa Ana Valley Rd.
Hollister, CA 95024
800-345-1504
www.mkballistics.com

Magma Engineering
P.O. Box 161
Queen Creek, AZ 85242
480-987-9008
www.magmaengr.com

MagSafe Ammo
4700 S. U.S. Hwy. 17-92
Casselberry, FL 32707
407-834-9966
www.magsafeonline.com

Magtech Ammunition
6845 20th Ave. S., Ste. 120
Centerville, MN 55038
800-466-7191
www.magtechammunition.com

Manhurin Equipement
15 Rue de Quimper
68060 Mulhouse Cedex
FRANCE

Mast Technology
P.O. Box 1026
Blue Springs, MO 64013
816-796-0480
www.bellammo.com

Mayville Engineering
715 South St.
Mayville, WI 53050
920-387-4500
www.mecreloaders.com

Meister Bullets
12752 S. Hwy. 169
Oologah, OK 74053
918-443-2707
www.meisterbullets.com

Metallwerk Elisenhutte
10 Elisenhutte
D-56377 Nassau/Lahn
GERMANY

Midway USA
5875 W. Van Horn Tavern Rd.
Columbia, MO 65203
800-243-3220
www.midwayusa.com

NATEC
11 Arkansas St.
Plattsburgh, NY 12903
518-324-5625
www.natec-us.com

New Lachaussee
Rue du Tige, 13
B-4040 Herstal
BELGIUM
www.lachaussee.com

Nike-Fiocchi Sporting Ammunitions
H-8184
Fuzfogyarterep, POB 22
HUNGARY
www.nike-fiocchi.hu

Nobel Sport
57 Rue Pierre Charron
F-75008 Paris
FRANCE
www.nobelsport.fr

Norma Precision
670 40 Amotfors
SWEDEN
www.norma.cc

Nosler
107 SW Columbia St.
Bend, OR 97702
800-285-3701
www.nosler.com

Novosibirsk LVE Plant
Novosibirsk, 630108
Stantsionnaya, 30 A
RUSSIA
www.lveplant.com

Old Western Scrounger
219 Lawn St.
Martinsburg, WV 25401
304-262-9870
www.ows-ammunition.com

PMC/Eldorado Cartridge
P.O. Box 62508
Boulder City, NV 89006
800-456-9182
www.pmcammo.com

Pegoraro Sport
Via F.lli Bandiera, 2
30031 Dolo
Veneto, ITALY
www.pegorarosport.com

PowerBelt Bullets
2316 E. Railroad St.
Nampa, ID 83687
800-376-4010
www.powerbeltbullets.com

Precision Ammunition
5402 E. Diana St.
Tampa, FL 33610
888-393-0694
www.precisionammo.com

Prvi Partizan
Milosa Obrenovica 2
31000 Uzice
SERBIA
www.prvipartizan.com

Quality Cartridge
P.O. Box 445
Hollywood, MD 20636
301-373-3719
www.qual-cart.com

RC Eximport srl
5 Via Tassinara
I-47100 Forli (FO)
ITALY
www.rc-cartridges.com

RCBS
605 Oro Dam Blvd.
Oroville, CA 95965
800-533-5000
www.rcbs.com

Ramba
Via Giorgio La Pira, 20
25020 Fiero
Brescia, ITALY
www.ramba.it

Rainier Ballistics
4500 15th St. E.
Tacoma, WA 98424
800-638-8722
www.rainierballistics.com

Redding Reloading Equipment
1089 Starr Rd.
Cortland, NY 13045
607-753-3331
www.redding-reloading.com

Remington Arms
P.O. Box 700
Madison, NC 27025-0700
800-243-9700
www.remington.com

Rio Ammunition
2650 Fountainview #207
Houston, TX 77057
713-266-3091
www.rioammo.com

RUAG Ammotec GmbH
Uttigenstrasse 67
CH-3602 Thun
GERMANY
www.ruag-ammotec.ch

Saga Cartuchos
Partida de la Caparrella s/n
25191 Lleida
SPAIN
www.saga.es

Samco Global Arms
P. O. Box 7323
Miami, FL 33152
305-593-9782
www.samcoglobal.com

Scharch Mfg.
10325 Co. Rd. 120
Salida, CO 81201
800-836-4683
www.scharch.com

SK Jagd-und Sportmunitions
Wilhelm-Dumling-Strasse 12
39218 Schoenebeck/E
GERMANY
www.skmunition.de

Sokol-R
Kossyakova, 15
140730 Roshal, Moscow region
RUSSIA

SNC Technologies
5 Montee des Arsenaux
Le gardeur (Quebec)
J5Z 2P4 CANADA
450-581-3080
www.snctec.com

Schuetzen Powder
7650 U.S. Hwy. 287, Ste. 100
Arlington, TX 76001
866-809-9704
www.schuetzenpowder.com

Sellier & Bellot USA
P.O. Box 7307
Shawnee Mission, KS 66207
800-960-2422
www.sb-usa.com

Sinclair International
2330 Wayne Haven St.
Fort Wayne, IN 46803
800-717-8211
www.sinclairintl.com

Speer Bullets
2299 Snake River Ave.
Lewiston, ID 83501
800-627-3640
www.speer-bullets.com

SSK Industries.
590 Woodvue Ln.
Wintersville, OH 43953
740-264-0176
www.sskindustries.com

Starline
1300 W. Henry
Sedalia, MO 65301
800-280-6660
www.starlinebrass.com

Swift Bullet
P.O. Box 27
Quinter, KS 67752
785-754-3959
www.swiftbullets.com

Thifan Industrie Sarl
275, Rue de Malitorne, B.P. 61
18230 St. Doulchard
FRANCE
www.sauvestre.com

Top Brass/Scharch Mfg.
10325 Co. Rd. 120
Salida, CO 81201
719-539-7242
www.scarch.com

Trust Eibarres
Murrategui, 9 (Azitain)
Apartado (P.O. Box) 32
20600 Eibar-SPAIN
www.trust-eibarres.com

Tula Cartridge Works
139 Marata
RUS-30004 Tula
RUSSIA
www.tcwammo.tula.ru

UEE Cartucheria Deportiva
Avda. del Partenon 16 bajo
28042 Madrid
SPAIN
www.ueec.es

Ultramax Ammunition
2112 Elk Vale Rd.
Rapid City, SD 57701
605-342-4141
www.ultramaxammunition.com

Ulyanovsk Machinery Plant SUE, PA
2 Metallistov St.
32007 Ulyanovsk
RUSSIA
www.ulmash.narod.ru

Valtro Europe
Via Capretti, 12
25136 Brescia
Brescia, ITALY
info@valtroeurope.it

Vasini F.lli. Costruzioni Meccaniche
Via Renzo Botti, 8
26100 Cremora
ITALY
www.vasini.com

Widener's Reloading and Shooting Supply
P.O. Box 3009 CRS
Johnson City, TN 37602
800-615-3006
www.wideners.com

West Coast Shot
32 Red Rock Rd.
Carson City, NV 89706
775-246-5588

Western Powders
P.O. Box 158
Miles City, MT 59301
800-497-1007
www.westernpowders.com

**Olin Corporation
(A Winchester Division)**
427 N. Shamrock St.
East Alton, IL 62024
618-258-2000
www.winchester.com

Wolf Performance Ammunition
P.O. Box 757
Placentia, CA 92871
888-757-WOLF
www.wolfammo.com

Woodleigh Bullets
P.O. Box 15
Murrabit, Victoria 3579
AUSTRALIA
www.woodleighbullets.com.au

Manufacturers and Distributors of Optical Sights and Accessories

Aimpoint
Jagershillgaten 15
SE-214 75 Malmo
SWEDEN

14103 Mariah Ct.
Chantilly, VA 20151-2113
877-AIMPOINT
www.aimpoint.com

Aimtech Mount Systems
P.O. Box 223
Thomasville, GA 31792
229-226-4313
www.aimtech-mounts.com

B-Square
8909 Forum Way
Ft. Worth, TX 76140
800-433-2909
www.b-square.com

Barska Worldwide
2215 E. Huntington Dr.
Duarte, CA 91010
888-666-6769
www.barska.com

Bo-Mar Tool and Manufacturing Co.
6136 State Hwy. 300
Longview, TX 75604
903-759-4784
www.bo-mar.com

Brownells
200 S. Front St.
Montezuma, IA 50171
800-741-0015
www.brownells.com

BSA Optics
3911 SW. 47th Ave., Ste. 914
Ft. Lauderdale, FL 33314
954-581-2144
www.bsaoptics.com

Burris Company
331 E. 8th St.
Greeley, CO 80631
970-356-1670
www.burrisoptics.com

Bushmaster Firearms
P.O. Box 1479
Windham, ME 04062
800-883-6229
www.bushmaster.com

Bushnell Performance Optics
9200 Cody
Overland Park, KS 66214
800-423-3537
www.bushnell.com

C-More Systems
P.O. Box 1750
Manassas, VA 20108
888-265-8266
www.cmore.com

Cabela's
One Cabela Dr.
Sidney, NE 69160
800-243-6626
www.cabelas.com

Carl Zeiss Optical, Inc.
3-5 Gloelstrasse
D-35576 Wetzlar
GERMANY

13005 N. Kingston Ave.
Chester, VA 23836
800-441-3005
www.zeiss.com/sports

Champion's Choice
201 International Blvd.
LaVergne, TN 37086
615-793-4066
www.champchoice.com

Conetrol Scope Mounts
10225 Hwy. 123 S.
Seguin, TX 78155
800-266-3876
www.conetrol.com

Deben Group Industries
Melton, Woodbridge
IP12 1RS
UNITED KINGDOM
www.deben.com

Docter Analytic Jena AG
Niederlassung Eisfeld Seerasen 2
98673 Eisfeld
GERMANY
www.docter-germany.com

Heinie Specialty Products
301 Oak St.
Quincy, IL 62301
877-SIGHTS1
www.heinie.com

Horus Vision
659 Huntington Ave.
San Bruno, CA 94066
650-583-5471
www.horusvision.com

Hunter Co.
3300 W. 71st Ave.
Westminster, CO 80030
800-676-4868
www.huntercompany.com

IOR Valdada
P.O. Box 270095
Littleton, CO 80127
303-979-4578
www.valdada.com

Ironsighter Co.
P.O. Box 85070
Westland, MI 48185
734-326-8731
www.ironsighter.com

Kahles North America
2 Slater Rd.
Cranston, RI 02920
866-606-8779
www.kahlesoptik.com

Karl Kaps & Co.
Europastrasse
35614 Asslar
GERMANY
www.kaps-optik.de

Kowa Optimed
20001 S. Vermont Ave.
Torrance, CA 90502
800-966-5692
www.kowa-usa.com

Laseraim Tools
P.O. Box 3548
Little Rock, AR 72203
501-375-2227
www.laseraimtools.com

LaserMax
3495 Winton Pl., Bldg. B
Rochester, NY 14623
800-LASER-03
www.lasermax-inc.com

Leapers
37250 Plymouth Rd.
Livonia, MI 48150
734-542-1500
www.leapers.com

Leupold & Stevens
14400 NW Greenbrier Pkwy.
Beaverton, OR 97006
503-646-9171
www.leupold.com

Lightforce USA
1040 Hazen Ln.
Orofino, ID 83544
208-476-9814
www.nightforcescopes.com

Marble's
420 Industrial Park
Gladstone, MI 49837
906-428-3710

Meade Instruments Corp.
6001 Oak Canyon
Irvine, CA 92618
949-451-1450
www.meade.com

Meopta-Optika
Kabelikova 1
750 02 Prerov
CZECH REPUBLIC
www.meopta.com

Millett Sights
16131 Gothard St.
Huntington Beach, CA 92647
714-842-5575
www.millettsights.com

**Nantong Universal Optical
Instrument Co.**
No.1 Pingchao
Industrial Park
Nantong City, Jiangsu Province
CHINA
www.zoscn.com

New England Custom Gun
438 Willow Brook Rd.
Plainfield, NH 03781
603-469-3450
www.newenglandcustomgun.com

Night Owl Optics
307 Seventh Ave., Ste. 2104
New York, NY 10001
800-444-5994
www.nightowloptics.com

Nikko Stirling
Room 2406, Lucky Mountain
Shangcheng Rd. 660
Pudong, Shanghai
200120 CHINA
www.nikkostirling.com

Nikon
1300 Walt Witman Rd.
Melville, NY 11747
631-547-4200
www.nikonsportoptics.com

Novak Sights
P.O. Box 4045
Parkersburg, WV 26104
304-428-2676
www.novaksights.com

Pentax USA
600 12th St., Ste. 300
Golden, CO 80401
800-877-0155
www.pentaxlightseeker.com

Redfield USA
201 Plantation Oak Dr.
Thomasville, GA 31792
800-323-3191
www.redfieldoptics.com

S&K Scope Mounts
RD 2, Box 21C
Sugar Grove, PA 16350-9308
www.scopemounts.com

Schmidt & Bender
P.O. Box 134
438 Willow Brook
Meriden, NH 03770
800-468-3450
www.schmidtbender.com

Shepherd Enterprises
P.O. Box 189
Waterloo, NE 68069
402-779-2424
www.shepherdscopes.com

Shinei Group Inc.
Pacico Bldg. #601
J-6-15-8 Tokyo
Honkomagome, Bunkyo-ku 113-0021
JAPAN
www.shirstone.com

Sightron
100 Jeffery Way, Ste. A
Youngsville, NC 27596
919-532-3000
www.sightron.com

Simmons Outdoor Group
201 Plantation Oak Dr.
Thomasville, GA 31792
800-285-0689
www.simmonsoptics.com

Steiner-Optik
Dr. Hans Frischstrasse 9
95448 Bayreuth
GERMANY

97 Foster Rd., Ste. 5
Moorestown, NJ 08057
800-257-7742
www.steiner-binoculars.com

Swarovski Optik North America
2 Slater Rd.
Cranston, RI 02920
401-734-1800
www.swarovskioptik.com

Swift Instruments
2055 Gateway Pl., Ste. 500
San Jose, CA 95110
800-523-4544
www.swift-optics.com

Talley Mfg.
P.O. Box 369
Santee, SC 29142
803-854-5700
www.talleyrings.com

Trijicon
49385 Shafer Ave.
P.O. Box 930059
Wixom, MI 48393
248-960-7700
www.trijicon.com

Truglo
710 Presidential Dr.
Richardson, TX 75081
972-774-0300
www.truglo.com

Ultra Dot Distribution
P.O. Box 362
Yankeetown, FL 34498
352-447-2255
www.ultradotusa.com

Unertl Ordnance Company
2900 S. Highland Dr., Bldg. 18 Unit C
Las Vegas, NV 89109
702-369-4092
www.unertloptics.com

U.S. Optics
5900 Dale St.
Buena Park, CA 90621
714-994-4901
www.usoptics.com

Valdada-IOR Optics
P.O. Box 270095
Littleton, CO 80127
303-979-4578
www.valdada.com

Weaver Optics
201 Plantation Oak Dr.
Thomasville, GA 31792
800-285-0689
www.weaveroptics.com

Weigand Combat Handguns
1057 S. Main Rd.
Mountaintop, PA 18707
570-868-8358
www.jackweigand.com

Williams Gun Sight Co.
P.O. Box 329
7389 Lapeer Rd.
Davison, MI 48423
800-530-9028
www.williamsgunsight.com

XS Sight Systems
2401 Ludelle
Fort Worth, TX 76105
888-744-4880
www.xssights.com

Note: Contact information for firms in the firearm and shooting and hunting accessories industry are provided as a service to readers. All contact information herein was correct at the time of original publication (2006), however, readers should be aware that in time some of this information will become outdated.

Chapter 20
APPENDICES

Proofs and Other Markings

Proof of a firearm has been defined as the "testing of a new small arm before sale to insure insofar as practicable its safety in the hands of its user."

Proving a firearm, as a test of safety, is done by firing a proof load developing higher pressure than that of the load normally used so there will be a margin of strength in the arm and, consequently, a measure of safety for the user.

Upon satisfactory completion of proof firing, the arm is usually stamped with proofmarks signifying that the arm has satisfactorily withstood the strain of proof pressure without perceptible or measurable change in the condition of the arm.

It is difficult to determine when proofmarks were first employed on firearms, but there is evidence that they were used in Europe as early as the 16th century, when gun barrels were proved and stamped by guild officials or city authorities.

In the early years of gunmaking, barrels were tested by firing them from a special bench into an earthen bank or backstop, and the French term for proof house, *banc d'epreuve*, recalls the procedure.

In course of time, proof of firearms became systematized in Europe; but, in this country, firearms proof is not required except for military arms, and there is no national proof house. The government has its own system of proof testing and proofmarks for military arms, and each commercial manufacturer conducts tests which he deems proper.

Although proof testing is not required, the established U.S. manufacturers are careful to protect their reputations by turning out soundly-made guns. The majority have their own distinctive marks consisting of letters or various symbols. Some of these marks are not proof marks, but merely manufacturer's symbols.

Proof among most Western European nations has been standardized under the Commission Internationale Permanente des Armes a Feu Portatives (Permanent International Commission of Small Arms—CIP), headquartered at the Liege Proof House. The commission, established in 1914, sets testing standards for member nations, which agree to recognize each other's products that meet CIP standards. The CIP mark allows firearms and ammunition to move freely among member nations. Arms and ammunition exported to Europe from the United States or other firearms-producing nations must meet CIP standards, and an American gun that has been exported to Europe will bear a proofmark from the receiving nation.

Proofmarks are stamped on the barrel, action components or stock, but most usually on barrel, receiver or frame. In some cases the gun must be disassembled to find them. There is a great variety of these marks, each with its special meaning. Other marks denote caliber, gauge, case length, bullet weight and other specifications.

Countries change their proof laws and procedures from time to time, and thus in attempting to learn the significance of proofmarks on a gun it is necessary to refer to a list of marks which were used when the gun was manufactured.

Typical proof of a commercial European gun consists of a first or "provisional" proof of the barrel in its unfinished state followed by a final or "definitive" proof of the complete gun when finished or almost finished.

There is also a "nitro" proof to indicate test with smokeless powder, voluntary proof of arms not ordinarily subject to proof, proof after repair, proof of guns imported into a country, and special proofs for rimfire arms, signal pistols and other types of small arms.

In order to clarify the significance of proofmarks, the Guardians of the Birmingham Proof House in England issued in 1953, and reprinted in 1958, a memorandum entitled "Limitation in the Proof of Small Arms," in which these comments are made:

"Perhaps because of the confidence created by the Proof Marks impressed on arms made in this country a confused idea appears to have grown up that the British Proof Marks are in fact a hall mark of quality...

"Proof is solely a test of the ability of a small arm to withstand the pressures and strains imposed on its parts by normal service use—and particularly the pressure developed by the propellant gases of the cartridge or load for which the arm is designed.

"Proof may therefore be described as a test of safety, but it is not a test of quality because the Proof Test is uniform for all arms of the same bore having the same chamber length...and each may qualify to be marked according to the Rules.

"It is part of the duty of the Proof Authorities to determine what is in fit condition for Proof and whether arms have passed or failed Proof but they are not the arbiters of what is fit for sale."

The proofmarks illustrated are representative of most important current ones. Some shown are obsolete, but are often encountered on older arms.

Austrian Proofmarks

Vienna   Ferlach   Vienna   Ferlach

Provisional barrel proof   Definitive smokeless proof

Definitive blackpowder proof   Discretionary superior proof
for shotguns

Belgian Proofmarks

Muzzleloading shotguns and smoothbores

Normal   Superior

Barrel   Lock   Barrel   Lock

Breechloading shotguns

Discretionary   Normal   Superior
  provisional   Required proof
  barrel proof   Barrel and action parts

Smallbore rifles   Smokless proof

 Blackpowder   Action   Barrel
         proof   parts   Action
                                              parts

Rifled arms

 Required proof
         Barrel
         Action parts

Belgian Proofmarks (continued)

Revolvers

 Blackpowder proof

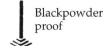 Smokeless proof

Barrel-frame

Cylinder

Barrel-frame cylinder

Self loading pistols Smokeless proof
Barrel
Action parts

Pistols for Flobert or revolver cartridges

 Blackpowder proof

 Smokeless proof

Barrel

Action parts

Barrel
Action parts

Barrel
Action parts

Foreign arms

Barrel
Action parts

Military arms

Barrel Action parts

Hard-tempered pieces may be marked

British Proofmarks

	LONDON	BIRMINGHAM
Provisional barrel proof		

Definitive smokeless proof

On action   On barrel

Definitive blackpowder proof

Special definitive proof

Reproof

Chilean Proofmarks

Arms proof

Czechoslovakian Proofmarks

Proofmark for alarm guns,
cattle-killers, stud drivers, etc.,
applied to barrel and action

Air Arms

Proofmark for
unfinished shotgun
barrels

Proofmark for shotguns,
smoothbore pistols, Flobert arms—
applied to barrel and action parts

Proofmark for rifled arms,
applied to barrel and action parts

German Proofmarks

Definitive
blackpowder
proof

Definitive
smokeless
proof

Superior
smokeless
proof

Distinctive marks of various proofhouses

Ulm   Berlin   Kiel   Hanover   Munich   Mellrichstadt   Cologne

East Germany

Normal proof

Superior proof

Repair proof

Date of proof (month and year)   **474**

Finnish Proofmarks

Normal proof

Blackpowder proof

Superior proof

French Proofmarks

Required Proofs

Normal proof
for finished
blackpowder arms

Supplementary
proof for
finished arms

Normal proof
for finished
smokeless arms

Blackpowder
reproof

Superior proof
for finished
smokeless arms

Proof for
rifled foreign
long arms

Proof for rifled
French long arms StETIENNE

Proof for French
short arms StETIENNE

Proof for foreign
short arms

Superior reproof

Discretionary Proofs

Normal proof for semi-finished barrels

Double proof for above

Triple proof for above

Hungarian Proofmarks

Discretionary
provisional proof

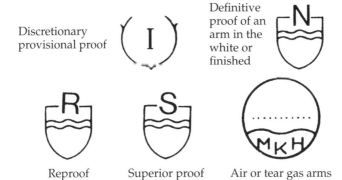

Definitive
proof of an
arm in the
white or
finished

Reproof   Superior proof   Air or tear gas arms

Italian Proofmarks

Distinctive mark of
the Gardone proofhouse
applies to all arms

Definitive
blackpowder
proof

Definitive
smokeless
proof

Discretionary superior
smokeless proof

Additional mark for arms proved
in a finished state

Spanish Proofmarks

Eibar proofmark applied to all arms

Blackpowder proof for muzzleloaders

Voluntary black-powder proof for breechloader barrels

Required smokeless proof for breechloading smoothbores

Supplementary smokeless proof for breechloading smoothbores

Proof for smallbore pistols and rifles

Required proof for rifled arms

Proof for foreign arms not carrying the CIP mark

Yugoslavian Proofmarks

Normal blackpowder proof for finished arms

Proofmark for action parts

Normal smokeless proof for finished arms

Proofmark for calibrating devices

Superior smokeless proof for finished arms

Proofmark for foreign arms

Supplementary mark indicating the arm has been proved in delivery condition

Mark indicating satisfactory barrel assembly

Yugoslavian Proofmarks

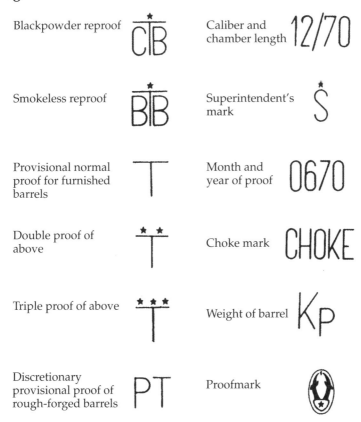

Blackpowder reproof	CB (with star)
Caliber and chamber length	12/70
Smokeless reproof	BB (with star)
Superintendent's mark	S (with star)
Provisional normal proof for furnished barrels	T
Month and year of proof	0670
Double proof of above	T (with two stars)
Choke mark	CHOKE
Triple proof of above	T (with three stars)
Weight of barrel	Kp
Discretionary provisional proof of rough-forged barrels	PT
Proofmark	(oval emblem)

Foreign Firearms Markings

A listing and translation of some commonly encountered markings

BELGIUM/FRANCE

acier—steel
arme etrangere—arm of foreign make
B. Blindee (Balle Blindee)—jacketed bullet
barillet—cylinder
brevet—patent
canon—barrel
CHOKE—smoothbore choke-bore barrels
CH. B. RAYE—partially rifled choke-bore barrels

521

et Cie.—& Co.
EXPRESS NON RAYE—non-rifled express guns
fondee—cast
non pour balle—not for ball
non raye—not rifled
poudre sans fumer—smokeless powder
poudre noir—blackpowder
P.V. (poudre vive)—smokeless powder proof
S.A. (Societe Anonyme)—joint-stock company

BRITAIN
F.T.R.—factory through repair
Nitro—smokeless
tons—long tons (2240 lbs.)

CZECH REPUBLIC/CZECHOSLOVAKIA
Ceska Zbrojovka-Narodni Podnik—Czech National Cooperative Arsenal
Vz. (Vzor)—model

GERMANY
A.G. (Aktiengesellschaft)—joint-stock company
Bl.G. (Bleigeschoss)—lead bullet
D (Dauerfeuer)—continuous or full-automatic fire
D.R.P. (Deutsches Reichspatent)—German patent
D.R.P.u.A.P.—German and foreign patents
D.R.G.M. (Deutsches Reichs-Gebrauchsmuster)—German registered design
E (Einzelfeuer)—semi-automatic fire
Fluss-stahl—fluid steel
Gew. (Gewehr)—rifle
G.m.b.H. (Gesellschaft mit beschrankter Haftung)—limited liability company
K.K. (Kleinkaliber)—smallbore
K.M.G. (Kupfermantelgeschoss)—copper-jacketed bullet
Kar. (Karabiner)—carbine
Kurz—short
M.G. (Maschinengewehr)—machine gun
M.P. (Maschinenpistole)—submachine gun
Nicht für Kugel—not for ball
Selbstlade-Pistole—self-loading pistol
Special-Gewehr-Lauf-Stahl—special gun barrel steel
Spitzgeschoss—pointed bullet
StG (Sturmgewehr)—assault rifle
St.M.G. (Stahlmantelgeschoss)—steel-jacketed bullet
.22 Lang für Buchsen—.22 Long Rifle
VEB (Volks-Eigene Betrieb)—National Cooperative Firm
Waffenfabrik—arms factory

ITALY
FINITO—gun proved in finished state
polvere vera—blackpowder
PSF (polvere senza fumo)—smokeless powder proof
Pistola Mitra (Pistola Mitragliatrice)—submachine gun
S.A. (Societa Anonima)—joint-stock company
S.p.A. (Societa per Azione)—corporation
S.r.l. (Societa a responsabilita limitata)—limited-liability company

POLAND
Wz. (Wzor)—model

SPAIN
Amatrelladora—machine gun
Avancarga—muzzleloading
Escopeta—shotgun
Polvora negra—blackpowder
Polvora sin humo—smokeless powder
Rayada—rifled
Retrocarga—breechloading
S.A. (Sociedad Anonima)—joint-stock company
S.A.L. (Sociedad Anonima Limitada)—limited liability company
S.R.C. (Sociedad Redito Comandito)—partnership
Subfusil—submachine gun
y Cia.—& Co.

SWEDEN
AB (Aktienbolaget)—joint-stock company
Gevarsfaktori—rifle factory
Specialstal—special steel
Vapenfabrik—arms factory

Historic U.S. Handgun Grip Marks

The idea of using an identifying mark on the grip of the handgun seems to have had its beginnings here in the middle 1870s. An important innovation was the introduction of molded hard rubber grips which permitted use of more elaborate designs than could be achieved with wood. The designs are usually found at the top of the grip on either side, or positioned about the central grip plate screw.

American Arms Co., Boston, Mass.; 1870-1893. Milwaukee, Wis.; 1893-1904. revolvers.

American Arms Co., Boston, Mass.; early 1870s to 1904.

Bliss & Goodyear, New Haven, Conn. 1866-1887. Hartford Arms was a trade name used by Bliss & Goodyear, Royal, Liberty, Gypsy and Bull's Eye revolvers.

Bliss & Goodyear, New Haven, Conn. revolvers.

Cody Mfg. Corp., Springfield, Mass. Cody Thunderbird cal. .22 revolver.

Colt's Patent Firearms Mfg. Co., Hartford, Conn.; 1836 to date.

Colt's Patent Firearms Mfg. Co., Hartford, Conn., 1836 to date. automatic arms.

Davis Warner Arms Corp., Assonet, Mass. Cal. .32 Infallible automatic pistol.

Eastern Arms Co., Chicopee Falls, Mass. Trade name for some guns made by Meriden Firearms Co.

Forehand & Wadsworth, Hopkins & Allen, Norwich, Conn., revolvers bearing either name.

Forehand Arms Co., Worcester, Mass. 1890-1900. Grips are believed to have been left over from the preceding firm, Forehand & Wadsworth. Used on both exposed-hammer and hammerless revolvers. Sold out to Hopkins & Allen.

Forehand & Wadsworth, Worcester, Mass.; 1871-1890. Also found on some arms produced by Forehand Arms Co.

Forehand & Wadsworth, Worcester, Mass.; 1871-1890

Andrew Fryberg & Co., Hopkinton, Mass. Revolvers made by Meriden Firearms Co. of Meriden, Conn.

Harrington & Richardson, Worcester, Mass.; 1871 to 1985. revolvers.

Harrington & Richardson, Worcester, Mass.; 1871 to date. Aetna 2½ revolver and White Star revolver.

Harrington & Richardson, Worcester, Mass.

Harrington & Richardson, Worcester, Mass. 7-shot cal. .32 revolver with patent date of May 28, 1876.

Harrington & Richardson, Worcester, Mass.

J.C. Higgins, Model 88 9-shot revolver.

High Standard Mfg. Co., New Haven, Conn. Hi-Standard Model "B" automatic pistol marked "Property of U.S."

High Standard Mfg. Corp., New Haven, Conn.

Hood Firearms Co., Norwich, Conn.; 1875-1880. F.W. Hood's Victoria revolver.

Hopkins & Allen, Norwich, Conn.; 1868-1915. Cal. .32 Dictator revolver.

Hopkins & Allen, Norwich, Conn. Arms made for Merwin, Hulbert & Co., agents.

Hopkins & Allen, Norwich, Conn. Revolvers made for Merwin, Hulbert & Co., agents.

Hopkins & Allen, Norwich, Conn.; 1868-1915. Czar, Blue Jacket 1½ and other revolvers.

Hopkins & Allen, Norwich, Conn.; 1868-1915, pistols and revolvers.

Hopkins & Allen, Norwich, Conn.; 1868-1915. Safety Police Cal. .32 revolvers.

Iver Johnson Co., Defender 89 birdshead grip revolver.

Iver Johnson Co. monogram around grip screw. Found on early grips with bulldog head facing forward.

Iver Johnson monogram around grip screw. Found on grips with owl or bulldog head.

Iver Johnson Co. Secret Service Special revolver. Jobbed by a firm in Chicago.

Iver Johnson Co., American Bulldog revolver with large eagle covering most of grip.

Iver Johnson Co., variation of eagle design covering most of grip.

525

Iver Johnson Arms & Cycle Works, Worcester, Mass.; 1871-1891. Fitchburg, Mass.; 1891 to date.

Iver Johnson Arms & Cycle Works, Worcester, Mass.; 1871-1891. Fitchburg, Mass. 1891 to date. Revolvers stamped "U.S. Revolver Co."

Kaiser, Maker unknown.

Henry M. Kolb, Philadelphia Pa. circa 1897-1911.; Baby Hammerless revolvers.

Maltby-Curtis Co., New York, N.Y. Exact dates unknown.

Maltby-Henley, New York, N.Y.; circa 1878-1890. Agents for guns produced under the John T. Smith patents. Spencer Safety Hammerless.

Maltby-Henley, New York, N.Y. Revolvers.

J.M. Marlin, New Haven, Conn. XX standard revolvers.

J.M. Marlin, New Haven, Conn.; 1870-1881. Early J.M. Marlin arms and some Marlin Fire Arms Co. arms.

Marlin Fire Arms Co., New Haven, Conn.; 1881 to date. revolvers.

Marlin Fire Arms Co., New Haven, Conn.; 1881 to date. Arms carrying above marking and also J.M. Marlin arms. #32 Standard 1878 revolvers.

Osgood Gun Works, Norwich, Conn.; circa 1880. Osgood Duplex revolver.

Reising Mfg. Corp., New York, N.Y. Reising automatic pistol.

E. Remington & Sons, Ilion, N.Y.; 1844-1886. No. 3 New Line revolvers.

Remington-UMC. Ilion, N.Y. Automatic pistols.

Remington Arms Co., Ilion, N.Y.; 1886-1902. Model 1890 .44-40 revolver.

T. E. Ryan, Norwich, Conn.;1890-1893. Marquis of Lorne, Napoleon, and Retriever revolvers.

Savage Arms Corp., Chicopee Falls, Mass. Model 101 single-shot pistol.

Savage Repeating Arms Corp., Utica, N.Y.; 1895-1899. Savage Arms Co.; 1899-1917. Savage Arms Corp.; 1917 to date. Cal .32 and .380 automatics.

R.F. Sedgely, Inc., Philadelphia, Pa. Circa 1910-1938. Successors to Henry M. Kolb. Baby Hammerless revolvers.

Sears-Roebuck Co., Chicago, Ill. revolvers.

C.S. Shattuck Arms Co., Hatfield, Mass.; 1875-1918. Cal. .32 revolvers made under Shattuck patent of Nov. 4, 1879.

C.S. Shattuck Arms Co., Hatfield, Mass.; 1875-1918. revolver.

Sheridan Products, Inc., Racine, Wis.

Smith & Wesson, Springfield, Mass.; 1857 to date. Standard trademark.

Smith & Wesson, Springfield, Mass.; Baby Russian revolvers.

Sturm, Ruger & Co. Southport, Conn. revolvers and automatic pistols.

Turner & Ross, Boston, Mass.; 1873-1885. Agents for arms made by Whitney at Whitneyville, Conn., and by Hopkins & Allen at Norwich, Conn. Czar revolvers.

Warner Arms Corp., Norwich, Conn. Cal .32 automatic pistol The Infallible.

Unknown. Pioneer brass-frame revolver, maker unknown.

Pioneer. Maker unknown. Distributed through Kruse Hardware Co. of Cincinnati, Ohio.

Dead Shot. Maker unknown.

Maker unknown. Inexpensive pocket revolvers; 1880-1890 period.

527

Multi-Barrel Guns

The German-speaking nations have been the most prolific producers of multi-barreled guns, so the German names have been traditional in referring to them. The three-barreled drilling is familiar to most shooters, but it was just the beginning for Germanic creativity.

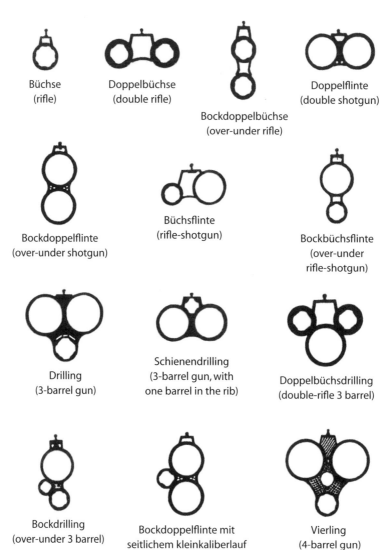

Büchse
(rifle)

Doppelbüchse
(double rifle)

Bockdoppelbüchse
(over-under rifle)

Doppelflinte
(double shotgun)

Bockdoppelflinte
(over-under shotgun)

Büchsflinte
(rifle-shotgun)

Bockbüchsflinte
(over-under
rifle-shotgun)

Drilling
(3-barrel gun)

Schienendrilling
(3-barrel gun, with
one barrel in the rib)

Doppelbüchsdrilling
(double-rifle 3 barrel)

Bockdrilling
(over-under 3 barrel)

Bockdoppelflinte mit
seitlichem kleinkaliberlauf
(over-under shotgun with
side-mounted rifle barrel)

Vierling
(4-barrel gun)

Chapter 21
INDEX